AP Biology
Investigative Labs:

An Inquiry-Based Approach

The College Board
New York, NY

■ ABOUT THE COLLEGE BOARD

The College Board is a mission-driven not-for-profit organization that connects students to college success and opportunity. Founded in 1900, the College Board was created to expand access to higher education. Today, the membership association is made up of over 6,000 of the world's leading educational institutions and is dedicated to promoting excellence and equity in education. Each year, the College Board helps more than seven million students prepare for a successful transition to college through programs and services in college readiness and college success — including the SAT® and the Advanced Placement Program®. The organization also serves the education community through research and advocacy on behalf of students, educators and schools. For further information, visit www.collegeboard.org.

■ AP® Equity and Access Policy

The College Board strongly encourages educators to make equitable access a guiding principle for their AP programs by giving all willing and academically prepared students the opportunity to participate in AP. We encourage the elimination of barriers that restrict access to AP for students from ethnic, racial and socioeconomic groups that have been traditionally underserved. Schools should make every effort to ensure their AP classes reflect the diversity of their student population. The College Board also believes that all students should have access to academically challenging course work before they enroll in AP classes, which can prepare them for AP success. It is only through a commitment to equitable preparation and access that true equity and excellence can be achieved.

The College Board acknowledges all the third party content that has been included in these materials and respects the Intellectual Property rights of others. If we have incorrectly attributed a source or overlooked a publisher, please contact us.

Page S121: Reprinted with permission from Micklos and Freyer, DNA Science 2e, © 2003 Cold Spring Harbor Laboratory Press.

FAST PLANTS® is a registered trademark of Wisconsin Alumni Research Foundation.

Item # for single copies: 130085374.

Item # for packages of five: 130085375.

Copies of this book may be ordered online through the College Board Store at http://store.collegeboard.com.

Editorial inquiries concerning this book should be directed to The College Board, 45 Columbus Avenue, New York, New York 10023-6992.

Third Printing

Contents

Acknowledgments v

Introduction S1

Chapter 1: What Is Inquiry? S3

Chapter 2: Written, Verbal, and Graphic Information S5

Chapter 3: Quantitative Reasoning in AP® Biology S9

▮ Big Idea 1: Evolution

Investigation 1: Artificial Selection S17

Investigation 2: Mathematical Modeling: Hardy-Weinberg S25

Investigation 3: Comparing DNA Sequences to Understand Evolutionary Relationships with BLAST S41

▮ Big Idea 2: Cellular Processes: Energy and Communication

Investigation 4: Diffusion and Osmosis S51

Investigation 5: Photosynthesis S61

Investigation 6: Cellular Respiration S71

▮ BIg Idea 3: Genetics and Information Transfer

Investigation 7: Cell Division: Mitosis and Meiosis S83

Investigation 8: Biotechnology: Bacterial Transformation S97

Investigation 9: Biotechnology: Restriction Enzyme Analysis of DNA S111

▮ Big Idea 4: Interactions

Investigation 10: Energy Dynamics S125

Investigation 11: Transpiration S135

Investigation 12: Fruit Fly Behavior S145

Investigation 13: Enzyme Activity S153

Appendix A: AP Biology Equations and Formulas A1

Appendix B: Constructing Line Graphs A3

Acknowledgments

The College Board would like to acknowledge the following individuals and committees for their commitment and dedication toward the completion of this project:

■ LAB AUTHORS AND MAJOR CONTRIBUTORS

- Stacy Baker, Convent of the Sacred Heart, New York, NY
- Spencer Benson, University of Maryland, College Park, MD
- Elizabeth Cowles, Eastern Connecticut State University, Willimantic, CT
- Arthur Eisenkraft, University of Massachusetts, Boston, MA
- Kim Foglia, Division Avenue Senior High School, Levittown, New York
- A. Daniel Johnson, Wake Forest University, Winston-Salem, NC
- John Jungck, Beloit College, Beloit, WI
- John Jack Kay, Iolani High School, Honolulu, HI
- Sue Offner, Lexington High School, Lexington, MA
- Peggy O'Neill Skinner, The Bush School, Seattle, WA
- Sharon Radford, The Paideia School, Atlanta, GA
- Gordon Uno, University of Oklahoma, Norman, OK
- Brad Williamson, University of Kansas, Lawrence, KS
- Julianne Zedalis, The Bishop's School, La Jolla, CA

■ AP LAB MANUAL VISION TEAM

In 2010, the College Board convened a group of subject matter and laboratory investigation experts to provide a model of excellence for what the investigative labs should be in AP science courses. These individuals worked diligently to create a vision for exemplary AP science labs that would serve to assist teachers in facilitating inquiry-based and student-directed investigative work. This vision also serves as the input for professional development and resource materials that will support the new course and lab investigations.

- Arthur Eisenkraft, University of Massachusetts, Boston, MA
- Eugenia Etkina, Rutgers University, Piscataway, NJ
- Nivedita Ganguly, University of Tennessee, Knoxville, TN
- Dolores Gende, Parish Episcopal School, Dallas, TX
- Peggy O'Neill Skinner, The Bush School, Seattle, WA
- Susan Singer, Carleton College, Northfield, MN
- Angelica Stacy, University of California, Berkeley, CA
- Peter Strom, Rutgers University, New Brunswick, NJ

- Gordon Uno, University of Oklahoma, Norman, OK
- Dave Yaron, Carnegie Mellon University, Pittsburgh, PA

■ OTHER CONTRIBUTORS

- AP Biology Commission
- AP Biology Consultants
- AP Biology Curriculum Development and Assessment Committee
- AP Biology Development Committee
- AP Biology Focus Group Participants
- *AP Biology Lab Manual* Reviewers
- AP Biology Lab Pilot Teachers
- AP Biology Readers
- Authors and Contributors of the 1990 *AP Biology Lab Manual* (and subsequent editions)
- BioPhase Committee
- College Board Science Academic Advisory Committee

Introduction

■ GOALS OF THE LABORATORY INVESTIGATIONS

Knowing a collection of facts about biology is beneficial only if you can use that information to understand and investigate a particular aspect of the natural world. AP® Biology lab investigations allow you to explore the natural world, and provide opportunities for you to choose to study what interests you most about each concept. Science is about the process of investigating, and should be a central part of your experience in AP Biology. Performing labs also gives you insight into the nature of science, and helps you appreciate the investigations and processes that result in the collection of facts that your textbook and your teacher often present to you.

This suite of AP Biology laboratory investigations helps you gain enduring understandings of biological concepts and the scientific evidence that supports them. The investigations allow you to develop and apply practices and skills used by scientists. You make observations, ask questions, and then design plans for experiments, data collection, application of mathematical routines, and refinement of testable explanations and predictions. As you work through your experiments, your teacher will ask follow-up questions to assess how well you understand key concepts. Finally, you will communicate your findings and your interpretation of them to your classmates and instructor(s).

For each investigation in this manual, you will find the following:

- Background information and clear learning objectives for each investigation
- Prelab questions, activities, software simulations, and other supplemental resources
- "Checklists" of prior skills and skills that will be developed
- Tips for designing and conducting investigations
- Safety concerns
- Lists of materials and supplies
- Methods of analyzing and evaluating results
- Means of communicating results and conclusions
- Postlab questions and activities
- Suggestions for extending the investigation(s)

CHAPTER 1:
What Is Inquiry?

How do we know what we know? Inquiry begins with observations you make about the natural world — a bare spot under a tree, a bird chirping repeatedly, or an unusual spot on your skin. If you follow such observations by a question, such as *What is causing that?*, you have begun an inquiry. Inquiry-based laboratory investigations allow you to discover information for yourself, and model the behavior of scientists as you observe and explore. Through inquiry, you use a variety of methods to answer questions you raise. These methods include laboratory and field investigations; manipulation of software simulations, models, and data sets; and meaningful online research. By designing experiments to test hypotheses, analyze data, and communicate results and conclusions, you appreciate that a scientific method of investigation is cyclic, not linear; each observation or experimental result raises new questions about how the world works, thus leading to open-ended investigations.

There are four levels of inquiry that lead to the student question. It is not reasonable to think that every part of a particular lab in AP Biology will be completely student directed. However, as written, the labs lead to a student-directed, inquiry-based investigation(s). The four levels of inquiry are as follows:

- **Confirmation**. At this level, you confirm a principle through an activity in which the results are known in advance.

- **Structured Inquiry**. At this level, you investigate a teacher-presented question through a prescribed procedure.

- **Guided Inquiry**. At this level, you investigate a teacher-presented question using procedures that you design/select.

- **Open Inquiry**. At this level, you investigate topic-related questions that are formulated through procedures that you design/select.

As you work on your investigations, your teacher may walk around the room and ask probing questions to provoke your thinking (e.g., *How are you changing the temperature? How are you recording the temperature?*). Your teacher may also ask about data and evidence (e.g., *Is there an alternative way to organize the data? Is there some reason the data may not be accurate? What data are important to collect? What are you hoping to find out? How will you communicate your results?*). This strategy will allow your teacher to diagnose and address any misconceptions immediately.

CHAPTER 2:
Written, Verbal, and Graphic Communication

Experimental results must be communicated to peers to have value. To understand the relationship among your hypothesis, procedures, and results, you should first take part in an informal small-group or class discussion of the experiment, including possible errors, changes in procedures, and alternative explanations for your data. Since many of the laboratory experiences described in this manual contain suggestions for further investigation, discussion of a given experiment can be a launching pad for independent work, culminating in a formal written report, poster, or oral presentation. Some possibilities for more permanent presentations are described below.

■ Mini-Posters and Presentations

At scientific conferences, many experiments are presented orally or via posters. Posters provide the advantage of clarity and brevity that articulate the essential elements of the research. In a class, an alternative to the standard oral presentation or a full-sized poster is a mini-poster session, which requires fewer materials and less time than a formal presentation. You can include the most important elements of a full-sized poster, present your work, and get feedback from your classmates in an informal setting. The essential elements of a mini-poster are as follows:

- Title

- Abstract

- Introduction with primary question, background context, and hypothesis

- Methodology

- Results, including graphs, tables, charts, and statistical analyses

- Conclusions, or your interpretation of your results based on your hypothesis

- Literature cited

An example of a mini-poster session can be found at ***http://www.nabt.org/ blog/2010/05/04/mini-posters-authentic-peer-review-in-the-classroom***. Such a session allows you to evaluate information on your own, and then discuss it with other students, mimicking authentic presentations and peer review.

■ Lab Notebooks/Portfolios

A lab notebook allows you to organize your work so that you have the information for a more formal report. Your lab notebook should contain the information necessary for making a formal report, which may include a prelab experimental outline with the following information:

- Members of work group

- Primary question for investigation

- Background observations and contextual information

- Hypothesis and rationale for the investigation

- Experimental design — strategies for testing hypothesis, using appropriate controls and variables

- Materials required

- Safety issues

- Procedure in sufficient detail so that someone could replicate your results

In addition, your lab notebook should contain the following:

- Results, including graphs, tables, drawings or diagrams, and statistical analysis

- Conclusion and discussion — Was the hypothesis supported? What additional questions remain for further investigation?

- References

A lab portfolio might contain finished lab reports, notes on individual projects, library research, reflections on particular lab experiences, and connections with other parts of the course, or a combination of these elements as requested by your teacher.

■ Lab Reports/Papers

A formal report or paper provides an effective method for you to organize your work, and mimics papers in scientific journals. Your teacher might provide a rubric for what information should be included. This type of report gives you writing experience and opportunities to reflect on your work. (Refer to page 10 for tips on constructing informative graphs to include in your report.) A sample rubric showing what your teacher will be looking for in your lab reports can be found at *http://www.biologycorner.com/worksheets/labreport_rubric.html*.

You also can see a good example of a descriptive lab report, "Examination of Protozoan Cultures to Determine Cellular Structure and Motion Pattern," at *http://www.ncsu.edu/labwrite/res/labreport/sampledescriptlab.html*.

Technology

There are numerous websites for posting class data, which can then provide a larger sample for analysis, comparison of different conditions in the experiment, or collaboration between students in different class sections and different schools. Your school's technology or media center personnel may recommend appropriate Web-based options.

Graphs

A graph is a visual representation of your data, and you want your graph to be as clear as possible to the reader for interpretation. First, you have to decide whether to use a scatter plot in order to draw a "best fit" line through data points, a bar graph, or some other representation with appropriate units. Use a line graph if your data are continuous (e.g., the appearance of product over time in an enzyme reaction). If your data are discontinuous (e.g., the amount of water consumption in different high schools), use a bar graph. Your teacher might have other suggestions.

A graph must have a title that informs the reader about the experiment. Labeling a graph as simply "Graph Number Four" doesn't tell the reader anything about the experiment, or the results. In comparison, the title "The Effect of Different Concentrations of Auxin on Root Growth" tells the reader exactly what was being measured. Make sure each line or bar on your graph is easily identifiable by the reader.

Axes must be clearly labeled with units.

- The x-axis shows the independent variable. Time is an example of an independent variable. Other possibilities for an independent variable might be light intensity, or the concentration of a hormone or nutrient.

- The y-axis denotes the dependent variable, or what is being affected by the condition (independent variable) shown on the x-axis.

- Intervals must be uniform. For example, if one square on the x-axis equals five minutes, each interval must be the same and not change to ten minutes or one minute. If there is a break in the graph, such as a time course over which little happens for an extended period, note this with a break in the axis and a corresponding break in the data line.

- For clarity, you do not have to label each interval. You can label every five or ten intervals, or whatever is appropriate.

- Label the x-axis and y-axis so that a reader can easily see the information.

More than one condition of an experiment may be shown on a graph using different lines. For example, you can compare the appearance of a product in an enzyme reaction at different temperatures on the same graph. In this case, each line must be clearly differentiated from the others — by a label, a different style, or color indicated by a key. These techniques provide an easy way to compare the results of your experiments.

Be clear as to whether your data start at the origin (0,0) or not. Do not extend your line to the origin if your data do not start there. In addition, do not extend your line beyond your last data point (extrapolation) unless you clearly indicate by a dashed line (or some other demarcation) that this is your prediction about what may happen.

For more detailed information about graphs, see Appendix B: Constructing Line Graphs.

CHAPTER 3:
Quantitative Reasoning in AP® Biology

Which would you choose? A brain biopsy or a CAT/MRI scan? A vaccine for 90%+ of the population with a risk of 0.001% suffering from side effects, or no vaccine at all? Fresh vegetables sprayed with competing bacteria, or vegetables sprayed with sterilants that are hazardous to ecosystems? To risk conviction of a crime based on a detective's hunch, or to be acquitted based on evidence provided by DNA markers? These are routine questions affected by the use of mathematics in science, including biology, medicine, public health, and agriculture.

To have a rich foundation in biology, you need to include and apply quantitative methods to the study of biology. This is particularly true for a laboratory experience. Quantitative reasoning is an essential part of inquiry in biology. Many mathematical tools (e.g., statistical tests) were developed originally to work out biological problems.

Mathematics can help biologists (and biology students) grasp and work out problems that are otherwise:

- Too big (such as the biosphere)
- Too slow (macroevolution)
- Too remote in time (early extinctions)
- Too complex (human brain)
- Too small (molecular structures and interactions)
- Too fast (photosynthesis)
- Too remote in space (life in extreme environments)
- Too dangerous or unethical (how infectious agents interact with human populations)

The laboratory investigations in this manual were chosen to provide you with an opportunity to do biology — to explore your own questions and try to find answers to those questions. Many of the investigations provide a preliminary, guided exploration to introduce you to a way of looking at a biology problem, or method for studying it, providing just enough familiarity with the topics so that you can begin asking your own questions and investigating them. An essential part of that exploration includes an introduction to various quantitative skills — mathematical routines, concepts, methods, or operations used to interpret information, solve problems, and make decisions — that you will need in order to explore the investigative topic adequately.

The quantitative skills you'll apply as you carry out the investigations in this lab manual are for the most part the same skills you have been acquiring in your mathematics courses. For many of the skills required in these labs, you already understand how to do the math, and these investigations simply extend the application of those math skills. Your teacher can help to guide you as you supplement and review the quantitative skills required for the various laboratory investigations in this manual.

To conceptually organize the scope and nature of the skills involved, refer to Figure 1:

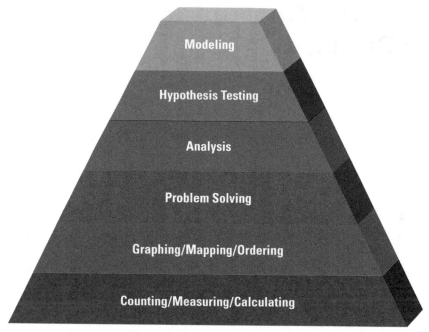

Figure 1. Pyramid of Quantitative Reasoning

The figure graphically organizes the quantitative skills featured in this lab manual. The skills labeled on the bottom of the pyramid are generally less complex, and require the application of standard procedures. As you move up the pyramid, the applications become more complex as you try to make sense out of data and biological phenomena. One of the important lessons about quantitative reasoning is that real data are "messy." The increasing complexity as you move up this pyramid does not necessarily indicate that the mathematical operations themselves are more complex. Good, first approximations of mathematical models often require only simple arithmetic. This chapter describes how the quantitative skills listed in the pyramid are applied when answering questions generated by various lab topics in this manual.

■ Counting, Measuring, and Calculating

At this point in your education, you may not feel that counting, measuring, and calculating represent much in the way of a "skill." And you'd be right in a theoretical world. The problem is that your investigation will explore the real world of biology, and that is messy.

For example, Investigation 1: Artificial Selection presents the problem of selection of quantitative variation in a population of plants. You identify a trait that can be quantified (counted), and then measure the variation in the population of plants by counting. This is not always as easy as it sounds. You will notice that some of the plants in your population are more hairy than others, so this is the trait you select. What do you count? All the hairs? Some of the hairs on specific parts of the plant? On how many plants? After observing one of your plants more closely, you see that it has very few (if any) hairs, but another plant has hundreds. These hairs are small. You have a limited amount of time to make your counts. How do you sample the population? After discussion with your lab partner(s), you and your class decide to count just the hairs on the first true leaf's petiole (stalk attaching the blade to the stem) — a much smaller and more reasonable amount to count, but you'll still need to work out whether or not it is a representative sample.

Measuring phenomena in the real world presents similar challenges. Investigation 10: Energy Dynamics introduces you to energy dynamics by measuring the biomass of growing organisms. How do you measure the mass of a small caterpillar? What about the water in the organism? Is water included in "biomass"? It is your challenge to come up with solutions to these problems, and to define all measurements carefully so that someone could measure in the same way you did and replicate the experiment. Perhaps you could measure a quantity of caterpillars and sacrifice a few caterpillars to estimate how much the "wet mass" of a caterpillar is biomass, and how much is water. You will have to perform relatively simple calculations, including percentages, ratios, averages, and means.

Nearly every lab investigation requires these kinds of operations and decisions. What is different about this manual is that the decisions are up to you. The manual doesn't make the decisions for you. There are almost always a number of reasonable, productive solutions to such problems. Make sure that your decisions are reasonable and provide a good solution to the problem you are studying.

Precision needed in the experiment is also a consideration and a decision you have to make. Increasing precision requires more time and resources. How precise do your data need to be for you to support or reject your hypothesis?

■ Graphing, Mapping, and Ordering: Histograms of Variation and/or Energy Flow Diagrams

To build on the previous two examples, consider how the data counted and measured should be represented — not numerically, but with graphs or diagrams. For example, consider the examination of the variation of a quantitative trait in a population of plants. How do you best represent these data? If you count the hairs (trichomes) in a population of 150 plants, do you present each data point on a graph, or do you compile the data into an overall picture? If all data points are the same, then there would be no need to present data graphically, but the messy reality is that the counts likely could vary from 0 to more than 50 hairs per plant. For this reason, a histogram (see Figure 2) is often used to represent the variability and distribution of population data.

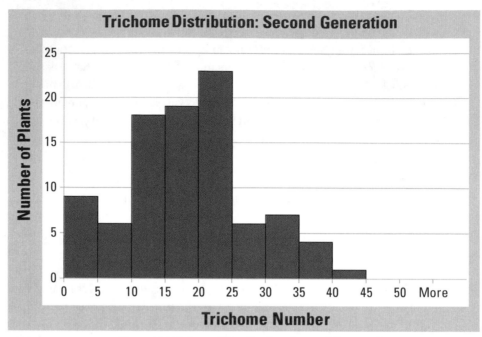

Figure 2. Trichome Distribution: Second Generation

In a histogram, the data are organized into bins with a defined range of values. For example, for the hairy plants the bin size might be 10 hairs, and bins defined in this manner might include 1–10 hairs, 11–20 hairs, 21–30 hairs, and so on. You simply count the number of plants that fall into each bin, and then graph the distribution as a bar graph — or in this case, a histogram. There are several challenges and decisions you'll have to make where your quantitative skills will be tested. For instance, what should you do about plants with 0 plant hairs? Do you include a separate bin for this one plant? How do you know what the "correct" bin size is? It is usually best to try several bin sizes, but you'll have to make the decision which bin size best captures the nature of the variation you are working with — messy.

Creating Diagrams, Charts, and Maps

Biology is the study of systems at several levels of organization, from molecules and cells to populations and ecosystems. When exploring a topic, such as energy dynamics in Investigation 10, creating a chart or map can help you to logically define the system components and the flows between those components, while simplifying a very complicated process. Creating such a chart is an exercise in logic and graphic design. Such a graphic representation of your work helps to communicate your thinking, and organizes your analysis and modeling structure. Figure 3 is one model of how a disease might infect a population.

Figure 3. A Disease's Infection of a Population

Your teacher may have suggestions on investigations of graphic representation methods you may want to employ to summarize your data and thoughts.

Problem Solving

All sorts of questions and problems are raised and solved during biological investigations. Such questions include the following:

- What is the inheritance pattern for a particular trait?

- What is the critical population size that will ensure genetic diversity in an isolated population?

- How are genes linked to each other on the same chromosome?

- How often do spontaneous mutations occur in a species of yeast?

- What is the Q_{10} temperature coefficient[1] for invertebrates in the Arctic?

- How does a change in ambient temperature affect the rate of transpiration in plants?

- How can the efficiency of transformation be calculated in bacteria exposed to plasmids containing a gene for antibiotic resistance?

Problem solving involves a complex interplay among observation, theory, and inference. For example, say that for one of your investigations you explore a typical dihybrid genetic cross like one you may have studied earlier in an introductory biology course. This time, however, you collect data from the F2 generation, and note four different phenotype combinations (observation). You count the number of each combination. Using your understanding of the role of chromosomes in inheritance, you work to make a theoretical prediction of what your results might be assuming independent assortment of genes (hypothesis). However, you find that the observed results don't quite match your expected results. Now what? You've been using quantitative thinking, and now it is time to extend the thinking into possible solutions to this problem.

---

1   Q_{10} temperature coefficient: a measure of the rate of change of a biological or chemical system as a consequence of increasing the temperature by 10 °C.

In this case, the deviation from expected may be due to random chance, or it may be due to a phenomenon known as linkage, where two genes are located close together on the same chromosome instead of on separate chromosomes. There is not enough space here to fully explore the strategies for solving such a problem, but realize that the challenge requires a different level of commitment on your part to work through the problem and solve it. Instead of the instructions for each lab investigation walking you through such problems step by step, this manual provides you with opportunities to explore problems you can solve on your own, which will give you a deeper learning experience.

Analysis

When you start to design your own investigations to answer your own questions, you may find that appropriate and adequate data analysis is a challenge. This is the result of having done too many investigations that have the analysis scripted for you. From the very first inkling of the question that you plan to investigate, you also should consider how you plan to analyze your data. Data analysis describes your data quantitatively. Descriptive statistics help to paint the picture of the variation in your data; the central tendencies, standard error, best-fit functions, and the confidence that you have collected enough data. Analysis helps you to make your case when arguing for your conclusion that your data meet accepted standards for reliability and validity. Data analysis is complex. Obviously, there is not enough space in this overview to do the topic justice, but do not let this deter you. Data analysis is an essential component of each investigation in this manual, and is integral to the communication process. Your teacher will be a valuable guide in this process.

Hypothesis Testing

In the investigations in this manual, you are asked to modify your question into an appropriate hypothesis. Your experimental design should provide evidence that will help you to conclude whether or not your hypothesis should be accepted. Part of the evidence needed to produce such a conclusion is based on a number of statistical tests that are designed for specific situations. You may be familiar with a statistical hypothesis test, such as a chi-square test or a T-test. These tests can help you to determine probability that the data you have sampled are significantly different from a theoretical population. You've undoubtedly read about such tests, as they are applied when testing new drug treatments or medical procedures. Your teacher can help guide you as you select the methods appropriate to your study. Deciding on the appropriate methods for hypothesis testing (statistical tests) before you carry out your experiment will greatly facilitate your experimental design.

■ Modeling

Not all biological research involves wet lab investigations[2]. Investigations also can involve a quantitative model. Quantitative models are often computer based. Thinking about and developing computer models may seem to be a new way of thinking and doing biology, but actually you've been constructing mental models of biological phenomena since you first began your study of biology. Models are simplifications of complex phenomena, and are important tools to help drive prediction and identify the important factors that are largely responsible for particular phenomena.

To develop a mathematical model, you must first define the relevant parameters or variables. For example, if you were creating a model of disease in a population, you might divide the population into three components: the part of the population that is susceptible but not infected, the part of the population that is infected, and the part of the population that has recovered from the disease. The probability of transmitting the infection and the probability for recovery are important parameters to define as well. The next step would be to graphically define these parameters and their relation to one another, as you did previously (see Figure 3).

With this graphic, you can imagine word equations that step through the process of a disease cycle in a population. These word equations can then be interpreted into the language of a spreadsheet to get something like Figure 4.

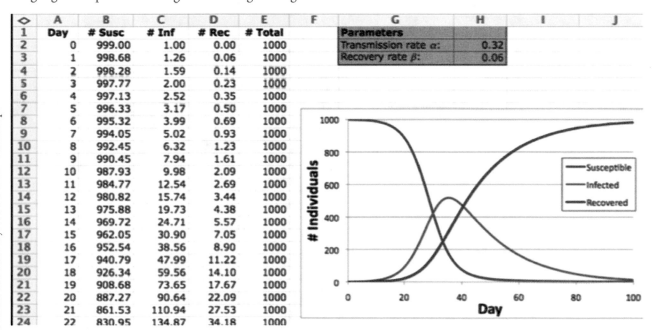

Source: Shodor/Project SUCCEED workshops

Figure 4. A Disease Cycle in a Population

---

2   Wet lab investigation: laboratories in which chemicals, drugs, or other material or biological matter are tested and analyzed requiring water, direct ventilation, and specialized piped utilities, as opposed to a computer-based lab.

Models help to provide insight and guidance for an investigation. They help to focus the investigation on parameters that are most influential. Models have to be checked against real data. The assumptions and the limitations of any model should be explicitly articulated. Building models is a challenge, but it is a challenge that, when met, pays very large dividends in learning.

■ REFERENCES

Johnson, A.D. 2009. 40 *Inquiry Exercises for the College Biology Lab*. Arlington, VA: NSTA Press.

http://shodor.org/succeed/curriculum/apprenticeship/Modeling/Excel/LessonPlan2/ Microsoft Excel II activity, Project Succeed workshops, Shodor.

Waterman, M., and E. Stanley. 2008. *Biological Inquiry: A Workbook of Investigative Cases for Campbell and Reece Biology*. 8th ed. San Francisco, CA: Pearson/Benjamin Cummings.

Big Idea 1

INVESTIGATION 1
ARTIFICIAL SELECTION

Can extreme selection change expression of a quantitative trait in a population in one generation?

■ BACKGROUND

Evolution is a process that has existed throughout the history of life on Earth. One of the key driving forces of evolution is natural selection, which is differential reproduction in a population — some organisms in a population may reproduce more than others and leave more viable offspring in the next population or generation. Differential reproduction results in a population with a genetic makeup that is different from that of the previous population. Thus, populations may change over time. This process of change is evolution. With natural selection, environmental factors play a key role in determining which organisms reproduce and how many of their offspring survive. In artificial selection, humans determine which organisms reproduce, allowing some individuals to reproduce more than others. What will happen to a population of these organisms over time when exposed to artificial selection?

For the first part of this investigation, you and your classmates will perform one round of artificial selection on a population of Wisconsin Fast Plants®. First, you will identify and quantify several traits that vary in the population and that you can quantify easily. You will then perform artificial selection by cross-pollinating only selected plants. You'll collect the seeds, plant them, and then sample the second-generation population and see if it is different from the previous one. Your results will generate questions, and you then will have a chance to test your own ideas about how selection works.

■ Learning Objectives
- To investigate natural selection as a major mechanism of evolution
- To convert a data set from a table of numbers that reflects a change in the genetic makeup of a population over time and to apply mathematical methods and conceptual understandings to investigate the cause(s) and effect(s) of this change
- To apply mathematical methods to data from a real population to predict what will happen to the population in the future
- To investigate how natural selection acts on phenotypic variations in populations
- To evaluate data-based evidence that describes evolutionary changes in the genetic makeup of a population over time due to changes in the environment
- To design an investigation based on your observations and questions related to the importance of a single trait in the life history of a plant

■ General Safety Precautions

When growing plants under lights, be careful to avoid any situation where water or fertilizer could come in contact with the electrical wires.

■ THE INVESTIGATIONS

■ Getting Started

In *On the Origin of Species*, Charles Darwin used artificial selection — the kind of selection that is used to develop domestic breeds of animals and plants — as a way to understand and explain natural selection. Like natural selection, artificial selection requires variation in the population under selection. For selection to work, the variations must be inheritable. To conduct artificial selection, humans decide on a specific trait of a plant or animal to enhance or diminish and then select which individuals with that desired trait will breed, producing the next generation and the next population.

Materials

- Lighting: light box systems (grow lights)
- Growing system: recycled plastic soda or water bottles
- Wicking: mason twine
- Fertilizer: Miracle-Gro Nursery Select All Purpose Water-Soluble Plant Food or Peters Professional with micronutrients
- Soil: Jiffy-Mix (soil mix, not potting soil)
- Vermiculite
- Fast Plants seed (Carolina Biological item 158888 works well and provides some additional options; it is heterozygous for two Mendelian traits, green/light green leaves and with anthocyanin [purple stems] and without anthocyanin. Other seed stocks, such as the standard Fast Plants seeds that can be purchased from Carolina Biological or Nasco, work as well.)
- Bee sticks for pollination
- Digital cameras to record the investigation
- Plastic magnifiers
- Laboratory notebook

■ Procedure

How will you know if artificial selection has changed the genetic makeup of your population? That is one of the questions you will be trying to answer. You then will have a chance to test your own ideas about how selection works.

Plant Cultivation: First-Generation Plants

Step 1 Prepare growing containers. Go to the Wisconsin Fast Plants website and find the instructions for converting small soda bottles into planting containers (*http://www.fastplants.org/grow.lighting.bottle.php*). Plan to use one-liter bottles or smaller. You can raise up to 6 plants per container.

Figure 1. Notice that the scissors are cutting along the bottom of the bottle curve. This provides better control.

Figure 2. Feed mason twine through a small hole in the lid.

Figure 3. The growing systems are ready for planting.

Figure 4. Soil is in place along with the wicking.

Figure 5. Mix fertilizer — one bottle cap of fertilizer in eight liters of water. Wet the soil gently until water drips from the wicks. Then fill the reservoirs with the dilute fertilizer solution. Plant the seeds carefully — about six to a bottle, uniformly spaced on the surface, not buried in the soil.

Figure 6. Cover with a light layer of vermiculite. Place the reservoirs — with fertilizer water, seeds on the surface of the soil, and a light layer of vermiculite on the soil — under the lights.

Step 2 Each day, check your plants and make sure that the reservoirs are full, especially on Fridays. These reservoirs have enough volume to last a three-day weekend for small plants.

As your plants grow, record your observations daily. Also try to identify a trait that you could measure or observe reliably. Look for variation in the plants you are growing and describe any you see in your notebook. Observe your classmates' plants as well. Are there also variations in their plants?

Note: Carefully read Steps 3–7 *before* the plants begin to flower.

Step 3 When the plants are about 7 to 12 days old (Figure 7), the class needs to choose 1–2 variable traits for artificial selection. Several variable traits can work for this. Compare your observations with those of other students. You want a trait that varies between plants in a single bottle but also varies between containers. The trait should not be something that is Yes or No, but rather something that varies within a range. That is, look for traits that you can score on a continuum (length, width, number, and so on).

If you and your classmates cannot identify a trait on your own, your teacher will provide additional guidance.

Trichomes

Figure 7. The plants here are 7–12 days old.

Step 4 Score each of your plants for the trait that your class chose to evaluate. You may need a magnifier to do this accurately. Don't be surprised if some plants are not very different from one another.

Step 5 In your lab notebook, compile a list of all the possible traits your class identified. Calculate appropriate descriptive statistics for the class data for the first generation: mean, median, range, standard deviation, etc. Create a histogram that shows the frequency distribution of the trait that you have selected. You can find help for this in Chapter 3.

Step 6 You are now ready to make selection decisions. Directional selection tends to move the variability of a trait in one direction or the other (increase or decrease the trait in the next population). As a class, pick a trait you want to try to affect. Find the top (or bottom) 10% of plants with that trait in the entire class's population (e.g., out of a population of 150 plants, the 15 hairiest plants), and mark any that are in your plant bottle container. Using scissors, cut off the tops of the remaining plants in your container (those not in the top 10%).

Step 7 Just as you did in Step 5, construct a new histogram and calculate descriptive statistics for the selected population of plants. Record the data in your lab notebook. Once you have finished, isolate these selected plants from the rest of the population. Move the bottles of selected plants to another light system so that the plants can finish out their life cycle in isolation. This population will serve as the parents for a new generation.

Step 8 On about day 14–16, when several flowers are present on each of the selected plants, cross-pollinate the selected plants with a single bee stick or pollinating device. Fast Plants are self-incompatible — each plant must be fertilized by pollen from another plant. Collect and distribute pollen from every flower on every plant in the selected population. Reserve this bee stick for only the selected population. Avoid contaminating with the pollen from the remaining Fast Plants. Pollinate flowers in the selected population for the next three days with the same bee stick. Be sure to record observations about pollination in your lab notebook. Likewise, with separate bee sticks you can pollinate the plants from the larger population, but be careful to keep them separate from the selected population.

Step 9 Maintain the plants through the rest of their life cycle. As the seedpods form be sure to limit each of the plants to 8 to 10 seedpods. Any more will likely result in poor seed quality. Once the seedpods start to turn yellow (about day 28–36), remove the fertilizer water from the reservoirs and allow the plants to dry for several days. After the plants and seedpods have dried (about a week later), harvest the seedpods from the selected population into a small paper bag for further drying. Be sure to record observations about the plants' life cycle in your lab notebook.

Step 10 Continue to monitor, pollinate, and maintain your control plants throughout the rest of their life cycle. Just be careful to keep the original population and the selected population separate.

Plant Cultivation: Second-Generation Plants

Step 11 You should now have two populations of second-generation seeds: (1) a population that is the offspring of the selected plants from generation one and (2) a population that is the offspring of the remaining plants from generation one. Take seeds from the selected population and plant them to grow the second generation of plants under conditions that are identical to those you used for generation one. Use new bottle containers or, if you choose to use the previous bottle systems, make sure that you thoroughly clean the systems and sterilize with a dilute (10%) bleach solution. Use new wicking cord and new soil. To get your seed, break open the seedpods into a small plastic petri dish lid.

Step 12 When the second-generation plants are about seven to 12 days old, reexamine the plants and score for the trait you selected. Score the plants at the same life history stage using the same method.

Step 13 Unless you plan on growing these plants for another generation (maybe another round of selection), you do not have to save these plants. You can discard them and clean up your growing equipment at this point.

Step 14 Compile, analyze, and graph the class data as you did for the first generation. What is the outcome of your artificial selection? Be sure to record this preliminary analysis in your notebook.

■ Analyzing and Evaluating Results

Up to this point of the investigation, your analysis has largely been descriptive, but your data should raise some questions.

- Are the two populations/generations before and after selection actually different?

- Are the means significantly different?

- Should you use median or mean as a measure of central tendencies at this point in the investigation?

- Compare your two graphs from the two populations. The chapter on quantitative methods in this lab manual (Chapter 3) provides some guidance here. Consider constructing a bar graph to compare the mean number of hairs per generation. Include error bars, but first determine what is appropriate.

- What statistical test could you apply to help you define your confidence about whether these two populations are different?

- Compare the second population to the parent subpopulation of generation one. How do these two populations compare? How does this comparison differ from your other comparison?

As you carry out your analysis, be sure to include your rationale for the quantitative methods you have chosen in your discussion. Did evolution occur in your Fast Plant population? Justify your conclusion in your laboratory notebook.

■ Designing and Conducting Your Investigation

In the previous steps, you quantified a variable trait and then selected about 10% of the plants in the population that strongly expressed that trait. You isolated this subpopulation from the larger population during pollination and the rest of the life cycle. You then planted the resulting second generation of seeds, raised the plants to a similar life stage as the previous population, and scored the variation in the second-generation plants. During this long process, you recorded your observations, reflections, and perhaps some questions in your laboratory notebook.

As you worked, you likely started to think about questions of your own. You might want to know why the trait you tested is even variable to start with. How does it help the plants grow and survive? You might also have identified some other trait that you want to explore instead of the one the class chose.

Does one form or another of the trait offer an advantage in the natural world? How could you test this? Phenotypic variation is the result of the interaction of the genotypic variation with the variables in the environment. How much of the variation that you studied could be the result of environmental differences?

You and your class may decide to do this work as a class (to distribute the work involved) or work in small groups. You will report your work to the class and possibly to other AP® Biology classes in a manner agreed upon by you and your instructor. Posters, lab reports, online reports, and oral presentations are all possible effective means of submitting your work for review.

■ Where Can You Go from Here?

An essential component of this investigation is to take it beyond the simple selection experiment. With the skills and knowledge gained in the selection experiment, you should be able to design new experiments to investigate the adaptive characteristics of the trait you studied.

Start with a question of your own regarding hairs or some other variable quantitative trait, such as plant height, stem color, or flower number. For instance, in a closely related plant, one investigation demonstrated that herbivore damage early in the plant's development led to increased trichome numbers in later leaves. Could herbivore damage influence the hairy trait expression? Design and carry out an investigation to answer your question.

INVESTIGATION 2

MATHEMATICAL MODELING: HARDY-WEINBERG*

How can mathematical models be used to investigate the relationship between allele frequencies in populations of organisms and evolutionary change?

■ BACKGROUND

Evolution occurs in populations of organisms and involves variation in the population, heredity, and differential survival. One way to study evolution is to study how the frequency of alleles in a population changes from generation to generation. In other words, you can ask *What are the inheritance patterns of alleles, not just from two parental organisms, but also in a population?* You can then explore how allele frequencies change in populations and how these changes might predict what will happen to a population in the future.

Mathematical models and computer simulations are tools used to explore the complexity of biological systems that might otherwise be difficult or impossible to study. Several models can be applied to questions about evolution. In this investigation, you will build a spreadsheet that models how a hypothetical gene pool changes from one generation to the next. This model will let you explore parameters that affect allele frequencies, such as selection, mutation, and migration.

The second part of the investigation asks you to generate your own questions regarding the evolution of allele frequencies in a population. Then you are asked to explore possible answers to those questions by applying more sophisticated computer models. These models are available for free.

This investigation also provides an opportunity for you to review concepts you might have studied previously, including natural selection as the major mechanism of evolution; the relationship among genotype, phenotype, and natural selection; and fundamentals of classic Mendelian genetics.

---

* Transitioned from the *AP Biology Lab Manual* (2001)

■ Learning Objectives

- To use a data set that reflects a change in the genetic makeup of a population over time and to apply mathematical methods and conceptual understandings to investigate the cause(s) and effect(s) of this change

- To apply mathematical methods to data from a real or simulated population to predict what will happen to the population in the future

- To evaluate data-based evidence that describes evolutionary changes in the genetic makeup of a population over time

- To use data from mathematical models based on the Hardy-Weinberg equilibrium to analyze genetic drift and the effect of selection in the evolution of specific populations

- To justify data from mathematical models based on the Hardy-Weinberg equilibrium to analyze genetic drift and the effects of selection in the evolution of specific populations

- To describe a model that represents evolution within a population

- To evaluate data sets that illustrate evolution as an ongoing process

■ General Safety Precautions

There are some important things to remember when computer modeling in the classroom. To avoid frustration, periodically save your work. When developing and working out models, save each new version of the model with a different file name. That way, if a particular strategy doesn't work, you will not necessarily have to start over completely but can bring up a file that had the beginnings of a working model.

If you have difficulty refining your spreadsheet, consider using the spreadsheet to generate the random samples and using pencil and paper to archive and graph the results.

As you work through building this spreadsheet you may encounter spreadsheet tools and functions that are not familiar to you. Today, there are many Web-based tutorials, some text based and some video, to help you learn these skills. For instance, typing "How to use the SUM tool in Excel video" will bring up several videos that will walk you through using the SUM tool.

■ THE INVESTIGATIONS

■ Getting Started

This particular investigation provides a lab environment, guidance, and a problem designed to help you understand and develop the skill of modeling biological phenomena with computers. There are dozens of computer models already built and available for free. The idea for this laboratory is for you to build your own from scratch. To obtain the maximum benefit from this exercise, you should not do too much background preparation. As you build your model and explore it, you should develop a more thorough understanding of how genes behave in population.

To help you begin, you might want to work with physical models of population genetics, such as simulations that your teacher can share with you. With these pencil-and-paper simulations, you can obtain some insights that may help you develop your computer model.

■ Procedure

It is easy to understand how microscopes opened up an entire new world of biological understanding. For some, it is not as easy to see the value of mathematics to the study of biology, but, like the microscope, math and computers provide tools to explore the complexity of biology and biological systems — providing deeper insights and understanding of what makes living systems work.

To explore how allele frequencies change in populations of organisms, you will first build a computer spreadsheet that models the changes in a hypothetical gene pool from one generation to the next. You need a basic familiarity with spreadsheet operations to complete this lab successfully. You may have taken a course that introduced you to spreadsheets before. If so, that will be helpful, and you may want to try to design and build your model on your own after establishing some guidelines and assumptions. Otherwise, you may need more specific guidance from your teacher. You can use almost any spreadsheet program available, including free online spreadsheet software such as Google Docs or Zoho (*http://www.zoho.com*), to complete the first section of your investigation.

In the second part of the investigation, you will use more sophisticated spreadsheet models or computer models to explore various aspects of evolution and alleles in populations. To understand how these complex tools work and their limitations, you first need to build a model of your own.

Building a Simple Mathematical Model

The real world is infinitely complicated. To penetrate that complexity using model building, you must learn to make reasonable, simplifying assumptions about complex processes. For example, climate change models or weather forecasting models are simplifications of very complex processes — more than can be accounted for with even the most powerful computer. These models allow us to make predictions and test hypotheses about climate change and weather.

By definition, any model is a simplification of the real world. For that reason, you need to constantly evaluate the assumptions you make as you build a model, as well as evaluate the results of the model with a critical eye. This is actually one of the powerful benefits of a model — it forces you to think deeply about an idea.

There are many approaches to model building; in their book on mathematical modeling in biology, Otto and Day (2007) suggest the following steps:

1. Formulate the question.

2. Determine the basic ingredients.

3. Qualitatively describe the biological system.

4. Quantitatively describe the biological system.

5. Analyze the equations.

6. Perform checks and balances.

7. Relate the results back to the question.

As you work through the next section, record your thoughts, assumptions, and strategies on modeling in your laboratory notebook.

Step 1 Formulate the question.

Think about a recessive Mendelian trait such as cystic fibrosis. Why do recessive alleles like cystic fibrosis stay in the human population? Why don't they gradually disappear?

Now think about a dominant Mendelian trait such as polydactyly (more than five fingers on a single hand or toes on a foot) in humans. Polydactyly is a dominant trait, but it is not a *common* trait in most human populations. Why not?

How do inheritance patterns or allele frequencies change in a population? Our investigation begins with an exploration of answers to these simple questions.

Step 2 Determine the basic ingredients.

Let's try to simplify the question *How do inheritance patterns or allele frequencies change in a population?* with some basic assumptions. For this model, assume that all the organisms in our hypothetical population are diploid. This organism has a gene locus with two alleles — *A* and *B*. (We could use *A* and *a* to represent the alleles, but *A* and *B* are easier to work with in the spreadsheet you'll be developing.) So far, this imaginary population is much like any sexually reproducing population.

How else can you simplify the question? Consider that the population has an infinite gene pool (all the alleles in the population at this particular locus). Gametes for the next generation are selected totally at random. What does that mean? Focus on answering that question in your lab notebook for a moment — it is key to our model. For now let's consider that our model is going to look only at how allele frequencies might change from generation to generation. To do that we need to describe the system.

Step 3 Qualitatively describe the biological system.

Imagine for a minute the life cycle of our hypothetical organism. See if you can draw a diagram of the cycle; be sure to include the life stages of the organism. Your life cycle might look like Figure 1.

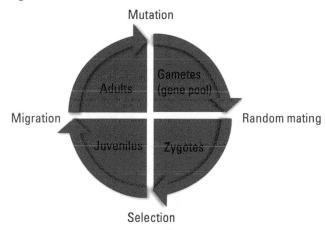

Figure 1. Life Stages of a Population of Organisms

To make this initial exploration into a model of inheritance patterns in a population, you need to make some important assumptions — all the gametes go into one infinite pool, and all have an equal chance of taking part in fertilization or formation of a zygote. For now, all zygotes live to be juveniles, all juveniles live to be adults, and no individuals enter or leave the population; there is also no mutation. Make sure to record these assumptions in your notebook; later, you will need to explore how your model responds as you change or modify these assumptions.

Step 4 Quantitatively describe the biological system.

Spreadsheets are valuable tools that allow us to ask *What if?* questions. They can repeatedly make a calculation based on the results of another calculation. They can also model the randomness of everyday events. Our goal is to model how allele frequencies change through one life cycle of this imaginary population in the spreadsheet. Use the diagram in Figure 1 as a guide to help you design the sequence and nature of your spreadsheet calculation.

Each part of the life cycle can be represented by a spreadsheet operation.

1. Set allele frequencies (assign a value to a cell).

2. Use the random function (RAND) to generate a random number which will be compared to the allele frequency from Step 1.

3. Compare the random number to allele frequency and assign the appropriate allele.

4. Repeat Steps 1–3 for the second allele.

5. Use the CONCATENATE function to combine the two alleles to form a zygote.

6. Copy this procedure (Steps 2–5) for multiple offspring.

Let's get started. The first step is to randomly draw gametes from the gene pool to form a number of zygotes that will make up the next generation.

To begin this model, let's define a couple of variables.

Let

$$p = \text{the frequency of the } A \text{ allele}$$
$$\text{and let } q = \text{the frequency of the } B \text{ allele}$$

Bring up the spreadsheet on your computer. The examples here are based on Microsoft® Excel, but almost any modern spreadsheet can work, including Google's online Google Docs (***https://docs.google.com***) and Zoho's online spreadsheet (***http://www.zoho.com***).

Hint: If you are familiar with spreadsheets, the RAND function, and using IF statements to create formulas in spreadsheets, you may want to skip ahead and try to build a model on your own. If these are not familiar to you, proceed with the following tutorial.

Somewhere in the upper left corner (in this case, cell D2), enter a value for the frequency of the *A* allele. This value should be between 0 and 1. Go ahead and type in labels in your other cells and, if you wish, shade the cells as well. This blue area will represent the gene pool for your model. (Highlight the area you wish to format with color, and right-click with your mouse in Excel to format.) This is a spreadsheet, so you can enter the value for the frequency of the *B* allele; however, when making a model it is best to have the spreadsheet do as many of the calculations as possible. All of the alleles in the gene pool are either *A* or *B*; therefore $p + q = 1$ and $1 - p = q$. In cell D3, enter the formula to calculate the value of *q*.

In spreadsheet lingo it is

$$=1\text{-}D2$$

Your spreadsheet now should look something like Figure 2.

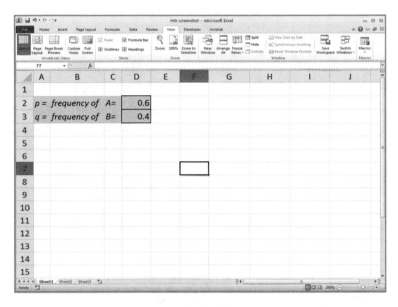

Figure 2

Let's explore how one important spreadsheet function works before we incorporate it into our model. In a nearby empty cell, enter the function (we will remove it later).

$$=\text{Rand}()$$

Note that the parentheses have nothing between them. After hitting *return*, what do you find in the cell? If you are on a PC, try hitting the F9 key several times to force recalculation. On a Mac, enter *cmd +* or *cmd =*. What happens to the value in the cell? Describe your results in your lab notebook.

The RAND function returns random numbers between 0 and 1 in decimal format. This is a powerful feature of spreadsheets. It allows us to enter a sense of randomness to our calculations if it is appropriate — and here it is when we are "randomly" choosing gametes from a gene pool. Go ahead and delete the RAND function in the cell.

Let's select two gametes from the gene pool. In cell E5, let's generate a random number, compare it to the value of *p*, and then place either an *A* gamete or a *B* gamete in the cell. We'll need two functions to do this, the RAND function and the IF function. Check the help menu if necessary.

Note that the function entered in cell E5 is

$$=IF(RAND()<=D\$2, ``A", ``B")$$

Be sure to include the *$* in front of the *2* in the cell address D2. It will save time later when you build onto this spreadsheet.

The formula in this cell basically says that if a random number between 0 and 1 is less than or equal to the value of *p*, then put an *A* gamete in this cell, or if it is not less than or equal to the value of *p*, put a *B* gamete in this cell. IF functions and RAND functions are very powerful tools when you try to build models for biology.

Now create the same formula in cell F5, making sure that it is formatted exactly like E5. When you have this completed, press the recalculate key to force a recalculation of your spreadsheet. If you have entered the functions correctly in the two cells, you should see changing values in the two cells. (This is part of the testing and retesting that you have to do while model building.) Your spreadsheet should look like Figure 3.

Try recalculating 10–20 times. Are your results consistent with what you expect? Do both cells (E5 and F5) change to *A* or *B* in the ratios you'd expect from your *p* value? Try changing your *p* value to 0.8 or 0.9. Does the spreadsheet still work as expected? Try lower *p* values. If you don't get approximately the expected numbers, check and recheck your formulas now, while it is early in the process.

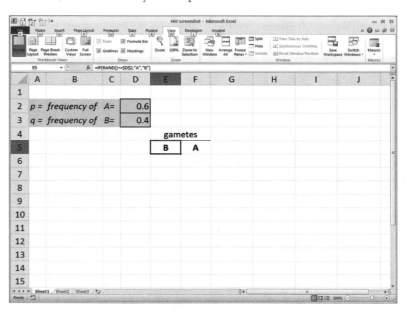

Figure 3

You could stop here and just have the computer recalculate over and over — similar to tossing a coin. However, with just a few more steps, you can have a model that will create a small number or large number of gametes for the next generation, count the different genotypes of the zygotes, and graph the results.

Copy these two formulas in E5 and F5 down for about 16 rows to represent gametes that will form 16 offspring for the next generation, as in Figure 4. (To copy the formulas, click on the bottom right-hand corner of the cell and, with your finger pressed down on the mouse, drag the cell downward.)

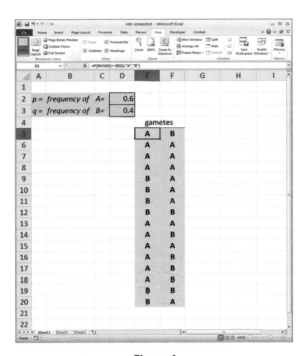

Figure 4

We'll put the zygotes in cell G5. The zygote is a combination of the two randomly selected gametes. In spreadsheet vernacular, you want to concatenate the values in the two cells. In cell G5 enter the function

$$=CONCATENATE(E5,F5)$$

Copy this formula down as far down as you have gametes, as in Figure 5 on the next page.

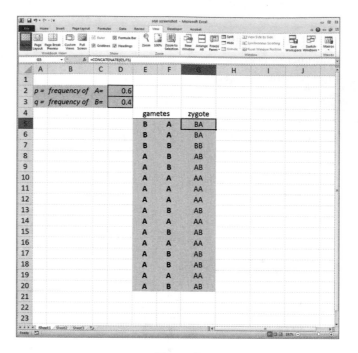

Figure 5

The next columns on the sheet, H, I, and J, are used for bookkeeping — that is, keeping track of the numbers of each zygote's genotype. They are rather complex functions that use IF functions to help us count the different genotypes of the zygotes.

The function in cell H5 is

$$=IF(G5=\text{"AA"},1,0)$$

This basically means that if the value in cell G5 is AA, then put a 1 in this cell; if not, then put a 0.

Enter the following very similar function in cell J5: =IF(G5="BB",1,0)

- Can you interpret this formula?

- What does it say in English?

Your spreadsheet now should resemble Figure 6.

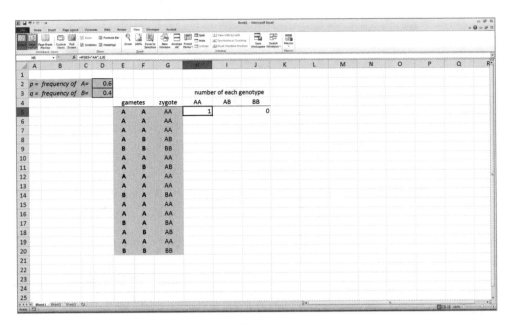

Figure 6

Now let's tackle the nested IF function. This is needed to test for either *AB* or *BA*.

In cell I5, enter the nested function:

$$=IF(G5=\text{"AB"},1,(IF(G5=\text{"BA"},1,0)))$$

This example requires an extra set of parentheses, which is necessary to nest functions. This function basically says that if the value in cell G5 is exactly equal to *AB*, then put a 1; if not, then if the value in cell G5 is exactly *BA*, put a 1; if it is neither, then put a 0 in this cell. Copy these three formulas down for all the rows in which you have produced gametes.

Enter the labels for the columns you've been working on — *gametes* in cell E4, *zygote* in cell G5, *AA* in cell H4, *AB* in cell I4, and *BB* in cell J4, as shown in Figure 7 on the next page.

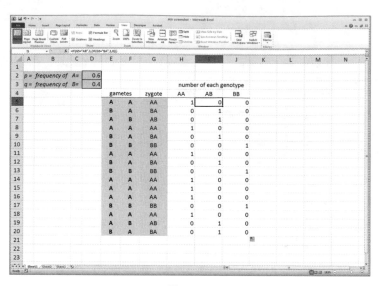

Figure 7

As before, try recalculating a number of times to make sure everything is working as expected. What is expected? If you aren't sure yet, keep this question in mind as you complete the sheet. You could use a *p* value of 0.5, and then you'd see numbers similar to the ratios you would get from flipping two coins at once. Don't go on until you are sure the spreadsheet is making correct calculations. Try out different values for *p*. Make sure that the number of zygotes adds up. Describe your thinking and procedure for checking the spreadsheet in your lab notebook.

Now, copy the cells E5 through J5 down for as many zygotes as you'd like in the first generation. Use the SUM function to calculate the numbers of each genotype in the H, I, and J columns. Use the genotype frequencies to calculate new allele frequencies and to recalculate new *p* and *q* values. Make a bar graph of the genotypes using the chart tool. Your spreadsheet should resemble Figure 8.

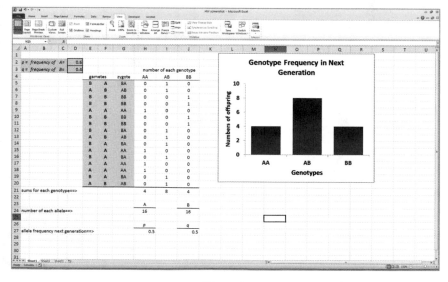

Figure 8

Testing Your Mathematical Model

You now have a model with which you can explore how allele frequencies behave and change from generation to generation. Working with a partner, develop a plan to answer this general question: *How do inheritance patterns or allele frequencies change in a population over one generation?* As you work, think about the following more specific questions:

- What can you change in your model? If you change something, what does the change tell you about how alleles behave?

- Do alleles behave the same way if you make a particular variable more extreme? Less extreme?

- Do alleles behave the same way no matter what the population size is? To answer this question, you can insert rows of data somewhere between the first row of data and the last row and then copy the formulas down to fill in the space.

Try out different starting allele frequencies in the model. Look for and describe the patterns that you find as you try out different allele frequencies. Develop and use a pattern to select your values to test and organize your exploration. In particular, test your model with extreme values and intermediate values. In your lab notebook, describe your observations and conclusions about the population inheritance patterns you discover.

Try adding additional generations to your model to look at how allele frequencies change in multiple generations. To do this, use your newly recalculated p and q values to seed the next generation. Once you've included the second generation, you should be able to copy additional generations so that your model looks something like Figure 9, with each new generation determining the new p and q values for the next.

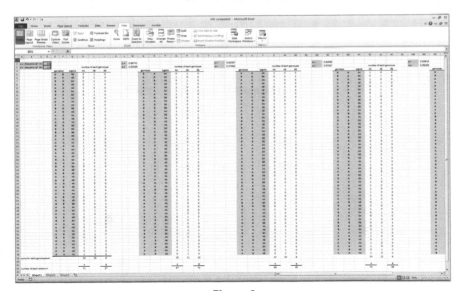

Figure 9

Try to create a graph of p values over several generations, for different-sized populations. See if you can detect a pattern of how population size affects the inheritance pattern. Be sure to try out both large and small populations of offspring.

This model relies on the RAND function to randomly select gametes from an infinite gene pool.

- What would happen if there were no randomness to this selection?

- What kind of pattern of genotypes would you expect in the next generation?

Creating a Formula that Predicts the Genotypes of the Next Generation

Here are two approaches to develop the formula. You might first try a graphical approach. Create a Punnet square, like Figure 10 and similar to what you might use to solve a Mendelian genetics problem. In this case, however, plot the values of p and q. Scale each side of the square based on the magnitude of the p or q values. Place this diagram in your lab notebook, and fill in the squares with variables and values, as in Figure 10.

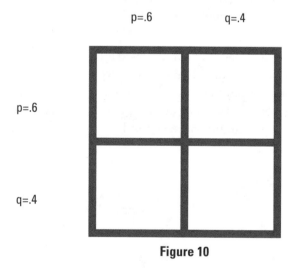

Figure 10

Of course, you could also calculate the expected results for the next generation.

Remember that $p + q = 1$

The probability of two A alleles combining in one organism in the next generation is p^2. The probability of two B alleles combining is q^2. The probability of a combination of AB is $p * q$, as is the probability of combination of BA alleles, for a total of $2pq$.

For the next generation, the formula that predicts genotypes is

$$(p + q)^2 = 1, \text{ which works out to: } p^2 + 2pq + q^2$$

Based on the calculations you made while testing your model, how would you answer the following questions?

- In the absence of random events (an infinitely large population), are the allele frequencies of the original population expected to change from generation to generation?

- How does this compare to a population that has random gamete selection but is small?

- What happens to allele frequencies in such a population? Is it predictable?

This mathematical model can predict allele frequencies from generation to generation. In fact, it is a *null* model. That is, in the absence of random events or other real-life factors that affect populations, the allele frequencies do not change from generation to generation. This is known as the Hardy-Weinberg equilibrium (H-W equilibrium). The H-W equilibrium is a valuable tool for population biologists because it serves as a baseline to measure changes in allele frequencies in a population. If a population is not in H-W equilibrium, then something else is happening that is making the allele frequencies change.

What factors can cause allele frequencies to change in a population? (Hint: There are many.) How could you model these factors using your spreadsheet?

■ Designing and Conducting Your Investigation

By this point you've been able to use your model to explore how random chance affects the inheritance patterns of alleles in large and small populations. Perhaps you've also been able to find some interesting patterns in how alleles behave across generations.

At the end of the last section you were asked what factors can cause allele frequencies to change in a population and how you would model them. Choose one of your answers, and try it out using your spreadsheet. This may involve adding multiple columns or rows along with a few extra operations. Keep the life cycle of your hypothetical population in mind as you develop additional strategies.

With your new spreadsheet model, generate your own questions regarding the evolution of allele frequencies in a population. From these questions (noted in your lab notebook), you need to develop hypotheses that you can test — those that allow you to easily manipulate the parameters of population size, number of generations, selection (fitness), mutation, migration, and genetic drift. Collect sufficient data by running your model repeatedly. Analyze your data. Formulate your conclusions and present a miniposter that supports your claim with sound reasoning and evidence to the class. Your teacher may have some ideas for questions to investigate.

Where Can You Go from Here?

An excellent extension to this laboratory is the following investigation:

McMahon, K. A. 2008. Supertasters—Updating the Taste Test for the A & P Laboratory. Pages 398–405, in Tested Studies for Laboratory Teaching, Volume 29 (K.L. Clase, Editor). Proceedings of the 29th Workshop/Conference of the Association for Biology Laboratory Education (ABLE).

Your teacher will provide the lab, or you can google "ABLE proceedings + supertaster" to access the lab.

There are few human traits that express the intermediate dominance necessary for testing for the null hypothesis. The supertaster trait described in this laboratory does express an intermediate phenotype; therefore, it creates an exemplary investigative population genetics laboratory.

REFERENCE

Otto, S. P. and T. Day (2007). A Biologist's Guide to Mathematical Modeling in Ecology and Evolution. Princeton University Press.
http://www.zoology.ubc.ca/biomath/

INVESTIGATION 3

COMPARING DNA SEQUENCES TO UNDERSTAND EVOLUTIONARY RELATIONSHIPS WITH BLAST

How can bioinformatics be used as a tool to determine evolutionary relationships and to better understand genetic diseases?

■ BACKGROUND

Between 1990–2003, scientists working on an international research project known as the Human Genome Project were able to identify and map the 20,000–25,000 genes that define a human being. The project also successfully mapped the genomes of other species, including the fruit fly, mouse, and *Escherichia coli*. The location and complete sequence of the genes in each of these species are available for anyone in the world to access via the Internet.

Why is this information important? Being able to identify the precise location and sequence of human genes will allow us to better understand genetic diseases. In addition, learning about the sequence of genes in other species helps us understand evolutionary relationships among organisms. Many of our genes are identical or similar to those found in other species.

Suppose you identify a single gene that is responsible for a particular disease in fruit flies. Is that same gene found in humans? Does it cause a similar disease? It would take you nearly 10 years to read through the entire human genome to try to locate the same sequence of bases as that in fruit flies. This definitely isn't practical, so a sophisticated technological method is needed.

Bioinformatics is a field that combines statistics, mathematical modeling, and computer science to analyze biological data. Using bioinformatics methods, entire genomes can be quickly compared in order to detect genetic similarities and differences. An extremely powerful bioinformatics tool is BLAST, which stands for Basic Local Alignment Search Tool. Using BLAST, you can input a gene sequence of interest and search entire genomic libraries for identical or similar sequences in a matter of seconds.

In this laboratory investigation, you will use BLAST to compare several genes, and then use the information to construct a *cladogram*. A cladogram (also called a phylogenetic tree) is a visualization of the evolutionary relatedness of species. Figure 1 is a simple cladogram.

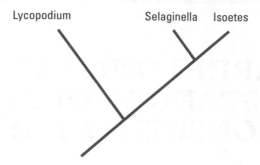

Figure 1. Simple Cladogram Representing Different Plant Species

Note that the cladogram is treelike, with the endpoints of each branch representing a specific species. The closer two species are located to each other, the more recently they share a common ancestor. For example, *Selaginella* (spikemoss) and *Isoetes* (quillwort) share a more recent common ancestor than the common ancestor that is shared by all three organisms.

Figure 2 includes additional details, such as the evolution of particular physical structures called shared derived characters. Note that the placement of the derived characters corresponds to when (in a general, not a specific, sense) that character evolved; every species above the character label possesses that structure. For example, tigers and gorillas have hair, but lampreys, sharks, salamanders, and lizards do not have hair.

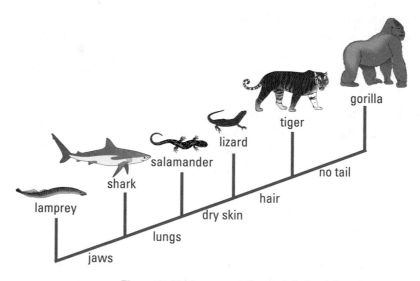

Figure 2. Cladogram of Several Animal Species

The cladogram above can be used to answer several questions. Which organisms have lungs? What three structures do all lizards possess? According to the cladogram, which structure — dry skin or hair — evolved first?

Historically, only physical structures were used to create cladograms; however, modern-day cladistics relies heavily on genetic evidence as well. Chimpanzees and humans share 95%+ of their DNA, which would place them closely together on a cladogram. Humans and fruit flies share approximately 60% of their DNA, which would place them farther apart on a cladogram.

Can you draw a cladogram that depicts the evolutionary relationship among humans, chimpanzees, fruit flies, and mosses?

Learning Objectives

- To create cladograms that depict evolutionary relationships

- To analyze biological data with a sophisticated bioinformatics online tool

- To use cladograms and bioinformatics tools to ask other questions of your own and to test your ability to apply concepts you know relating to genetics and evolution

General Safety Precautions

There are no safety precautions associated with this investigation.

THE INVESTIGATIONS

Getting Started

Your teacher may assign the following questions to see how much you understand concepts related to cladograms before you conduct your investigation:

1. Use the following data to construct a cladogram of the major plant groups:

Table 1. Characteristics of Major Plant Groups

Organisms	Vascular Tissue	Flowers	Seeds
Mosses	0	0	0
Pine trees	1	0	1
Flowering plants	1	1	1
Ferns	1	0	0
Total	3	1	2

2. GAPDH (glyceraldehyde 3-phosphate dehydrogenase) is an enzyme that catalyzes the sixth step in glycolysis, an important reaction that produces molecules used in cellular respiration. The following data table shows the percentage similarity of this gene and the protein it expresses in humans versus other species. For example, according to the table, the GAPDH gene in chimpanzees is 99.6% identical to the gene found in humans, while the protein is identical.

Table 2. Percentage Similarity Between the GAPDH Gene and Protein in Humans and Other Species

Species	Gene Percentage Similarity	Protein Percentage Similarity
Chimpanzee *(Pan troglodytes)*	99.6%	100%
Dog *(Canis lupus familiaris)*	91.3%	95.2%
Fruit fly *(Drosophila melanogaster)*	72.4%	76.7%
Roundworm *(Caenorhabditis elegans)*	68.2%	74.3%

a. Why is the percentage similarity in the gene always lower than the percentage similarity in the protein for each of the species? (Hint: Recall how a gene is expressed to produce a protein.)

b. Draw a cladogram depicting the evolutionary relationships among all five species (including humans) according to their percentage similarity in the GAPDH gene.

Online Activities

You can also prepare for the lab by working through the following online activities:

- "The Evolution of Flight in Birds"
  http://www.ucmp.berkeley.edu/education/explorations/reslab/flight/main.htm
  This activity provides a real-world example of how cladograms are used to understand evolutionary relationships.

- "What did T. rex taste like?"
  http://www.ucmp.berkeley.edu/education/explorations/tours/Trex /index.html

- "Journey into Phylogenetic Systematics"
  http://www.ucmp.berkeley.edu/clad/clad4.html

■ Procedure

A team of scientists has uncovered the fossil specimen in Figure 3 near Liaoning Province, China. Make some general observations about the morphology (physical structure) of the fossil, and then record your observations in your notebook.

Little is known about the fossil. It appears to be a new species. Upon careful examination of the fossil, small amounts of soft tissue have been discovered. Normally, soft tissue does not survive fossilization; however, rare situations of such preservation do occur. Scientists were able to extract DNA nucleotides from the tissue and use the information to sequence several genes. Your task is to use BLAST to analyze these genes and determine the most likely placement of the fossil species on Figure 4.

©AMNH, Mick Ellison

Figure 3. Fossil Specimen

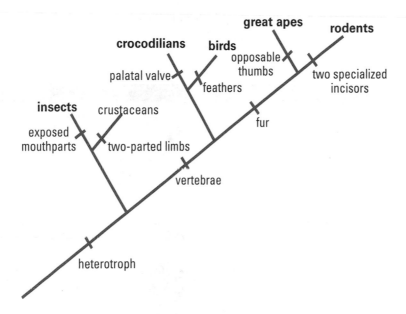

Figure 4. Fossil Cladogram

Step 1 Form an initial hypothesis as to where you believe the fossil specimen should be placed on the cladogram based on the morphological observations you made earlier. Draw your hypothesis on Figure 4.

Step 2 Locate and download gene files. Download three gene files from the AP Biology Investigative Labs page at AP Central: *http://apcentral.collegeboard.com/apc/ members/courses/teachers_corner/218954.html*.

Step 3 Upload the gene sequence into BLAST by doing the following:

   a. Go to the BLAST homepage: *http://blast.ncbi.nlm.nih.gov/Blast.cgi*

   b. Click on "Saved Strategies" from the menu at the top of the page.

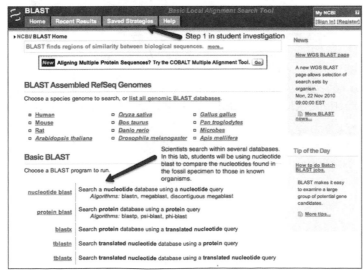

Figure 5

c. Under "Upload Search Strategy," click on "Browse" and locate one of the gene files you saved onto your computer.

d. Click "View."

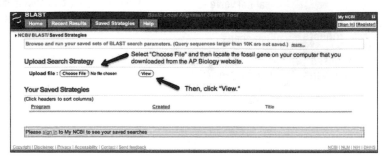

Figure 6

e. A screen will appear with the parameters for your query already configured. NOTE: Do not alter any of the parameters. Scroll down the page and click on the "BLAST" button at the bottom.

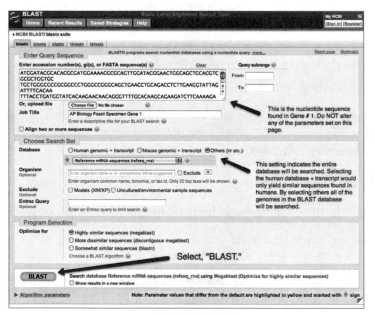

Figure 7

f. After collecting and analyzing all of the data for that particular gene (see instructions below), repeat this procedure for the other two gene sequences.

Step 4 The results page has two sections. The first section is a graphical display of the matching sequences.

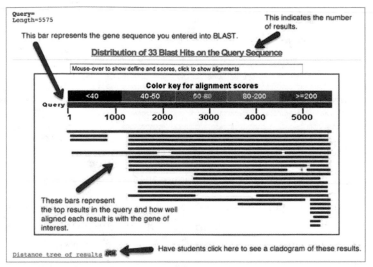

Figure 8

Scroll down to the section titled "Sequences producing significant alignments." The species in the list that appears below this section are those with sequences identical to or most similar to the gene of interest. The most similar sequences are listed first, and as you move down the list, the sequences become less similar to your gene of interest.

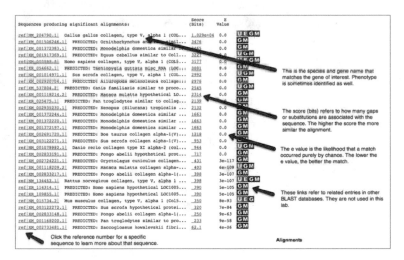

Figure 9

If you click on a particular species listed, you'll get a full report that includes the classification scheme of the species, the research journal in which the gene was first reported, and the sequence of bases that appear to align with your gene of interest.

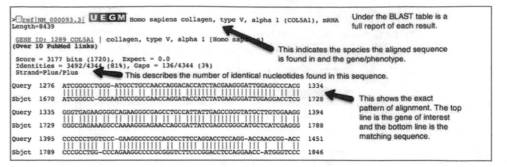

Figure 10

If you click on a particular species listed, you'll get a full report that includes the species' classification scheme, the research journal in which the gene was first reported, and the sequence of bases that appear to align with your gene of interest.

If you click on the link titled "Distance tree of results," you will see a cladogram with the species with similar sequences to your gene of interest placed on the cladogram according to how closely their matched gene aligns with your gene of interest.

■ Analyzing Results

Recall that species with common ancestry will share similar genes. The more similar genes two species have in common, the more recent their common ancestor and the closer the two species will be located on a cladogram.

As you collect information from BLAST for each of the gene files, you should be thinking about your original hypothesis and whether the data support or cause you to reject your original placement of the fossil species on the cladogram.

For each BLAST query, consider the following:

- The higher the score, the closer the alignment.

- The lower the e value, the closer the alignment.

- Sequences with e values less than 1e-04 (1 x 10-4) can be considered related with an error rate of less than 0.01%.

1. What species in the BLAST result has the most similar gene sequence to the gene of interest?

2. Where is that species located on your cladogram?

3. How similar is that gene sequence?

4. What species has the next most similar gene sequence to the gene of interest?

Based on what you have learned from the sequence analysis and what you know from the structure, decide where the new fossil species belongs on the cladogram with the other organisms. If necessary, redraw the cladogram you created before.

■ Evaluating Results

Compare and discuss your cladogram with your classmates. Does everyone agree with the placement of the fossil specimen? If not, what is the basis of the disagreement?

On the main page of BLAST, click on the link "List All Genomic Databases." How many genomes are currently available for making comparisons using BLAST? How does this limitation impact the proper analysis of the gene data used in this lab?

What other data could be collected from the fossil specimen to help properly identify its evolutionary history?

■ Designing and Conducting Your Investigation

Now that you've completed this investigation, you should feel more comfortable using BLAST. The next step is to learn how to find and BLAST your own genes of interest. To locate a gene, you will go to the Entrez Gene website (***http://www.ncbi.nlm.nih.gov/gene***). Once you have found the gene on the website, you can copy the gene sequence and input it into a BLAST query.

Example Procedure

One student's starting question: What is the function of actin in humans? Do other organisms have actin? If so, which ones?

1. Go to the Entrez Gene website (***http://www.ncbi.nlm.nih.gov/gene***) and search for "human actin."

2. Click on the first link that appears and scroll down to the section "NCBI Reference Sequences."

3. Under "mRNA and Proteins," click on the first file name. It will be named "NM 001100.3" or something similar. These standardized numbers make cataloging sequence files easier. Do not worry about the file number for now.

4. Just below the gene title click on "FASTA." This is the name for a particular format for displaying sequences.

5. The nucleotide sequence displayed is that of the actin gene in humans.

6. Copy the entire gene sequence, and then go to the BLAST homepage (***http://blast.ncbi.nlm.nih.gov/Blast.cgi***).

7. Click on "nucleotide blast" under the Basic BLAST menu.

8. Paste the sequence into the box where it says "Enter Query Sequence."

9. Give the query a title in the box provided if you plan on saving it for later.

10. Under "Choose Search Set," select whether you want to search the human genome only, mouse genome only, or all genomes available.

11. Under "Program Selection," choose whether or not you want highly similar sequences or somewhat similar sequences. Choosing somewhat similar sequences will provide you with more results.

12. Click BLAST.

Below is a list of some gene suggestions you could investigate using BLAST. As you look at a particular gene, try to answer the following questions:

- What is the function in humans of the protein produced from that gene?

- Would you expect to find the same protein in other organisms? If so, which ones?

- Is it possible to find the same gene in two different kinds of organisms but not find the protein that is produced from that gene?

- If you found the same gene in all organisms you test, what does this suggest about the evolution of this gene in the history of life on earth?

- Does the use of DNA sequences in the study of evolutionary relationships mean that other characteristics are unimportant in such studies? Explain your answer.

Suggested Genes to Explore	Families or Genes Studied Previously
ATP synthase	Enzymes
Catalase	Parts of ribosomes
GAPDH	Protein channels
Keratin	
Myosin	
Pax1	
Ubiquitin	

- How do these factors alter diffusion rates?

- Why are gradients important in diffusion and osmosis?

- What is the explanation for the fact that most cells are small and have cell membranes with many convolutions?

- Will water move into or out of a plant cell if the cell has a higher water potential than the surrounding environment?

- What would happen if you applied saltwater to a plant?

- How does a plant cell control its internal (turgor) pressure?

■ **Procedure 1:** Surface Area and Cell Size

Cell size and shape are important factors in determining the rate of diffusion. Think about cells with specialized functions, such as the epithelial cells that line the small intestine or plant root hairs.

- What is the shape of these cells?

- What size are the cells?

- How do small intestinal epithelial and root hair cells function in nutrient procurement?

Materials

- 2% agar containing NaOH and the pH-indicator dye phenolphthalein
- 1% phenolphthalein solution
- 0.1M HCl
- 0.1 M NaOH
- Squares of hard, thin plastic (from

- disposable plates); unserrated knives; or scalpels from dissection kits
- Metric rulers
- Petri dishes and test tubes
- 2% agar with phenolphthalein preparation

Step 1 Place some phenolphthalein in two test tubes. Add 0.1 M HCl to one test tube, _Photo 2x_ swirl to mix the solutions, and observe the color. Using the same procedure, add 0.1 _Photo 2x_ M NaOH to the other test tube. Remember to record your observations as you were instructed.

- Which solution is an acid?

- Which solution is a base?

- What color is the dye in the base? In the acid?

- What color is the dye when mixed with the base?

Step 2 Using a dull knife or a thin strip of hard plastic, cut three blocks of agar of different sizes.

These three blocks will be your models for cells.
- What is the surface area of each of your three cells?
- What is the total volume of each of your cells?
- If you put each of the blocks into a solution, into which block would that solution diffuse throughout the entire block fastest? Slowest? How do you explain the difference?

■ Alternative Method

Mix one packet of unflavored gelatin with 237 mL of water: add 2.5 mL 1% phenolphthalein and a few drops of 0.1 M NaOH. The solution should be bright pink. Pour the gelatin mixture into shallow pans and refrigerate overnight.

You may use white vinegar in place of the 0.1 M HCl.

■ Designing and Conducting Your Investigation

Using the materials listed earlier, design an experiment to test the predictions you just made regarding the relationship of surface area and volume in the artificial cells to the diffusion rate using the phenolphthalein–NaOH agar and the HCl solution. Once you have finished planning your experiment, have your teacher check your design. When you have an approved design, run your experiment and record your results. Do your experimental results support your predictions?

■ Procedure 2: Modeling Diffusion and Osmosis

You are in the hospital and need intravenous fluids. You read the label on the IV bag, which lists all of the solutes in the water.
- Why is it important for an IV solution to have salts in it?
- What would happen if you were given pure water in an IV?
- How would you determine the best concentration of solutes to give a patient in need of fluids *before* you introduced the fluids into the patient's body?

In this experiment, you will create models of living cells using dialysis tubing. Like cell membranes, dialysis tubing is made from a material that is selectively permeable to water and some solutes. You will fill your model cells with different solutions and determine the rate of diffusion.

- How can you use weights of the filled cell models to determine the rate and direction of diffusion? What would be an appropriate control for the procedure you just described?

- Suppose you could test other things besides weights of the dialysis tubes. How could you determine the rates and directions of diffusion of water, sucrose, NaCl, glucose, and ovalbumin?

- Will protein diffuse? Will it affect the rate of diffusion of other molecules?

Materials

- Distilled or tap water
- 1 M sucrose
- 1 M NaCl
- 1 M glucose
- 5% ovalbumin (egg white protein)
- 20 cm-long dialysis tubing
- Cups
- Balances

Step 1 Choose up to four pairs of different solutions. One solution from each pair will be in the model cell of dialysis tubing, and the other will be outside the cell in the cup. Your fifth model cell will have water inside and outside; this is your control. Before starting, use your knowledge about solute gradients to predict whether the water will diffuse into or out of the cell. Make sure you label the cups to indicate what solution is inside the cell and inside the cup.

Step 2 Make dialysis tubing cells by tying a knot in one end of five pieces of dialysis tubing. Fill each "cell" with 10 mL of the solution you chose for the inside, and knot the other end, leaving enough space for water to diffuse into the cell.

Step 3 Weigh each cell, record the initial weight, and then place it into a cup filled with the second solution for that pair. Weigh the cell after 30 minutes and record the final weight.

Step 4 Calculate the percent change in weight using the following formula:
(final – initial)/initial X 100. Record your results.

- Which pair(s) that you tested did not have a change in weight? How can you explain this?

- If you compared 1 M solutions, was a 1 M NaCl solution more or less hypertonic than a 1 M sucrose solution? What is your evidence? What about 1 M NaCl and 1 M glucose and 1 M sucrose?

- Does the protein solution have a high molarity? What is evidence for your conclusion?

- How could you test for the diffusion of glucose?

- Based on what you learned from your experiment, how could you determine the solute concentration inside a living cell?

■ Designing and Conducting Your Investigation

Living cell membranes are selectively permeable and contain protein channels that permit the passage of water and molecules. In some respects, the dialysis tubing you used is similar to a cell membrane, and you can use it to explore osmosis in greater depth. Think about the questions that came up as you worked through the investigation. What unanswered questions do you still have about osmosis that you could investigate further?

Using the available materials, design an investigation to answer one of your questions. Have your teacher check your design first. Remember to record your results, and be sure to use appropriate controls.

These questions can help jump-start your thinking.

- What factors determine the rate and direction of osmosis?

- What would you predict if you used a starch solution instead of the protein?

- Can you diagram the flow of water based upon the contents of your model cell and the surrounding solution?

- When will the net osmosis rate equal zero in your model cells? Will it ever truly be zero?

- Based upon your observations, can you predict the direction of osmosis in living cells when the cells are placed in various solutions?

- How is the dialysis tubing functionally different from a cellular membrane?

■ Procedure 3: Observing Osmosis in Living Cells

The interactions between selectively permeable membranes, water, and solutes are important in cellular and organismal functions. For example, water and nutrients move from plant roots to the leaves and shoots because of differences in water potentials. Based upon what you know and what you have learned about osmosis, diffusion, and water potential in the course of your investigations, think about these questions.

- What would happen if you applied saltwater to the roots of a plant? Why?

- What are two different ways a plant could control turgor pressure, a name for internal water potential within its cells? Is this a sufficient definition for turgor pressure?

- Will water move into or out of a plant cell if the cell has a higher water potential than its surrounding environment?

Step 1 Start by looking at a single leaf blade from either *Elodea* (a water plant) or a leaf-like structure from *Mnium hornum* (a moss) under the light microscope. If you need assistance, your teacher will show you how to place specimens on a slide.

- Where is the cell membrane in relation to the cell wall? Can you see the two structures easily? Why or why not?

- What parts of the cell that you see control the water concentration inside the cell?

Back in Procedure 2 you tested diffusion and osmosis properties of several solutions. Now you are going to determine how they affect plant cell turgor pressure.

- What changes do you expect to see when the cells are exposed to the solutions?
- How will you know if a particular treatment is increasing turgor pressure? If it is reducing turgor pressure?
- How could you determine which solution is isotonic to the cells?

Step 2 Test one of the four solutions from Procedure 2 and find out if what you predicted is what happens. When you are done, ask other students what they saw. Be sure to record all of your procedures, calculations, and observations.

■ Designing and Conducting Your Investigation

Materials

- Potatoes, sweet potatoes, or yams
- Cork borers or french fry cutter
- Balances
- Metric rulers
- Cups
- Color-coded sucrose solutions of different, but unlabeled, concentrations prepared by your teacher

Design an experiment to identify the concentrations of the sucrose solutions and use the solutions to determine the water potential of the plant tissues. (You might want to review the information on water potential described in Understanding Water Potential.) Use the following questions to guide your investigation:

- How can you measure the plant pieces to determine the rate of osmosis?
- How would you calculate the water potential in the cells?
- Which solution had a water potential equal to that of the plant cells? How do you know?
- Was the water potential in the different plants the same?
- How does this compare to your previous determinations in the *Elodea* cells?
- What would your results be if the potato were placed in a dry area for several days before your experiment?
- When potatoes are in the ground, do they swell with water when it rains? If not, how do you explain that, and if so, what would be the advantage or disadvantage?

■ Analyzing Results

1. Why are most cells small, and why do they have cell membranes with many convolutions?

2. What organelles inside the cell have membranes with many convolutions? Why?

3. Do you think osmosis occurs when a cell is in an isotonic solution? Explain your reasoning.

■ Where Can You Go from Here?

Do you think that fungal cells have turgor pressure? Design an experiment to test your hypothesis.

INVESTIGATION 5
PHOTOSYNTHESIS

What factors affect the rate of photosynthesis in living leaves?

■ BACKGROUND

Photosynthesis fuels ecosystems and replenishes the Earth's atmosphere with oxygen. Like all enzyme-driven reactions, the rate of photosynthesis can be measured by either the disappearance of substrate or the accumulation of product (or by-products).

The general summary equation for photosynthesis is

$$2\,H_2O + CO_2 + light \rightarrow carbohydrate\ (CH_2O) + O_2 + H_2O$$

What could you measure to determine the rate of photosynthesis?
- Production of O_2 (How many moles of O_2 are produced for one mole of sugar synthesized?)

  or
- Consumption of CO_2 (How many moles of CO_2 are consumed for every mole of sugar synthesized?)

In this investigation, you will use a system that measures the accumulation of oxygen.

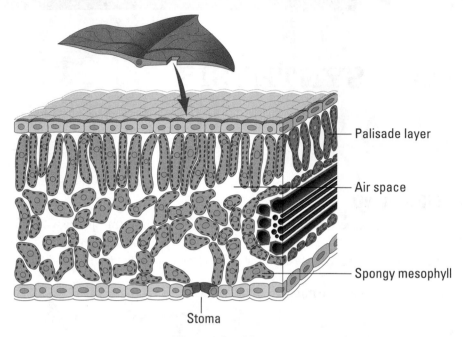

Palisade layer

Air space

Spongy mesophyll

Stoma

Figure 1. Leaf Anatomy

Because the spongy mesophyll layer of leaves (shown in Figure 1) is normally infused with gases (O_2 and CO_2), leaves — or disks cut from leaves — normally float in water. What would you predict about the density of the leaf disk if the gases are drawn from the spongy mesophyll layer by using a vacuum and replaced with water? How will that affect whether or not the leaf floats? If the leaf disk is placed in a solution with an alternate source of carbon dioxide in the form of bicarbonate ions, then photosynthesis can occur in a sunken leaf disk. As photosynthesis proceeds, oxygen accumulates in the air spaces of the spongy mesophyll, and the leaf disk will once again become buoyant and rise in a column of water. Therefore, the rate of photosynthesis can be *indirectly* measured by the rate of rise of the leaf disks. However, there's more going on in the leaf than that! You must also remember that cellular respiration is taking place at the same time as photosynthesis in plant leaves. (Remember that plant cells have mitochondria, too!) What else could be going on that might affect this process? Aerobic respiration will consume oxygen that has accumulated in spongy mesophyll. Consequently, the two processes counter each other with respect to the accumulation of oxygen in the air spaces of the spongy mesophyll. So now you have a more robust measurement tool — the buoyancy of the leaf disks is actually an indirect measurement of the *net* rate of photosynthesis occurring in the leaf tissue.

■ Learning Objectives

- To design and conduct an experiment to explore the effect of certain factors, including different environmental variables, on the rate of cellular photosynthesis

- To connect and apply concepts, including the relationship between cell structure and function (chloroplasts); strategies for capture, storage, and use of free energy; diffusion of gases across cell membranes; and the physical laws pertaining to the properties and behaviors of gases

■ General Safety Precautions

You must wear safety goggles or glasses, aprons, and gloves because you will be working in close proximity to exposed lightbulbs that can easily shatter.

Be careful to keep your solutions away from the electrical cord of your light source. Follow your teacher's instructions.

If you investigate temperature as a variable in Designing and Conducting Your Investigation, there is no need to heat any solution beyond 50–60°C.

Most but not all syringes are capable of withstanding the vacuum created in this procedure without failure. However, you should test the syringes beforehand.

■ THE INVESTIGATIONS

■ Getting Started

To study photosynthesis, review the properties of light and how it interacts with matter. In addition to your textbook, the Concord Consortium has a Java-based Web activity that will review the properties of light and the ways in which visible light interacts with matter in the process of photosynthesis. This multistep activity uses visualizations, animations, and a molecular modeling engine that does an excellent job of making abstract concepts understandable. To explore this activity, enter these terms in your search engine: "concord consortium molecular workbench photosynthesis."

While going through this activity, record any questions in your laboratory notebook. These questions and others that occur to you while working through the steps in Procedure can serve as a basis for your own investigation in Designing and Conducting Your Investigation.

■ Procedure

In this part of the lab, you will learn how the floating leaf disk technique can measure the rate of photosynthesis by testing a variable that you know affects photosynthesis. Later, you will apply this technique (or computer-based probes) to test a variable that you choose. It is important for you to develop a few skills during this part of the investigation in order to carry out your own investigation. For the floating disk technique, the most challenging skill is getting the disks to sink. Don't just watch someone do this; make sure you can get the disks to sink as well.

Materials

- Baking soda (sodium bicarbonate)
- Liquid soap (approximately 5 mL of dishwashing soap in 250 mL of water)
- 2 plastic syringes without needle (10 mL or larger)
- Living leaves (spinach, ivy, etc.)
- Hole punch
- 2 clear plastic cups
- Timer
- Light source

Figure 2. Materials

When immersed in water, oxygen bubbles are usually trapped in the air spaces of the spongy mesophyll in the plant leaf. By creating a vacuum in this experimental procedure, the air bubbles can be drawn out of the spongy mesophyll, and the space is refilled by the surrounding solution. This allows the leaf disks to sink in the experimental solution. If the solution has bicarbonate ions and enough light, the leaf disk will begin to produce sugars and oxygen through the process of photosynthesis. Oxygen collects in the leaf as photosynthesis progresses, causing the leaf disks to float again. The length of time it takes for leaf disks to float again is a measure of the net rate of photosynthesis. This process is shown in Figure 3.

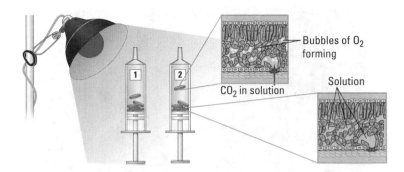

Figure 3. Photosynthesis at Work

Question: If the leaf disks are treated in a way you know increases the net rate of photosynthesis, should they start to float faster or slower? Why?

Step 1 Prepare 300 mL of 0.2% bicarbonate solution for each experiment. The bicarbonate will serve as a source of carbon dioxide for the leaf disks while they are in the solution.

Step 2 Pour the bicarbonate solution into a clear plastic cup to a depth of about 3 cm. Label this cup "With CO_2." Fill a second cup with only water to be used as a control group. Label this cup "Without CO_2." Throughout the rest of the procedure you will be preparing material for both cups, so do everything for both cups simultaneously.

Step 3 Using a pipette, add one drop of a dilute liquid soap solution to the solution in each cup. It is critical to avoid suds. If either solution generates suds, then dilute it with more bicarbonate or water solution. The soap acts as a surfactant or "wetting agent" — it wets the hydrophobic surface of the leaf, allowing the solution to be drawn into the leaf and enabling the leaf disks to sink in the fluid.

Figure 4. Dilute Liquid Soap Solution Added to Cup

Step 4 Using a hole punch, cut 10 or more uniform leaf disks for each cup. Avoid major leaf veins. (The choice of plant material is perhaps the most critical aspect of this procedure. The leaf surface should be smooth and not too thick.)

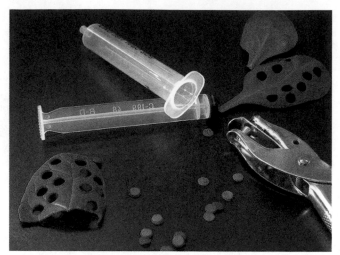

Figure 5. Leaf Disks

Step 5 Draw the gases out of the spongy mesophyll tissue and infiltrate the leaves with the sodium bicarbonate solution by performing the following steps:

a. Remove the piston or plunger from both syringes. Place the 10 leaf disks into each syringe barrel.

b. Replace the plunger, but be careful not to crush the leaf disks. Push in the plunger until only a small volume of air and leaf disk remain in the barrel (<10%).

c. Pull a small volume (5 cc) of sodium bicarbonate plus soap solution from your prepared cup into one syringe and a small volume of water plus soap into the other syringe. Tap each syringe to suspend the leaf disks in the solution. Make sure that, with the plunger inverted, the disks are suspended in the solution. Make sure no air remains. Move the plunger to get rid of air from the plunger before you attempt Step d.

d. You now want to create a vacuum in the plunger to draw the air out of the leaf tissue. This is the most difficult step to master. Once you learn to do this, you will be able to complete the entire exercise successfully. Create the vacuum by holding a finger over the narrow syringe opening while drawing back the plunger (see Figure 6a). Hold this vacuum for about 10 seconds. While holding the vacuum, swirl the leaf disks to suspend them in the solution. Now release the vacuum by letting the plunger spring back. The solution will infiltrate the air spaces in the leaf disk, causing the leaf disks to sink in the syringe. If the plunger does not spring back, you did not have a good vacuum, and you may need a different syringe. You may have to repeat this procedure two to three times in order to get the disks to sink. **(If you have any difficulty getting your disks to sink after three tries, it is usually because there is not enough soap in the solution. Try adding a few more drops of soap to the cup and replacing the liquid in the syringe.)** Placing the disks under vacuum more than three times can damage the disks.

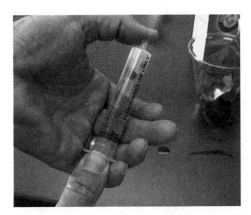

Figure 6a. Creating a Vacuum in the Plunger

Figure 6b. Sinking Leaf Disks

Step 6 Pour the disks and the solution from the syringe into the appropriate clear plastic cup. Disks infiltrated with the bicarbonate solution go in the "With CO_2" cup, and disks infiltrated with the water go in the "Without CO_2" cup.

Step 7 Place both cups under the light source and start the timer. At the end of each minute, record the number of floating disks. Then swirl the disks to dislodge any that stuck against the side of the cups. Continue until all of the disks are floating in the cup with the bicarbonate solution.

Figure 7a. Cup Under Light Source

Figure 7b. Disks Floating in Cup with Bicarbonate Solution

Step 8 To make comparisons between experiments, a standard point of reference is needed. Repeated testing of this procedure has shown that the point at which 50% of the leaf disks are floating (the median or ET_{50}, the Estimated Time it takes 50% of the disks to float) is a reliable and repeatable point of reference for this procedure.

Step 9 Record or report findings.

■ Designing and Conducting Your Investigation

What factors affect the rate of photosynthesis in living plants?

1. Once you have mastered the floating disk technique, you will design an experiment to test another variable that might affect the rate of photosynthesis. Some ideas include the following, but don't limit yourself to just these:

- What environmental variables might affect the net rate of photosynthesis? Why do you think they would affect it? How do you predict they would affect it?

- What features or variables of the plant leaves might affect the net rate of photosynthesis? How and why?

- Could the way you perform the procedure affect the outcome? If the outcome changes, does it mean the net rate of photosynthesis has changed? Why do you think that?

Note: If you are truly stumped, your instructor can give you some guidance. Keep in mind that leaves with hairy surfaces should be avoided. Ivy and spinach work well, but many others do as well. Differences between plants may be one of the ideas that you want to investigate.

2. Use your results to prepare a lab report/mini-poster for a classroom peer review presentation. See Chapter 2 for guidance on this.

■ Additional Guidelines

1. Consider combining variables as a way to describe differences between different plants. For instance, if you investigate how light intensity affects the rate of photosynthesis, you might generate a "photosynthesis light response curve"—the rate of photosynthesis at different light intensities. The shape of this curve may change for different plants or plants in different light environments. The "light response curve" is a form of measurement itself. How do you think a light response curve (the first variable) for a shade-grown leaf compares to that of a sun-grown leaf? In this situation, sun versus shade is the second variable. Comparing light response curves is a standard research technique in plant physiological ecology.

2. When you compare the ET_{50} across treatments, you will discover that there is an inverse relationship between ET_{50} and the rate of photosynthesis — ET_{50} goes down as rate of photosynthesis goes up, which plots a graph with a negative slope. This creates a seemingly backward graph when plotting your ET_{50} data across treatments, as shown in Figure 8a. To correct this representation and make a graph that shows increasing rates of photosynthesis with a positive slope, the ET_{50} term can be modified by taking its inverse, or $1/ET_{50}$. This creates a more traditional direct relationship graph, as shown in Figure 8b.

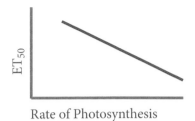

Figure 8a. Inverse Relationship   **Figure 8b. Direct Relationship**

3. Don't forget to include other appropriate data analyses as you prepare and study your discussion and conclusions. In particular for this investigation, you should somehow indicate the variability in your data. The ET_{50} measurement is calculated from the median. To indicate the spread of your data, you could use error bars around the ET_{50} point that express that variation, or you might consider using "box and whisker" plots.

CELLULAR RESPIRATION*

What factors affect the rate of cellular respiration in multicellular organisms?

■ BACKGROUND

Living systems require free energy and matter to maintain order, to grow, and to reproduce. Energy deficiencies are not only detrimental to individual organisms, but they cause disruptions at the population and ecosystem levels as well. Organisms employ various strategies that have been conserved through evolution to capture, use, and store free energy. Autotrophic organisms capture free energy from the environment through photosynthesis and chemosynthesis, whereas heterotrophic organisms harvest free energy from carbon compounds produced by other organisms. The process of cellular respiration harvests the energy in carbon compounds to produce ATP that powers most of the vital cellular processes. In eukaryotes, respiration occurs in the mitochondria within cells.

If sufficient oxygen is available, glucose may be oxidized completely in a series of enzyme-mediated steps, as summarized by the following reaction:

$$C_6H_{12}O_6 + 6O_{2(g)} \rightarrow 6CO_{2(g)} + 6H_2O + energy$$

More specifically,

$$C_6H_{12}O_6 + 6O_2 \rightarrow 6CO_2 + 6H_2O + \frac{686 \text{ kilocalories of energy}}{\text{mole of glucose oxidized}}$$

The chemical oxidation of glucose has important implications to the measurement of respiration. From the equation, if glucose is the energy source, then for every molecule of oxygen consumed, one molecule of carbon dioxide is produced.

Suppose you wanted to measure the overall rate of cellular respiration.

- What specific things could you measure?

- Which of these might be easier or harder to measure?

In Procedures, you will learn how to calculate the rate of cellular respiration by using a respirometer system (either microrespirometers or gas pressure sensors with computer interface). These measure relative volume (changes in pressure) as oxygen is consumed by germinating plant seeds. As oxygen gas is consumed during respiration, it is normally

---

* Transitioned from the *AP Biology Lab Manual* (2001)

replaced by CO_2 gas at a ratio of one molecule of CO_2 for each molecule of O_2. Thus, you would expect no change in gas volume to result from this experiment. However, in the following procedure the CO_2 produced is removed by potassium hydroxide (KOH). KOH reacts with CO_2 to form the solid potassium carbonate (K_2CO_3) through the following reaction:

$$CO_2 + 2KOH \rightarrow K_2CO_3 + H_2O$$

Thus, as O_2 is consumed, the overall gas volume in the respirometer decreases. The change in volume can be used to determine the rate of cellular respiration. Because respirometers are sensitive to changes in gas volume, they are also sensitive to changes in temperature and air pressure; thus, you need to use a control respirometer. What would be a good control for this procedure? Talk with another student for a minute, and come up with at least one possible control you could use.

As you work through Procedures, think about this question: What factors can affect the rate of cellular respiration? In Designing and Conducting Your Investigation, you will design and conduct an experiment(s) to investigate at least one of your responses to this question or some other question you have. Your exploration will likely generate even more questions about cellular respiration.

The investigation also provides an opportunity for you to apply and review concepts that you have studied previously, including the relationship between cell structure and function (mitochondria); enzymatic activity; strategies for capture, storage, and use of free energy; diffusion of gases across cell membranes; and the physical laws pertaining to the properties and behaviors of gases.

■ Learning Objectives

- To learn how a respirometer system can be used to measure respiration rates in plant seeds or small invertebrates, such as insects or earthworms

- To design and conduct an experiment to explore the effect of certain factors, including environmental variables, on the rate of cellular respiration

- To connect and apply concepts, including the relationship between cell structure and function (mitochondria); strategies for capture, storage, and use of free energy; diffusion of gases across cell membranes; and the physical laws pertaining to the properties and behaviors of gases

■ General Safety Precautions

You must wear safety goggles or glasses, aprons, and gloves during this investigation(s) because KOH (or the alternative, NaOH in Drano) is caustic. Follow your teacher's instructions when using the hot glue gun to seal microrespirometers. Do not work in the laboratory without your teacher's supervision.

■ THE INVESTIGATIONS

■ Getting Started

Your teacher may assign the following questions to see how much you understand concepts related to respiration before you design and conduct your own investigation:

1. Why is it necessary to correct the readings of the respirometers containing seeds with the readings taken from respirometers containing only glass beads? Your answer should refer to the concepts derived from the general gas law:

$$PV = nRT$$

Where

P = pressure of the gas

V = volume of the gas

n = number of moles of the gas

R = the gas constant (its value is fixed)

T = temperature of the gas

2. What happens to the volume of the gas being measured (O_2 consumption or CO_2 production) when the temperature or pressure changes during the experiment? If pressure and temperature remain constant, will the volume of gas in the respirometers increase or decrease? Please explain.

Hint: Several tutorials and animations explaining the general gas law are available online (e.g., *http://www.nclark.net/GasLaws*).

3. Imagine that you are given 25 germinating pea seeds that have been placed in boiling water for five minutes. You place these seeds in a respirometer and collect data. Predict the rate of oxygen consumption (i.e., cellular respiration) for these seeds and explain your reasons.

4. Imagine that you are asked to measure the rate of respiration for a 25 g reptile and a 25 g mammal at 10°C. Predict how the results would compare, and justify your prediction.

5. Imagine that you are asked to repeat the reptile/mammal comparison of oxygen consumption, but at a temperature of 22°C. Predict how these results would differ from the measurements made at 10°C, and explain your prediction in terms of the metabolism of the animals.

6. What difficulties would there be if you used a living green plant in this investigation instead of germinating seeds?

■ Procedures

The rate of cellular respiration can be measured by several methods, and two reliable methods are detailed below. Your teacher will tell you which method you will use to measure the rate of respiration in germinating plant seeds at room temperature.

■ Option 1: Using Microrespirometers to Measure the Rate of Cellular Respiration

Materials

- Germinating/nongerminating Wisconsin Fast Plants seeds or seeds of several species of plants, including grasses; small animals, such as crickets or earthworms; small glass beads; or dry, baked seeds
- Safety goggles or glasses, aprons, and gloves
- 1 mL plastic tuberculin syringes without needles
- Thin-stem plastic dropping pipettes
- 40 μL plastic capillary tubes or plastic microhematocrits

- Hot glue gun; absorbent and nonabsorbent cotton
- 3 or 4 one-quarter inch flat metal washers
- Celsius thermometer, centimeter rulers, permanent glass-marking pens
- Constant-temperature water bath
- Manometer fluid (soapy water with red food coloring)
- 15% solution of KOH, potassium hydroxide solution (or NaOH, Drano)

Figure 1. Materials

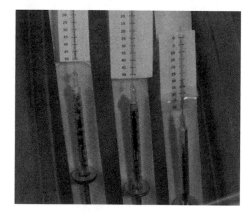

Figure 2. Microrespirometer Assembly

Constructing a Microrespirometer

Measuring the rate of respiration is more technically challenging than many lab procedures because there are many places for potential error in the assembly and use of equipment. The advantages of the microrespirometer method as described by Richard E. Lee in *American Biology Teacher* include low cost, reliability, simplicity, and rapid response. A modification of the Lee method is described at ***http://www.elbiology. com/labtools/Microrespirometers.html***. However, for the sake of convenience, the procedure is outlined below. **Hint**: Read each step before doing it! You need to assemble two microrespirometers: one for measuring the rate of respiration in germinating seeds and the other for the control.

Step 1 Plug in the hot glue gun and allow it to heat up.

Step 2 Take a tuberculin syringe (without a needle) and make sure that its plunger is pushed all the way in.

Step 3 Carefully insert a 40 µL plastic capillary tube into the syringe where the needle normally would be. Insert it as far as the plunger tip but no farther. This will help prevent the capillary from becoming plugged with glue.

Step 4 While holding the capillary tube straight up, add a small amount of hot glue around its base (where it meets the syringe) to seal the capillary to the syringe. Keep the capillary pointed straight up until the glue cools — this should not take long. If needed, add a bit more glue to ensure an airtight seal between the capillary and syringe. (See Figure 3.)

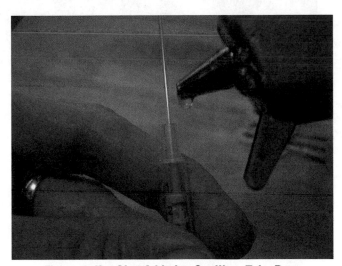

Figure 3. Hot Glue Added to Capillary Tube Base

Step 5 After the glue has cooled, pull back on the plunger and make sure that the glue has not plugged the capillary. If the capillary is plugged, carefully remove the glue and capillary and start over.

Preparing the Microrespirometer

Step 1 Draw a small quantity of manometer fluid (soapy water with red food coloring) into the full length of the microrespirometer's capillary tube. Then eject the fluid back out of the capillary. This coats the inside of the tube with a thin soapy film that helps prevent the manometer fluid from sticking.

Step 2 Carefully insert a small plug of absorbent cotton into the barrel of the microrespirometers, all the way into the 0 mL or cc mark. You can pack this cotton to the end with the barrel of a clean thin-stem pipette. (See Figure 4.)

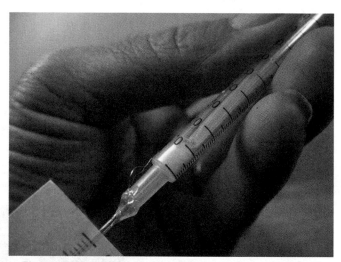

Figure 4. Cotton Inserted into Microrespirometer Barrel

Step 3 Add one small drop of 15% KOH (or NaOH, Drano) to the cotton in the microrespirometers. Do not add too much! **CAUTION: Make sure you are wearing gloves and safety goggles to protect your eyes because KOH is caustic.**

Step 4 Add a small plug of nonabsorbent cotton on top of the absorbent cotton plug already inside the barrel of the microrespirometers. You can pack the cotton to the end with the barrel of a clean thin-stem pipette. (This nonabsorbent plug is needed to protect the seeds from the caustic KOH.)

Step 5 Slowly reinsert the syringe plunger. **CAUTION: Be sure to point the capillary tip into a sink or container**. There may be excess KOH in the syringe that might squirt from the end of the capillary. Push the plunger in until it reaches the cotton so that any excess KOH is removed.

Step 6 Remove the plunger to add seeds.

Step 7 Add 0.5 mL of germinating seeds to the microrespirometers. Push the plunger in to the 1.0 mL mark. This creates a sealed microrespirometer chamber with a 1.0 mL volume.

Step 8 Place three to four washers around the barrel of the microrespirometers. The washers provide weight so that the microrespirometers will sink.

Step 9 Place the microrespirometers in a room temperature (about 20°C) water bath. You must maintain the temperature of the water bath for the experiment. Adjust the level of the water bath so that the capillary tube is sticking out of the water while the barrel of the microrespirometers is completely submerged. You will not be able to read the capillary tube easily unless it is out of the water. Make sure the top end of the capillary tube is open (not sealed).

Setting Up Your Control

Because a microrespirometer is sensitive to changes in gas volume, it is also sensitive to changes in temperature and air pressure. To compensate for any changes, you will use control microrespirometers. The control respirometer is set up just like the microrespirometer except that it contains nonliving matter (e.g., small glass beads or dry, baked seeds) instead of germinating seeds.

Step 1 Add 0.5 mL of beads or baked seeds to the second microrespirometer you assembled. Reinsert the syringe plunger and push it to the 1.0 mL mark. This seals the chamber and creates a chamber that has the same volume as the experimental microrespirometer.

Step 2 Place three to four washers around the barrel of the control.

Step 3 Place the assembled control in the water bath next to the experimental microrespirometer. Adjust the level of the water bath so the capillary tube is sticking out of the water while the barrel of the control is completely submerged. In order to easily read the capillary tube, it must be out of the water. Make sure the top end of the capillary tube is open (not sealed).

The respirometers must be airtight, and they are sensitive to environmental changes, including bumping the lab table. Once the respirometers have reached equilibrium, they should not be touched or moved, nor should anything else be added to or taken out of the water baths (including your hands!).

Collecting Data

Step 1 Prepare a table like Table 1 to record your data and observations in your lab notebook. You will need to record data for both the experimental and control microrespirometers.

Table 1. Results for Option 1, Using Microrespirometers

A Total Time (Min.)	B Water Bath Temperature (20°C)	C Total Distance Fluid Has Moved (cm)	D Change in Fluid Position During Time Interval (cm)
0			
5			
10			
15			
20			
25			

Step 2 Place the experimental and control microrespirometers into the 20°C water bath. Wait 5 minutes to allow the temperature in the microrespirometers to equalize.

Step 3 Use a dropping pipette to add one small drop of manometer fluid to the tip of each capillary tube (see Figure 5). If everything is working properly, the drop will be sucked down into the capillary tube. The manometer fluid will seal the chamber of the microrespirometers. (You should use the plunger on the control microrespirometers to get the manometer fluid into the capillary. Pull on the plunger until the manometer drop is about halfway down the capillary.)

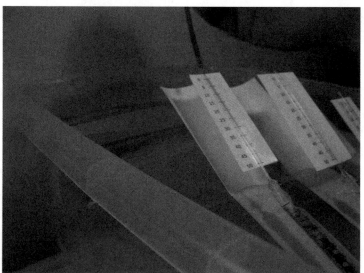

Figure 5. Manometer Fluid Added to Capillary Tube Tip

Step 4 As oxygen is consumed by cellular respiration, the manometer fluid plug will move toward the chamber. Record the starting position of each plug by marking its position on the capillary with a marker. Be sure to mark the bottom edge of the plug. These are your Time 0 marks. Begin timing once you have made the Time 0 marks.

Step 5 At 5-minute intervals, mark the position of the manometer fluid for each capillary tube. Be sure to mark the bottom edge of the fluid plug. Continue marking the positions until the fluid in the microrespirometers has traveled the entire length of the capillary, or until 25 minutes have passed.

Step 6 At the end of 25 minutes, remove the microrespirometers from the water bath. Use a centimeter ruler to measure the distance from the initial mark (Time 0 mark) to each of the 5-minute intervals marked on each capillary tube. Record your measurements in the correct column of your data table.

Step 7 Calculate the change in fluid position during each time interval. To do this, subtract the fluid position at the beginning of the time interval from the fluid position at the end of the time interval. Record your values.

Step 8 Repeat the calculations for your control microrespirometer.

Step 9 Using the values you obtained for the control microrespirometer, correct for any changes in volume that you measure that may be attributed to changes in temperature and air pressure.

Figure 6 shows how the microrespirometer works.

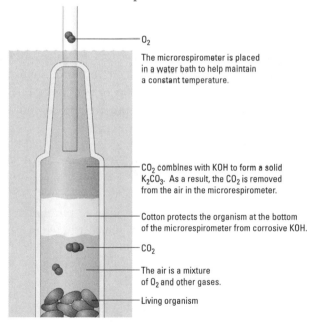

The microrespirometer is placed in a water bath to help maintain a constant temperature.

CO$_2$ combines with KOH to form a solid K$_2$CO$_3$. As a result, the CO$_2$ is removed from the air in the microrespirometer.

Cotton protects the organism at the bottom of the microrespirometer from corrosive KOH.

CO$_2$

The air is a mixture of O$_2$ and other gases.

Living organism

O$_2$

Figure 6. Microrespirometer

■ Analyzing Results

1. Use your data table to construct a graph. Your goal is to determine respiration rate. How should you plot your data? Which variable will be on the x-axis, and which will be on the y-axis?

2. From the graph, determine the rate of respiration for the germinating seeds at 20°C. **Hint**: Go back and think about what the units of measurement would be for respiration. How can you get a value with those units from your graph?

3. What additional questions can you explore about cellular respiration using the same respirometers from this experiment?

4. In the next part of this investigation, you will design and conduct your own experiments to answer questions that you raised in Procedures. Do you have any suggestions for improving the design of microrespirometers or procedure for measuring oxygen consumption/cellular respiration?

Option 2: Using Gas Pressure Sensors with Computer Interface to Measure the Rate of Cellular Respiration

Gas pressure sensors can be used to measure the rate of cellular respiration by measuring the amount of O_2 consumed, the amount of CO_2 produced, or both simultaneously. Your teacher will provide written instructions or perhaps ask you to download information from the manufacturer's website or another online resource. If you are unfamiliar with the use of probes with a computer interface, you will need to spend time learning how to collect data using the equipment.

■ General Procedure

1. Use a gas pressure sensor to measure the rate of cellular respiration in germinating seeds at 20°C over a 25-minute time interval or as per instructed by your teacher.

2. What additional questions can you explore about cellular respiration from this experiment?

3. In the next part of this investigation, you will design and conduct your own experiments to answer questions that you raised in the first part of the investigation. Do you have any suggestions for improving the procedure provided for measuring oxygen consumption/cellular respiration using a gas pressure sensor with computer interface?

■ Designing and Conducting Your Investigation

Now that you have learned how to measure the rate of cellular respiration in germinating seeds, you have a tool for exploring questions on your own. Think about the process of cellular respiration.

- When does it occur? Are there any situations when living cells are not respiring?

- Why might some living cells respire more than others?

- Are there differences between major groups of organisms in how fast they respire?

- What is the difference, if any, in the rate of cellular respiration between germinating seeds and nongerminating seeds?

- Does the temperature of germinating seeds affect the rate of cellular respiration? Do plant seeds consume more oxygen at higher temperatures than at lower temperatures?

- Do germinating seeds just starting to germinate consume oxygen at a greater rate than seeds that have been germinating for several days (age dependence)?

- Do seeds such as Wisconsin Fast Plant seeds (which store energy as oil) respire at a different rate from small grass seeds (which store energy as starch)?

- Do small seeds of spring flowers, weeds, or grasses respire at a different rate from seeds from summer, fall, or winter plants?

- Do seeds from monocot plants respire at different rates from dicot plants?

- Do available nutrients affect the rate of respiration in germinating seeds?

- Can the same respirometer system be used to measure the rate of respiration in small invertebrates, such as insects or earthworms?

Step 1 Design an experiment to investigate one of your own questions about cellular respiration or one of the questions above using microrespirometers or gas pressure sensors. When identifying your design, be sure to address the following:

- What is the essential question being addressed?

- What assumptions are made about the question(s) being addressed? Can those assumptions be verified?

- Will the measurements you choose to make provide the necessary data to answer the question under study?

- Did you include a control in your experiment?

- What are possible sources of error in the experiment(s)?

Step 2 Make a hypothesis, which should include a prediction about the effect of the factor(s) you chose to investigate on the rate of cellular respiration.

Step 3 Conduct your experiment(s) and record data and any answers to your questions in your laboratory notebook or as per instructed by your teacher.

Step 4 Record your data using appropriate methods, such as the example table provided in Procedures. Then graph the results to show the effect of the factors/variables you investigated on the rate of cellular respiration. Calculate the rate(s) of cellular respiration for each factor/variable.

■ Analyzing Results

1. Your teacher may suggest that you perform statistical analysis of your data, comparing results of the experimental variable(s) to the controls. You should at least express the uncertainty of your measurements with error bars. You may want to review Chapter 3 for more information about statistical analysis.

2. How was the rate of cellular respiration affected by the experimental variable(s) you chose as compared to the control(s)?

3. Compare class data to explain how different variables affect rates of cellular respiration.

■ Evaluating Results

1. Was your initial hypothesis about the effect of your factor on the rate of cellular respiration supported? Why or why not?

2. What were some challenges you had in performing your experiment? Did you make any incorrect assumptions?

3. Were you able to perform without difficulty the mathematical routines required to analyze your data? If not, what calculations were challenging or required help from your classmates or teacher?

■ Where Can You Go from Here?

If time is available, ask your teacher if you can extend the investigation to explore answers to other questions that might have been raised as you conducted your experiment(s). For example, if you originally investigated the effect of temperature on metabolic rate in plant seeds, you might want to explore a different aspect, such as the effect of temperature on metabolic rate in small invertebrates, such as insects or earthworms, or the relationship between the mass of an organism and its rate of respiration.

INVESTIGATION 7
CELL DIVISION: MITOSIS AND MEIOSIS

How do eukaryotic cells divide to produce genetically identical cells or to produce gametes with half the normal DNA?

■ BACKGROUND

One of the characteristics of living things is the ability to replicate and pass on genetic information to the next generation. Cell division in individual bacteria and archaea usually occurs by binary fission. Mitochondria and chloroplasts also replicate by binary fission, which is evidence of the evolutionary relationship between these organelles and prokaryotes.

Cell division in eukaryotes is more complex. It requires the cell to manage a complicated process of duplicating the nucleus, other organelles, and multiple chromosomes. This process, called the cell cycle, is divided into three parts: interphase, mitosis, and cytokinesis (Figure 1). Interphase is separated into three functionally distinct stages. In the first growth phase (G_1), the cell grows and prepares to duplicate its DNA. In synthesis (S), the chromosomes are replicated; this stage is between G_1 and the second growth phase (G_2). In G_2, the cell prepares to divide. In mitosis, the duplicated chromosomes are separated into two nuclei. In most cases, mitosis is followed by cytokinesis, when the cytoplasm divides and organelles separate into daughter cells. This type of cell division is asexual and important for growth, renewal, and repair of multicellular organisms.

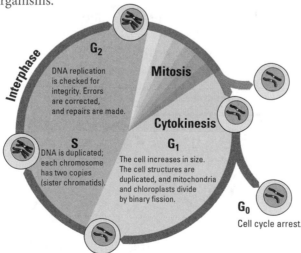

Figure 1. The Cell Cycle Showing G_1, S, and G_2 Phases, Mitosis, and Cytokinesis

Cell division is tightly controlled by complexes made of several specific proteins. These complexes contain enzymes called cyclin-dependent kinases (CDKs), which turn on or off the various processes that take place in cell division. CDK partners with a family of proteins called cyclins. One such complex is mitosis-promoting factor (MPF), sometimes called maturation-promoting factor, which contains cyclin A or B and cyclin-dependent kinase (CDK). (See Figure 2a.) CDK is activated when it is bound to cyclin, interacting with various other proteins that, in this case, allow the cell to proceed from G_2 into mitosis. The levels of cyclin change during the cell cycle (Figure 2b). In most cases, cytokinesis follows mitosis.

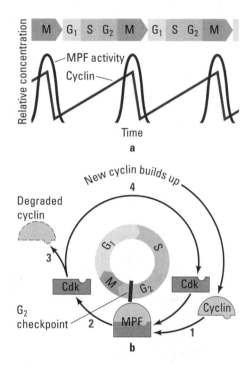

Figure 2. MPF Production During the Cell Cycle

As shown in Figure 3, different CDKs are produced during the phases. The cyclins determine which processes in cell division are turned on or off and in what order by CDK. As each cyclin is turned on or off, CDK causes the cell to move through the stages in the cell cycle.

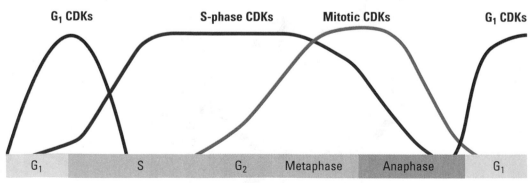

Figure 3. Levels of CDKs During the Cell Cycle

Cyclins and CDKs do not allow the cell to progress through its cycle automatically. There are three checkpoints a cell must pass through: the G_1 checkpoint, G_2 checkpoint, and the M-spindle checkpoint (Figure 4). At each of the checkpoints, the cell checks that it has completed all of the tasks needed and is ready to proceed to the next step in its cycle. Cells pass the G_1 checkpoint when they are stimulated by appropriate external growth factors; for example, platelet-derived growth factor (PDGF) stimulates cells near a wound to divide so that they can repair the injury. The G_2 checkpoint checks for damage after DNA is replicated, and if there is damage, it prevents the cell from going into mitosis. The M-spindle (metaphase) checkpoint assures that the mitotic spindles or microtubules are properly attached to the kinetochores (anchor sites on the chromosomes). If the spindles are not anchored properly, the cell does not continue on through mitosis. The cell cycle is regulated very precisely. Mutations in cell cycle genes that interfere with proper cell cycle control are found very often in cancer cells.

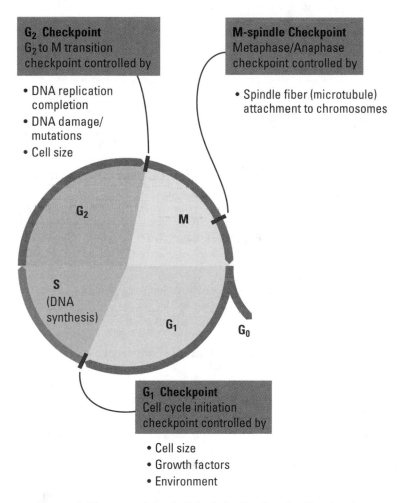

Figure 4. Diagram of the Cell Cycle Indicating the Checkpoints

Learning Objectives

- To describe the events in the cell cycle and how these events are controlled
- To explain how DNA is transmitted to the next generation via mitosis
- To explain how DNA is transmitted to the next generation via meiosis followed by fertilization
- To understand how meiosis and crossing over leads to increased genetic diversity, which is necessary for evolution

General Safety Precautions

You must be careful when preparing specimens for viewing under the compound microscope. Always cover the cover slip with a scientific cleaning wipe, such as a Kimwipe, and press down using a pencil eraser.

You should wear safety goggles or glasses and disposable gloves when handling the chemicals and razor blades in Parts 2 and 5. All materials should be disposed of properly as per your teacher's instructions.

THE INVESTIGATIONS

Getting Started

These questions are designed to see how well you understand and can explain the key concepts related to cell division before you begin your investigations.

1. How did you develop from a single-celled zygote to an organism with trillions of cells? How many mitotic cell divisions would it take for one zygote to grow into an organism with 100 trillion cells?

2. How is cell division important to a single-celled organism?

3. What must happen to ensure successful cell division?

4. How does the genetic information in one of your body cells compare to that found in other body cells?

5. What are some advantages of asexual reproduction in plants?

6. Why is it important for DNA to be replicated prior to cell division?

7. How do chromosomes move inside a cell during cell division?

8. How is the cell cycle controlled? What would happen if the control were defective?

■ Procedures

■ Part 1: Modeling Mitosis

You will investigate mitosis using models. Your teacher will give you sockosomes, Pop-It Beads, clay chromosomes, or pipe-cleaner chromosomes.

Review chromosome duplication and movement using these model chromosomes. Think about these questions as you review the cell cycle and mitosis.

- If a cell contains a set of duplicated chromosomes, does it contain any more genetic information than the cell before the chromosomes were duplicated?

- What is the significance of the fact that chromosomes condense before they are moved?

- How are the chromosome copies, called sister chromatids, separated from each other?

- What would happen if the sister chromatids failed to separate?

■ Part 2: Effects of Environment on Mitosis

Scientists reported that a fungal pathogen, may negatively affect the growth of soybeans (*Glycine max*). Soybean growth decreased during three years of high rainfall, and the soybean roots were poorly developed. Close relatives of *R. anaerobis* are plant pathogens and grow in the soil. A lectin-like protein was found in the soil around the soybean roots. This protein may have been secreted by the fungus. Lectins induce mitosis in some root apical meristem tissues. In many instances, rapid cell divisions weaken plant tissues.

You have been asked to investigate whether the fungal pathogen lectin affects the number of cells undergoing mitosis in a different plant, using root tips.

- What is your experimental hypothesis? Your null hypothesis? Are these the same?

- How would you design an experiment with onion bulbs to test whether lectins increase the number of cells in mitosis?

- What would you measure, and how would you measure it?

- What would be an appropriate control for your experiment?

Your teacher will provide you with untreated and lectin-exposed roots. You should be comfortable identifying cells in mitosis or in interphase before you begin examining the chromosome squashes.

Preparing Chromosome Squashes

1. Place the onion root tip in 1 M HCl for 4 minutes.

2. Transfer the tip to Carnoy's fixative for 4 minutes.

3. Remove the slide from Coplin jar containing 70% ethanol, dry with a scientific cleaning wipe, and label it.

4. Place the tip on the slide and cut off the distal 2 mm portion of the tip; discard the remainder of the tip.

5. Cover the root tip piece with carbol-fuschin stain for 2 minutes.

6. Blot off excess stain and cover the tip with 1–2 drops of H_2O.

7. Gently tease the root tip apart with dissecting probes or needles. Place the cover slip over the root tip and cover the cover slip with a scientific cleaning wipe.

8. Firmly press down on the cover slip with the eraser end of a pencil. Do not twist the slide, and be careful not to break the cover slip.

Counting Cells and Analyzing Data

1. Observe the cells at high magnification (400–500 X).

2. Look for well-stained, distinct cells.

3. Within the field of view, count the cells in each phase. Repeat the counts in two other root tips.

4. Collect the class data for each group, and calculate the mean and standard deviation for each group. You must make a table in your notebook for the class data.

5. Compare the number of cells from each group in interphase and in mitosis.

Table 1. Onion Root Tip Cell Phase Data; Treatment Group_____

Tip	Number of Cells		
	Interphase	Mitotic	Total
1			
2			
3			
Total			

Table 2. Table of Observed Values (o)

	Interphase	Mitosis	Total
Control	A	B	A + B
Treated	C	D	C + D
Total	A + C	B + D	A + B + C + D = N

1. Collect the class data and enter the values into Table 1; these are the observed values for the four groups.

2. Use the data from Table 1 to calculate the totals using the formulas found in Table 2. (For example, A equals the number of interphase cells in the control group.)

3. Use the totals from Table 2 to calculate the expected values (e) using the formulas from Table 3.

4. Enter the observed values (o) from Table 2 and expected values (e) from Table 3 for each group into Table 4. Calculate the chi-square (χ^2) value for the data by adding together the numbers in the right column.

5. Compare this value to the critical value in Table 5.

Table 3. Table of Expected Values (e)

	Interphase	Mitosis
Control	$\dfrac{(A + B)(A + C)}{N}$	$\dfrac{(A + B)(B + D)}{N}$
Treated	$\dfrac{(C + D)(A + C)}{N}$	$\dfrac{(C + D)(B + D)}{N}$

Table 4. Calculation of Chi-Square Value

Group	Observed (o)	Expected (e)	(o - e)	$(o - e)^2$	$(o - e)^2/e$
Control Interphase					
Control Mitosis					
Treated Interphase					
Treated Mitosis					

Total of $(o - e)^2/e$ = chi-square (χ^2) =

Table 5. Critical Values of the Chi-Square Distribution

Probability	Degrees of Freedom (DF)				
	1	2	3	4	5
0.05	3.84	5.99	7.82	9.49	11.1
0.01	6.64	9.21	11.3	13.2	15.1
0.001	10.8	13.8	16.3	18.5	20.5

1. The degrees of freedom (df) equals the number of treatment groups minus one multiplied by the number of phase groups minus one. In this case, there are two treatment groups (control, treated) and two phase groups (interphase, mitosis); therefore df = (2 - 1) (2 - 1) = 1.

2. The ρ value is 0.05, and the critical value is 3.84. If the calculated chi-square value is greater than or equal to this critical value, then the null hypothesis is rejected. If the calculated chi-square value is less than this critical value, the null hypothesis is not rejected.

■ Postlab Review

- What was the importance of collecting the class data?
- Was there a significant difference between the groups?
- Did the fungal pathogen lectin increase the number of root tip cells in mitosis?
- What other experiments should you perform to verify your findings?
- Does an increased number of cells in mitosis mean that these cells are dividing faster than the cells in the roots with a lower number of cells in mitosis?
- What other way could you determine how fast the rate of mitosis is occurring in root tips?

■ DESIGNING AND CONDUCTING YOUR INVESTIGATION

Now that you have worked with the root tip model system, design and conduct an investigation to determine what biotic or abiotic factors or substances in the environment might increase or decrease the rate of mitosis in roots. For instance, what factors in the soil might affect the rate of root growth and development? Consider, for example, abiotic soil factors such as salinity and pH or biotic factors, including roundworms, that might alter root growth.

■ Part 3: Loss of Cell Cycle Control in Cancer

Many of us have family members who have or have had cancer. Cancer can occur when cells lose control of their cell cycle and divide abnormally. This happens when tumor-suppressor genes, such as p53 or Rb (retinoblastoma), are mutated. There are many questions you should consider before beginning your investigation.

Review from Part 1

- How is the cell cycle controlled in normal cells?

- What are cyclins and cyclin-dependent kinases? What do these proteins do in a cell?

Prelab Questions for Part 3

- How are normal cells and cancer cells different from each other?

- What are the main causes of cancer?

- What goes wrong during the cell cycle in cancer cells?

- What makes some genes responsible for an increased risk of certain cancers?

- Do you think that the chromosomes might be different between normal and cancer cells?

The last question is the focus of this part of the lab. With your group, form a hypothesis as to how the chromosomes of a cancer cell might appear in comparison to a normal cell and how those differences are related to the behavior of the cancer cell.

For each of the following cases, look at pictures of the chromosomes (karyotype) from normal human cells. Compare them to pictures of the chromosomes from cancer cells. For each case, count the number of chromosomes in each type of cell, and discuss their appearance. Then answer the following questions.

- Do your observations support your hypothesis?

- If not, what type of information might you need to know in order to understand your observations?

- If yes, what type of information can you find that would validate your conclusions?

Case 1: HeLa cells

HeLa cells are cervical cancer cells isolated from a woman named Henrietta Lacks. Her cells have been cultured since 1951 and used in numerous scientific experiments. Henrietta Lacks died from her cancer not long after her cells were isolated. Lacks's cancer cells contain remnants of human papillomavirus (HPV), which we now know increases the risk of cervical cancer.

- From your observations, what went wrong in Henrietta Lacks's cervical cells that made them cancerous?

- How does infection with human papillomavirus virus (HPV) increase the risk of cervical cancer?

Your teacher may ask you to read *The Immortal Life of Henrietta Lacks* by Rebecca Skloot. As you read it, think about the following questions:

- Should tissue be removed from a patient without his or her consent for research?

- How was the HeLa cell line cultured?

- What virus infected Henrietta Lacks and may have caused her cervical cancer? What cellular process is affected by this virus?

- Was there bias in the way Henrietta Lacks was treated at Johns Hopkins?
- Put the use of HeLa cells on trial. Debate what is more important: an individual's rights to his/her own body tissues or the medical knowledge gained by studying a patient's tissues?
- Should Henrietta Lacks's family be compensated for the discoveries made using her cells?
- Do companies or universities have the right to patent discoveries made using a patient's tissues or genes without consulting the patient?
- What other legal and ethical questions are raised in this book?

■ Case 2: Philadelphia Chromosomes

In normal cells, mitosis usually is blocked if there is DNA damage. Sometimes, though, DNA damage makes cells divide more often. Certain forms of leukemia have a unique feature called a Philadelphia chromosome. Look at the karyotype of leukemia cells in Figure 5, and answer the following questions:

- What happens in a normal cell if the DNA has mutations?
- What would happen if cells with mutated DNA replicated?
- How do cells monitor DNA integrity?
- How are the chromosomes different in the cancer cells compared to normal cells?
- How could these differences lead to cancer?

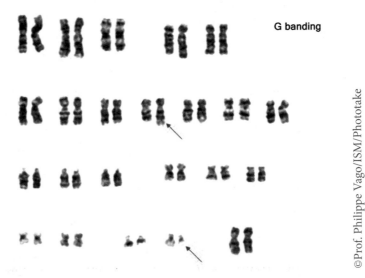

G banding

©Prof. Philippe Vago/ISM/Phototake

Figure 5. Karyotype of a Patient with Chronic Myelogenous Leukemia Indicating Chromosomal Deformity

■ Part 4: Modeling Meiosis

Meiosis resembles mitosis but serves a very different purpose. Meiosis is a cell division resulting in the halving, or reduction, of chromosome number in each cell. A diploid organism has two sets of chromosomes (2n), while a haploid cell or organism has one set (1n). Meiosis produces gametes (ova and sperm) in animals and spores in fungi, plants, and protists. Three other important characteristics of meiosis are the exchange of genetic material ("crossing over") between homologous chromosomes, the independent assortment of the chromosomes, and the separation of alleles of the same gene (Figure 6). These characteristics, along with random fertilization, increase the genetic variability in the offspring. These mechanisms are essential to our understanding of genetics and evolution in sexually reproducing organisms.

The hallmark of sexual reproduction is the great diversity seen in the gametes and in the resulting offspring produced by fertilization. Meiosis is integral to this process because this type of cell division produces the sex cells, gametes. Before you begin the modeling exercise, your teacher will ask you to discuss these questions.

- How do sexually reproducing organisms produce gametes from diploid progenitors?

- How does the process increase gamete diversity?

- What are the outcomes from independent assortment and crossing over?

- How does the distance between two genes or a gene and a centromere affect crossover frequencies?

Use the model chromosomes from Part 1 to explain meiosis and crossing-over events. During your investigation, answer the following questions:

- When is the DNA replicated during meiosis?

- Are homologous pairs of chromosomes exact copies of each other?

- What is crossing over?

- What physical constraints control crossover frequencies?

- What is meant by independent assortment?

- How can you calculate the possible number of different kinds of gametes?

- What happens if a homologous pair of chromosomes fails to separate, and how might this contribute to genetic disorders such as Down syndrome and cri du chat syndrome?

- How are mitosis and meiosis fundamentally different?

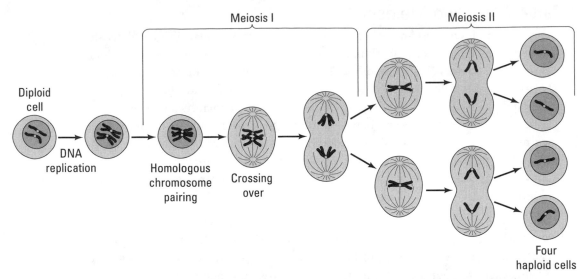

Figure 6. Meiotic Cell Division Emphasizing Chromosome Movement

Meiosis I

Meiosis II

Diploid cell

DNA replication

Homologous chromosome pairing

Crossing over

Four haploid cells

■ Part 5: Meiosis and Crossing Over in *Sordaria*

The fungus *Sordaria fimicola* exchanges genetic material when two mycelia meet and fuse. The resulting zygote undergoes meiosis to produce asci; each ascus contains eight haploid spores. A single gene determines the spore color. (See Figures 7 and 8.)

A cross was made between wild type (+; black) and tan (tn) strains. The resulting zygote produces either parental type asci, which have four black and four tan spores in a row (4:4 pattern), or recombinant asci, which do not have this pattern.

- How do you explain the differences between the recombinant asci and the parental types?

- What meiotic event can account for this difference?

- Using the model chromosomes from Part 4, predict the possible meiotic outcomes.

1. Place a drop of water onto the microscope slide.

2. Gently scrape some perithecia from the agar plate near where the two strains meet.

3. Place a cover slip over the perithecia and put a scientific cleaning wipe over the cover slip.

4. Gently press down on the cover slip using the eraser end of a pencil.

5. Count at least 50 asci, and score them as either parental or recombinant (crossing over).

6. Enter the data in Table 3 and make the calculations. One map unit equals one percent recombination. The percent of asci showing recombination divided by 2 equals the map units separating the spore-color gene from the centromere. The percent of asci showing recombination is divided by 2 because only half of the spores in each ascus are the result of a crossing-over event.

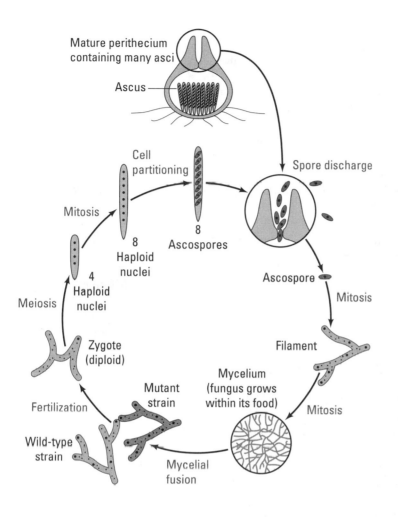

Figure 7. *Sordaria* Life Cycle

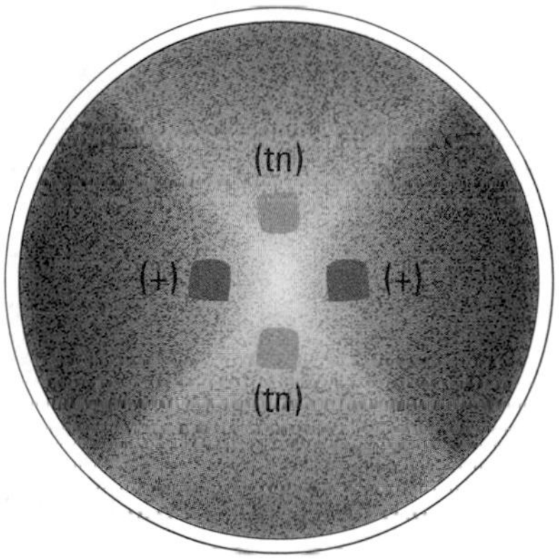

Figure 8: *Sordaria* Cross Plate

Table 3. Analysis of Results

Number of Asci Showing 4:4 Pattern	Number of Asci Showing Crossover	Total # of Asci	% Asci Showing Crossover Divided by 2	Gene to Centromere Distance (Map Units)

■ Evaluating Results

1. Why did you divide the percentage of asci showing crossover (recombinant) by 2?

2. The published map distance between the spore color gene and the centromere is 26 map units. How did the class data compare with this distance?

3. How can you account for any disparities between the class data and the published data?

4. Illustrate what happened during meiosis to produce the results you found.

5. Do you think the Philadelphia chromosome is a result of crossing over as seen in this part of the investigation or some other chromosomal abnormality? Explain your answer.

6. Do you think the cell cycle described for mitosis could be applied to meiosis as well? Explain your answer.

■ Where Can You Go from Here?

1. Can the same (or any) environmental factors you tested above affect the amount of crossing over that occurs in *Sordaria*? How would you set up an experiment to test this? For example, how does humidity or pH affect the crossover frequency?

2. Revisit the learning objectives stated earlier. Do you better understand mitosis and meiosis? Could you teach this to another class?

3. How do the mechanisms of cell replication affect genetic diversity and evolution? Consider the mechanisms such as crossing over, independent assortment, segregation, nondisjunction, and random fertilization.

4. Prepare a video or write and produce a play about the process of chromosome movement.

5. Investigate how growth factors affect the cell cycle. This will help you review cell communication.

6. Research what tumor suppressors do in the cell cycle and which types of cancers may be caused by mutations in tumor suppressor genes. Specific examples include human papillomavirus (HPV), retinoblastoma protein (Rb), BRCA1 and BRCA2, and p53.

INVESTIGATION 8

BIOTECHNOLOGY: BACTERIAL TRANSFORMATION*

How can we use genetic engineering techniques to manipulate heritable information?

■ BACKGROUND

Are genetically modified foods safe? There is ongoing debate about whether it is safe to eat fruit and vegetables that are genetically modified to contain toxins that ward off pests. For instance, biotechnologists have succeeded in inserting a gene (Bt) from the bacterium *Bacillus thuringiensis* into the corn genome. When expressed, the Bt toxin kills caterpillars and controls earworms that damage corn, but is the corn safe for human consumption?

Genetic information passed from parent to offspring via DNA provides for continuity of life. In order for information in DNA to direct cellular activities, it must be transcribed into RNA. Some of the RNAs are used immediately for ribosomes or to control other cellular processes. Other RNAs are translated into proteins that have important roles in determining metabolism and development, i.e., cellular activities and phenotypes (traits). When the DNA of a cell changes, the RNAs and proteins they produce often change, which in turn changes how that cell functions.

DNA inside a cell can change several ways. It can be mutated, either spontaneously or after the DNA replication machinery makes an error. Biotechnologists may cause an intentional mutation in a cell's own DNA as a way to change how that cell behaves. The most powerful tool biotechnologists have, though, is the ability to transfer DNA from one organism to another and make it function there. With this tool, they can make cells produce novel protein products the cells did not make previously.

Examples of this powerful tool are all around us. Insulin that people take to control their blood sugar levels is often made from engineered bacteria. Some vaccines, as well as enzymes used for manufacturing denim jeans, are also made using engineered cells. In the near future, engineered bacteria and other cells being developed could help clean up spilled oil or chemicals, produce fuel for cars and trucks, and even store excess carbon dioxide to help slow global climate change. Can you think of other possible applications of genetic engineering? However, biotechnology and human manipulation of DNA raise several ethical, social, and medical issues, such as the safety of genetically modified foods. Can you think of other issues to consider?

---

* Transitioned from the *AP Biology Lab Manual* (2001)

This biotechnology depends on plasmids, small circles of DNA that were found first in bacteria. Plasmids allow molecular biologists to manipulate genetic information in a laboratory setting to understand more fully how DNA operates. Plasmids also let us move DNA from one bacterium to another easily.

In this investigation, you will learn how to transform *Escherichia coli (E. coli)* bacteria with DNA it has not possessed before so that it expresses new genetic information. Bacterial cells that are able to take up exogenous (external) genetic material are said to be "competent" and are capable of being transformed. You also will calculate transformation efficiency to find out how well the *E. coli* took up the "foreign" DNA. Using these techniques, you will have the opportunity to explore the field of biotechnology further. You might want to explore the following questions:

- What causes mutations in bacteria? Can mutations affect plasmids?

- What is the function of plasmids in bacteria?

- Do cells take up more plasmids in some conditions and less in others?

By learning and applying these fundamental skills, you will acquire the tools to conduct more sophisticated biotechnology investigations, including designing your own experiments to manipulate DNA.

This investigation also provides you with the opportunity to review, connect, and apply concepts that you have studied previously, including cell structure of bacteria; structure and function of cell membranes, enzymes, and DNA and RNA; transcription and translation; the operon model of the regulation of gene expression; evolution and natural selection; and interactions between organisms and their environment.

Interspersed within each investigation are supplemental activities designed to keep you on track and to provide opportunities for you to take a deeper dive into the concepts. Your teacher may assign these activities for homework or ask that you do them as you work through each investigation.

■ Learning Objectives

- To demonstrate the universality of DNA and its expression

- To explore the concept of phenotype expression in organisms

- To explore how genetic information can be transferred from one organism to another

- To investigate how horizontal gene transfer is a mechanism by which genetic variation is increased in organisms

- To explore the relationship between environmental factors and gene expression

- To investigate the connection between the regulation of gene expression and observed differences between individuals in a population of organisms

■ General Safety Precautions

Basic Sterile Technique

When working with and culturing bacteria, it is important not to introduce contaminating bacteria or fungi into the experiment. Because these microorganisms are ubiquitous, i.e., you can find them everywhere — on fingertips, bench tops, lab tables, etc. — you must avoid these contaminating surfaces. When working with inoculation loops, bulb pipettes, micropipettes, and agar plates, do not touch the tips of them (or, in the case of agar, the surface itself) or place them directly onto contaminating surfaces. Be sure to wash your hands before beginning the procedure and after — and cover your sneezes. Do not eat, drink, apply cosmetics, or use personal electronic devices in the work area.

Working with *E. coli*

The host *E. coli* used in this investigation, plasmids, and the subsequent transformants created by their combination are *not* pathogenic (disease-causing) bacteria like the *E. coli* O157:H7 strain that has been in the news. However, handling *E. coli* requires appropriate microbiological and safety procedures. Your teacher will provide instructions, but these practices include, but are not limited to, the following:

- Decontaminating work surfaces once a day and after any spill of viable material with a 10% household bleach solution

- Decontaminating all contaminated liquid or solid wastes before disposal [This can be done in an autoclave (20 minutes at 121°C) or in a 10% bleach solution (soaked for 20 minutes).]

- Washing your hands after handling organisms containing recombinant DNA and before leaving the lab

- Wearing protective eyewear and disposable gloves

- Not eating, drinking, applying cosmetics, or using personal electronic devices, such as iPods and cell phones, in the work area

■ THE INVESTIGATIONS

■ Getting Started

DNA provides the instructions necessary for the survival, growth, and reproduction of an organism. When genetic information changes, either through natural processes or genetic engineering, the results may be observable in the organism. These changes may be advantageous for the long-term survival and evolution of a species, but it also may be disadvantageous to the individuals who possess the different genetic information.

In bacteria, genetic variation does not happen by mutation alone. It also can be introduced through the lateral (horizontal) transfer of genetic material between cells. Some bacteria undergo conjugation, which is direct cell-to-cell transfer. Other bacteria acquire DNA by transduction (viral transmission of genetic information). The third route is transformation, which is uptake of "naked" DNA from the environment outside the cell.

(You may have previously studied transformation in a different context. In an experiment conducted in 1928, Frederick Griffith, seeking a vaccine against a virulent strain of pneumonia, suggested that bacteria are capable of transferring genetic information through transformation. Little did Griffith know that his work would provide a foundation for genetic engineering and recombinant DNA technology in the 21st century.)

The concept of cell transformation raises the following questions, among others:

- To transform an organism to express new genetic information, do you need to insert the new gene into every cell in a multicellular organism or just one? Which organism is best suited for total genetic transformation — one composed of many cells or one composed of a single cell?

- Can a genetically transformed organism pass its new traits on to its offspring? To get this information, which would be a better candidate for your investigation — an organism in which each new generation develops and reproduces quickly or one that does this more slowly?

- Based on how you answered the first two sets of questions, what organism would be a good choice for investigating genetic transformation — a bacterium, earthworm, fish, or mouse?

If your answer to the last question is "bacterium," you are on the right track. Genetic transformation of bacteria most often occurs when bacteria take up plasmids from their environment. Plasmids are not part of the main DNA of a bacterium. They are small, circular pieces of DNA that usually contain genes for one or more traits that may be beneficial to survival. Many plasmids contain genes that code for resistance to antibiotics like ampicillin and tetracycline. [Antibiotic-resistant bacteria are responsible for a number of human health concerns, such as methicillin-resistant *Staphylococcus aureas* (MRSA) infections.] Other plasmids code for an enzyme, toxin, or other protein that gives bacteria with that plasmid some survival advantage. In nature, bacteria may swap these beneficial plasmids from time to time. This process increases the variation between bacteria — variation that natural selection can act on. In the laboratory, scientists use plasmids to insert "genes of interest" into an organism to change the organism's phenotype, thus "transforming" the recipient cell. Using restriction enzymes, genes can be cut out of human, animal, or plant DNA and, using plasmids as vectors (carriers of genetic information), inserted into bacteria. If transformation is successful, the recipient bacteria will express the newly acquired genetic information in its phenotype (Figure 1).

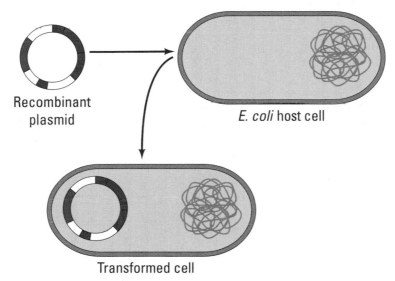

Figure 1. Transformation of Bacteria

In nature, the efficiency of transformation is low and limited to relatively few bacterial strains. Also, bacteria can take up DNA only at the end of logarithmic growth; at this time, the cells are said to be "competent." In the lab, you have discovered several ways to increase the rate of transformation. Now, rather than just a few bacteria taking up a plasmid you want them to use, millions of bacteria can be transformed. The number of bacteria that take up a plasmid successfully is called the "transformation efficiency." This is one of the values you will calculate in this lab unit.

In this investigation, you will use a predefined procedure to transform *E. coli* bacteria with a plasmid carrying a foreign gene. There are several different plasmids your instructor can choose from; you will be instructed about which one to work with for this unit.

E. coli is an ideal organism for the molecular geneticist to manipulate because it naturally inhabits the human colon and easily can be grown in a nutrient medium such as LB broth.

But what is *E. coli's* natural or pre-transformation phenotype?

- Observe the colonies of *E. coli* grown on the starter LB/agar plate provided by your teacher to glean some information before you determine if any genetic transformation has occurred. What traits do you observe in pre-transformed bacteria? Record your observations in your laboratory notebook.

- Some bacteria are naturally resistant to antibiotics, but others are not. How could you use two LB/agar plates, some *E. coli*, and some ampicillin (an antibiotic) to determine how *E. coli* cells are affected by ampicillin?

- What would you expect your experimental results to indicate about the effect of ampicillin on the *E. coli* cells? Do you think that exposure to ampicillin will cause the *E. coli* cells to evolve resistance to ampicillin? Why or why not?

- How will you be able to tell if host *E. coli* cells have been genetically transformed? (**Hint**: You will need some information from your teacher about the plasmid you will be using.)

■ Procedure

Your teacher will provide you with a plasmid containing one or more genes. The plasmid likely will contain the gene for resistance to ampicillin (pAMP), an antibiotic that is lethal to many bacteria, including *E. coli* cells. This transformation procedure involves the following three main steps to introduce the plasmid DNA into the *E. coli* cells and to provide an environment for the cells to express their newly acquired genes:

1. Adding $CaCl_2$

2. "Heat shocking" the cells

3. Incubating the cells in nutrient broth for a short time before plating them on agar

Materials

Your Workstation
- *E. coli* starter plate prepared by your teacher
- Poured agar plates prepared by your teacher, most likely the following:
    - 2 LB agar plates
    - 2 LB/amp agar (LB agar containing ampicillin) plates
- Transformation solution ($CaCl_2$, pH 6.1) kept *ice cold*
- LB nutrient broth
- Sterile inoculation loops
- 100–1000 µL sterile bulb pipettes
- 1–10 µL micropipettes with sterile tips
- Microcentrifuge tubes

- Microcentrifuge tube holder/float
- Container full of crushed ice
- Marking pen

Common Workstation
- DNA plasmid (most likely pAMP at 0.005 µg/µL)
- 42°C water bath and thermometer
- 37°C incubator
- 20 µL adjustable-volume micropipettes and tips (optional)
- 10% household bleach
- Biohazardous waste disposal bags
- Masking or lab tape

In your lab notebook, record data, answers to questions, and any questions that arise during this part of the activity.

Step 1 Form lab teams, as instructed by your teacher. Familiarize yourself with sterile technique, materials and lab equipment, and safety procedures for handling bacteria and decontaminating the work area.

Step 2 Label one closed microcentrifuge tube (micro test tube) "+ plasmid" and one tube "-plasmid." (What do the "+" and "-" symbols mean?) Label both tubes with your group's number (e.g., G2), and place them in the microcentrifuge tube holder/float.

Step 3 Carefully open the tubes and, using a 100–1000 μL bulb pipette with a sterile tip, transfer 250 μL of the ice cold transformation solution ($CaCl_2$) into each tube. (Note that "μl" and "μL" are alternative symbols for the same volumetric measurement.)

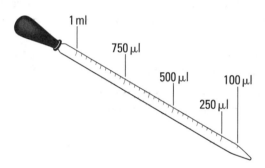

Figure 2. Measuring Volume with a Pipette

Step 4 Place both tubes on (into) the ice.

Step 5 Use a sterile inoculation loop to pick up a single colony of bacteria from your starter plate. Be careful not to scrape off any agar from the plate. Pick up the "+ plasmid" tube and immerse the loop into the $CaCl_2$ solution (transforming solution) at the bottom of the tube. Spin the loop between your index finger and thumb until the entire colony is dispersed in the solution. Appropriately discard the loop.

Step 6 Use a new sterile 100–1,000 μL micropipette to repeatedly pulse the cells in solution to thoroughly resuspend the cells. (Note that the clear transformation solution will become cloudy as the *E. coli* cells are suspended.) Place the tube back on the ice.

Step 7 Using a new sterile inoculation loop, repeat Steps 5 and 6 for the "- plasmid" tube.

CAUTION: Keep your nose and mouth away from the tip end when pipetting suspension culture to avoid inhaling any aerosol!

Step 8 Using a 1–10 μL micropipette with a sterile tip, transfer 10 μL of the plasmid solution *directly into the* E. coli *suspension* in the "+ plasmid" tube. Tap tube with a finger to mix, but avoid making bubbles in the suspension or splashing the suspension up the sides of the tube. Do not add the plasmid solution into the "- plasmid" tube! (Why not?)

Step 9 Incubate both tubes ("+ plasmid" and "- plasmid") on ice for 10 minutes. Make sure the bottom of the tubes make contact with the ice.

Step 10 While the tubes are sitting on ice, label each of your agar plates on the bottom (not the lid) as directed by your teacher.

Step 11 Following the 10-minute incubation at 0°C, remove the tubes from the ice and "heat shock" the cells in the tubes. It is critical that the cells receive a sharp and distinct shock! Make sure the tubes are closed tightly! Place the tubes into a test tube holder/ float, and dunk the tubes into the water bath, set at 42°C, for exactly 50 seconds. Make sure to push the tubes all the way down in the holder so that the bottom of the tubes with the suspension makes contact with the warm water.

Step 12 When the 50 seconds have passed, place both tubes back on ice. For best transformation results, the change from 0°C to 42°C and then back to 0°C must be rapid. Incubate the tubes on ice for an additional two minutes.

Step 13 Remove the holder containing the tubes from the ice and place on the lab counter. Using a 100–1,000 µL micropipette with sterile tip, transfer 250 µL of LB nutrient broth to the "+ plasmid" tube. Close the tube and gently tap with your finger to mix. Repeat with a new sterile micropipette for the "- plasmid" tube.

Step 14 Incubate each tube for 10 minutes at room temperature.

Step 15 Use a 10–1,000 µL micropipette with sterile tip to transfer 100 µL of the transformation ("+ plasmid") and control ("- plasmid") suspensions onto the appropriate LB and LB/Amp plates. Be sure to use a separate pipette for each of the four transfers.

Step 16 Using a new sterile inoculation loop for each plate, spread the suspensions evenly around the surface of the agar by quickly "skating" the flat surface of the sterile loop back and forth across the plate surface (Figure 3). Do not poke or make gashes in the agar! Your teacher might suggest that you use small sterile glass beads to spread the suspensions by gently rocking the beads across the surface of the agar. Allow the plates to set for 10 minutes.

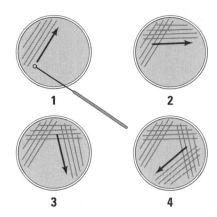

Figure 3. Technique for Plating Bacteria on Agar

Step 17 Stack your plates and tape them together. Place the stack upside down in the 37°C incubator for 24 hours or as per instructed by your teacher.

■ Analyzing Results

Think about these questions *before* collecting data and analyzing your results. Be sure to record your answers in your laboratory notebook.

1. On which of the plates would you expect to find bacteria most like the original non-transformed *E. coli* colonies you initially observed? Why?

2. If there are any genetically transformed bacterial cells, on which plate(s) would they most likely be located? Again, why?

3. Which plates should be compared to determine if any genetic transformation has occurred? Why?

4. What barriers might hinder the acquisition of plasmids?

5. How can the procedures described above (addition of CI_2 and "heat shocking") help facilitate the introduction of plasmids into the *E. coli* cells?

Consider the amount of bacterial growth you see on each plate. What color are the colonies? How many bacterial colonies are on each plate? Additional questions you might want to consider include the following:

1. Do your results support your original predictions about the "+ plasmid" transformed *E. coli* cells versus "- plasmid" nontransformed cells?

2. Which of the traits that you originally observed for *E. coli* did not seem to become altered? Which traits seem now to be significantly different after performing the transformation procedure?

3. What evidence suggests that the changes were due to the transformation procedures you performed?

4. What advantage would there be for an organism to be able to turn on or off particular genes in response to certain conditions?

5. Was your attempt at performing a genetic transformation successful? If so, *how* successful?

By calculating transformation efficiency, you can measure the success of your transformation quantitatively.

■ Calculating Transformation Efficiency

Your next task is to learn how to determine the extent to which you genetically transformed *E. coli* cells. This quantitative measurement is referred to as the transformation efficiency. What is the importance of quantifying how many cells have been transformed? In many applications, it is important to transform as many cells as possible. For example, in some forms of gene therapy, cells are collected from the patient, transformed in the laboratory, and then put back into the patient. The more cells that are transformed to produce the needed protein, the more likely the therapy will work.

Calculating transformation efficiency gives you an indication of how effective you were in getting plasmids carrying new information into host bacterial cells. In this example, transformation efficiency is a number that represents the total number of bacterial cells that express the gene for ampicillin resistance divided by the amount of DNA plasmid used in the experiment. The transformation efficiency is calculated using the following formula.

$$\text{Transformation efficiency} = \frac{\text{Total number of colonies growing on the agar plate}}{\text{Amount of DNA spread on the agar plate (in μg)}}$$

What two pieces of information will you need to calculate the efficiency of your transformation? Be sure to record all calculations.

1. Calculate the total number of transformed cells.

Observe the number of colonies visible on your LB/amp plate. Do not open the plate! Each colony on the plate can be assumed to be derived from a single cell. As individual cells reproduce, more and more cells are formed and develop into what is termed a colony. Thus, the most direct way to determine the total number of bacteria that were transformed with the plasmid is to count the colonies on the plate.

2. Calculate the amount of plasmid DNA in the bacterial cells spread on the LB/amp plate.

You need two pieces of information to find out the amount of plasmid DNA in the bacterial cells spread on the LB/amp plate: a) the total amount of DNA with which you began the experiment and b) the fraction of the DNA in the bacteria that actually got spread onto the LB/amp plate.

Once you determine this information, you will multiply the total amount of plasmid DNA used in the transformation times the fraction of DNA you spread on the LB/amp plate.

a. Calculate the total amount (mass) of plasmid DNA.

The total amount (mass) of DNA with which you began the experiment is equal to the product of the concentration and the total volume used, or

DNA in μg = (concentration of DNA of μg/μL) x (volume of DNA in μL)

In this example, assume you used 10 μL of plasmid at a concentration of 0.005 pAMP μg/μL.

- Calculate the amount (mass) of plasmid DNA (pAMP) in μg per 1 μL of solution.
- Calculate the total amount of DNA used in this experiment.

How will you use this information?

b. Calculate the fraction of plasmid DNA that actually got spread onto the LB/amp plate.

Since not all the DNA you added to the bacterial cells will be transferred to the agar plate, you need to calculate what fraction of the DNA was actually spread onto the LB/amp plate.

$$\text{Fraction of DNA used} = \frac{\text{Volume spread on the LB/amp plate (μL)}}{\text{Total sample volume in test tube (μL)}}$$

Calculate the fraction of plasmid DNA you spread on the LB/amp plate.

(Hint: Refer to the procedure and your notes. How many microliters of cells containing DNA did you spread onto the plate? What was the total volume of solution in the test tube? Did you add *all* the volumes?)

c. Calculate the micrograms of plasmid DNA that you spread on the LB/amp plate.

To answer this question, you multiply the total mass of plasmid DNA used times the fraction of plasmid DNA you spread on the LB/amp plate.

DNA spread in µg = Total amount of DNA used in µg x fraction of DNA used

What does this number tell you?

3. Calculate transformation efficiency.

Look at your calculations. Fill in the blanks with the correct numbers.

Number of colonies on the LB/amp plate: _____

Micrograms of plasmid DNA spread on the plate: _____

Now calculate the efficiency of the transformation.

Transformation efficiency = $\dfrac{\text{Total number of colonies growing on the agar plate}}{\text{Amount of DNA spread on the LB/amp plate (in µg)}}$

4. What does this mean?

Transformation efficiency calculations result in very large, and very small, numbers. For both very large and very small numbers, scientists often use a mathematical shorthand referred to as scientific notation. For example, if the calculated transformation efficiency is 1,000 bacteria/µg of DNA, they often report this as 10^3 transformants/µg.

How would scientists report 10,000 transformants/µg in scientific notation?

Suppose scientists calculated an efficiency of 5,000 bacteria/µg of DNA. How would they report this in scientific notation?

a. Report your calculated transformation efficiency in scientific notation.

b. What does your calculation of transformation efficiency mean?

c. Biotechnologists generally agree that the transformation protocol that you have just completed has a transformation efficiency of between 8.0×10^2 and 7.0×10^3 transformants per microgram of DNA. How does your transformation efficiency compare? What factors could explain a transformation efficiency that was greater or less than predicted?

■ Evaluating Results

1. What are some challenges you had in performing your investigation? Did you make any incorrect assumptions?

2. What are some possible sources of error in the transformation procedure? If you had to repeat the procedure, what are ways to minimize potential sources of error?

3. Were you able to perform without difficulty the mathematical routines required to calculate transformation efficiency? Which calculations, if any, were challenging or required help from your classmates or teacher?

4. Can you suggest other preliminary activities that would have better prepared you to tackle the investigation?

5. Does a bacterial cell take in a plasmid with genes the cell already possesses? If so, would this affect your calculations?

■ Designing and Conducting Your Investigation

Think about these questions again for a minute.

- What causes mutations in bacteria? Can mutations affect plasmids? How would you be able to tell if any observed changes in phenotypes are due to the expression of genes carried on plasmids and are not attributed to a possible mutagen?

- Do bacteria take up more in plasmid in some conditions and less in others? What conditions favor uptake, and which ones inhibit it?

- What other questions do you have about plasmids and transformation?

You can either design an investigation focusing on the information below OR design one based on a question(s) or observation you had as you worked through the genetic transformation you just conducted. Be sure that your experiment applies the science skills you acquired as you worked through this investigation. Make sure that your teacher approves your plan.

You should have noted satellites around the transformed colonies. (Satellites are smaller colonies that grow around the larger transformed colony.) What observations can you make about the satellites? Do they look like transformed bacteria? How can you tell if the satellites contain the plasmid? Design and conduct an experiment to determine if the *E. coli* satellite colonies from your genetic transformation experiment are transformed, too. Available to you are the same chemicals, supplies, and equipment you used in the previous investigation.

■ Where Can You Go from Here?

The background to this investigation asks you to think about several applications of genetic transformation, including genetically modified food and possible ethical, social, or medical issues raised by the manipulation of DNA by biotechnology. Why are these "issues"? What questions are posed by genetic engineering? In terms of what you have learned about biotechnology, how would you respond to the quote from Michael Crichton's novel and film *Jurassic Park*: "Just because science can do something doesn't mean that it should"?

INVESTIGATION 9

BIOTECHNOLOGY: RESTRICTION ENZYME ANALYSIS OF DNA*

How can we use genetic information to identify and profile individuals?

■ THE SCENARIO

"OMG! Is that blood?" Laurel nearly broke Marcus's arm as she tried to push past him into the classroom.

Marcus grabbed the sleeve of her cardigan and yanked her back. "Don't! Can't you see the glass?" Laurel tried knocking his hand free, but the 6'4" varsity basketball captain held tight. He made her settle for looking from under his armpit.

Not that what she saw would make any sense. Their AP Biology lab looked like a riot scene. Four chairs and a potted plant were overturned in the center of the room, and broken pieces of glass were scattered across the floor along with several wet red drops. Plink ... plink ... plink. Marcus's eyes were drawn to the teacher's desk where droplets of brownish liquid fell from a paper cup and collected in a puddle on the linoleum.

"What happened?" Laurel asked. "Did somebody get hurt?" Laurel and her classmates had gathered in front of the door and strained to see inside Room 102.

Marcus inspected the scene and raised his right arm above his head, his fingers spread apart as if taking a shot from the free throw line. "Stay back!"

"Where's Ms. Mason?" Laurel said. "She told me I could meet her before class to review for the quiz."

"Okay, folks, keep it down." Mr. Gladson, the teacher in the classroom next door, came into the hall. His white lab coat was streaked with several rust-colored stains. The pungent odor of formaldehyde permeated the corridor. "In case you haven't noticed, the bell has rung." He wiped his nose with a tissue and then tossed it into a nearby trash can. A girl's fake shriek from inside the anatomy lab rose above the buzz of Marcus's classmates.

"What's going on?" Bobby's high-pitched whine was unmistakable — and so was the scent of his bubble gum.

"I think something might've happened to Ms. Mason," Marcus said. He dug around in his backpack and pulled out a magnifying glass. "We've got a crime scene to process."

---

* Transitioned from the *AP Biology Lab Manual* (2001)

"Go figure," Laurel said. "Sherlock Holmes in a varsity jacket."

For the next hour, Marcus and Laurel searched the classroom and discovered several pieces of "evidence" that Marcus described in his biology notebook:

- Ten small drops on floor confirmed by Kastle-Meyer test to be blood

- Shard of glass from a broken 500-mL Erlenmeyer flask, edge smeared with a reddish stain

- Paper cup with lipstick stains, presumed to be Ms. Mason's, found on her desk

- Wad of bubble gum stuck underneath overturned chair

- Mr. Gladson's discarded tissue recovered from trash can in hall outside Room 102

- Bobby's test on photosynthesis with large "F" scrawled in red ink on first page

- Copy of email from Mr. Gladson to Ms. Mason asking her to give up position as department chair

Marcus's new game was afoot!

■ BACKGROUND

Applications of DNA profiling extend beyond what we see on television crime shows. Are you sure that the hamburger you recently ate at the local fast-food restaurant was actually made from pure beef? DNA typing has revealed that often "hamburger" meat is a mixture of pork and other nonbeef meats, and some fast-food chains admit to adding soybeans to their "meat" products as protein fillers. In addition to confirming what you ate for lunch, DNA technology can be used to determine paternity, diagnose an inherited illness, and solve historical mysteries, such as the identity of the formerly anonymous individual buried at the Tomb of the Unknown Soldier in Washington, D.C.

DNA testing also makes it possible to profile ourselves genetically — which raises questions, including *Who owns your DNA and the information it carries?* This is not just a hypothetical question. The fate of dozens of companies, hundreds of patents, and billions of dollars' worth of research and development money depend on the answer. Biotechnology makes it possible for humans to engineer heritable changes in DNA, and this investigation provides an opportunity for you to explore the ethical, social, and medical issues surrounding the manipulation of genetic information.

■ Learning Objectives

In this investigation, you will learn how to use restriction enzymes and gel electrophoresis to create genetic profiles. You will use these profiles to help Marcus and Laurel narrow the list of suspects in the disappearance of Ms. Mason.

■ General Safety Precautions

Never handle gels with your bare hands. An electrophoresis apparatus can be dangerous because it is filled with a highly conductive salt solution and uses DC current at a voltage strong enough to cause a small shock. Always turn the power supply switch

"OFF" and wait 10 seconds before making any connection. Connect BOTH supply leads to the power supply (black to black and red to red, just like when you jump-start a car battery) BEFORE turning on the power supply. Your teacher will tell you for how long and at how many volts (usually 50 volts) you should run your gel. After use, turn off the power supply, and then disconnect BOTH leads from the power supply. *Remember, power supply on last ... and off first.*

■ THE INVESTIGATIONS

■ Getting Started

■ Activity I: Restriction Enzymes

The DNA samples collected from the crime scene have been digested with restriction enzymes to generate smaller pieces of DNA, which will then be used to create DNA profiles of suspects.

Restriction enzymes are essential tools for analyzing DNA structure, and more than 200 enzymes are now available commercially. Each restriction enzyme is named for the bacterium in which it was first identified; for example, *Eco*RI was the first enzyme purified from *Escherichia coli,* and *Hin*dIII was the third enzyme isolated from *Haemophilus influenzae.* Scientists have hypothesized that bacteria use these enzymes during DNA repair and as a defense against their infection by bacteriophages. Molecular biologists use restriction enzymes to manipulate and analyze DNA sequences (Johnson 2009).

How do restriction enzymes work? These enzymes digest DNA by cutting the molecule at specific locations called restriction sites. Many restriction enzymes recognize a 4- to 10-nucleotide base pair (bp) palindrome, a sequence of DNA nucleotides that reads the same from either direction. Some restriction enzymes cut (or "cleave") DNA strands exactly in the center of the restriction site (or "cleavage site"), creating blunt ends, whereas others cut the backbone in two places, so that the pieces have single-stranded overhanging or "sticky" ends of unpaired nucleotides.

You have a piece of DNA with the following template strand:

5'-AAAGTCGCTGGAATTCACTGCATCGAATTCCCGGGGCTATATATGGAATTCGA-3'

1. What is the sequence of the complementary DNA strand? Draw it directly below the strand.

2. Assume you cut this fragment with the restriction enzyme *Eco*RI. The restriction site for *Eco*RI is 5'-GAATTC-3', and the enzyme makes a *staggered* ("sticky end") cut between G and A on both strands of the DNA molecule. Based on this information, draw an illustration showing how the DNA fragment is cut by *Eco*RI and the resulting products.

Two pieces of DNA that are cut with the same restriction enzyme, creating either sticky ends or blunt ends, can be "pasted" together using DNA ligase by reconnecting bonds, *even if the segments originated from different organisms.* An example of combining two "sticky end" sequences from different sources is shown in Figure 1. The ability of enzymes to "cut and paste" DNA fragments from different sources to make recombinant DNA molecules is the basis of biotechnology.

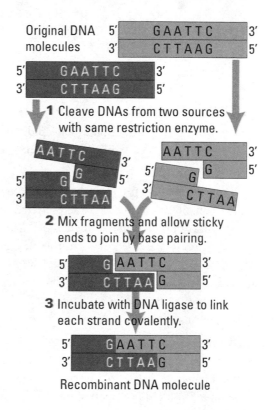

Figure 1. Recombinant DNA Using Restriction Enzymes

■ Activity II: DNA Mapping Using Restriction Enzymes

One application of restriction enzymes is restriction mapping. Restriction mapping is the process of cutting DNA at specific sequences with restriction enzymes, separating the fragments from each other by a process called gel electrophoresis (without pasting any fragments together), and then estimating the size of those fragments. The size and number of DNA fragments provide information about the structure of the original pieces of DNA from which they were cut.

Restriction mapping enables scientists to create a genetic signature or DNA "fingerprint" that is unique to each organism. The unique fragments, called restriction fragment length polymorphisms (RFLPs), can, for instance, be used to confirm that a mutation is present in one fragment of DNA but not in another, to determine the size of an unknown DNA fragment that was inserted into a plasmid, to compare the genomes of different species and determine evolutionary relationships, and to compare DNA samples from different individuals within a population. This latter application is widely used in crime scene investigations.

Consider your classmates. More than 99% of your DNA is the same as their DNA. The small difference is attributed to differences in your genetic makeup, with each person having a genetic profile or "fingerprint" as unique as the ridges, arches, loops, and grooves at the ends of his or her fingers.

- Based on this information, can you make a prediction about the products of DNA from different sources cut with the same restriction enzymes? Will the RFLP patterns produced by gel electrophoresis produced by DNA mapping be the same or different if you use just one restriction enzyme? Do you have to use many restriction enzymes to find differences between individuals? Justify your prediction.

- Can you make a prediction about the RFLP patterns of identical twins cut with the same restriction enzymes? How about the RFLP patterns of fraternal twins or triplets?

Now that you understand the basic idea of genetic mapping by using restriction enzymes, let's explore how DNA fragments can be used to make a genetic profile.

■ Activity III: Basic Principles of Gel Electrophoresis

Creating DNA profiles depends on gel electrophoresis. Gel electrophoresis separates charged molecules, including nucleic acids and amino acids, by how fast they migrate through a porous gel under the influence of an electrical current. Your teacher will likely prepare the gel ahead of time by dissolving agarose powder (a gelatinlike substance purified from seaweed) in a current-carrying buffer. The gel solidifies around a comb placed at one end, forming wells into which you can load DNA fragments. When an electrical current is passed through the gel, the RFLPs (fragments) migrate from one pole to the other. Gel electrophoresis can separate DNA fragments from about 200 to 50,000 base pairs (bp).

- Why do DNA fragments migrate through the gel from the *negatively* charged pole to the *positively* charged pole?

The general process of gel electrophoresis is illustrated in Figure 2.

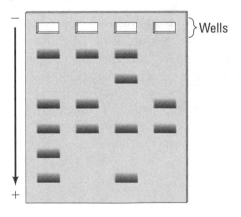

Figure 2. General Process of Gel Electrophoresis

■ Procedures

Learning to Use Gel Electrophoresis

To determine whose blood was on the classroom floor crime scene, you will need to be familiar with the techniques involved in creating genetic profiles using gel electrophoresis. The steps in the general procedure are described below. After you familiarize yourself with the procedure, you will analyze DNA profiles resulting from an "ideal" or mock gel before using what you have learned to conduct an independent investigation. In Designing and Conducting Your Investigation, you will use these skills to narrow the list of suspects in the disappearance of Ms. Mason based on DNA evidence collected at the crime scene.

Materials

Your Workstation
- 20 μL vials of DNA fragments prepared using restriction enzymes
- Rack for holding samples
- 3 plastic bulb transfer pipettes (or similar devices)
- Permanent marker
- Gel electrophoresis chamber
- Power supply

- Staining tray
- Semi-log graph paper
- Ruler

Common Workstation
- 0.8% agarose solution (or gel, if prepared by teacher)
- 1 X TAE (tris-acetate-EDTA) buffer
- Methylene blue stain

Record data and any answers to questions in your lab notebook.

Casting the Agarose Gel

Before proceeding, your teacher will direct you to short online videos that show how to prepare an agarose gel, load DNA samples into the wells in the gel, and run an electrophoresis.

Step 1 Seal the ends of the gel-casting tray with tape, dams, or any other method appropriate for the gel box that you are using. Insert the well-forming comb. Place the gel-casting tray out of the way on the lab bench so that the agarose poured in the next step can set undisturbed. (Your teacher might cast the gel for you ahead of time.)

Step 2 Carefully pour the liquid gel into the casting tray to a depth of 5–6 mm. The gel should cover only about one-half the height of the comb teeth (Figure 3). While the gel is still liquid, use the tip of a pipette to remove any bubbles.

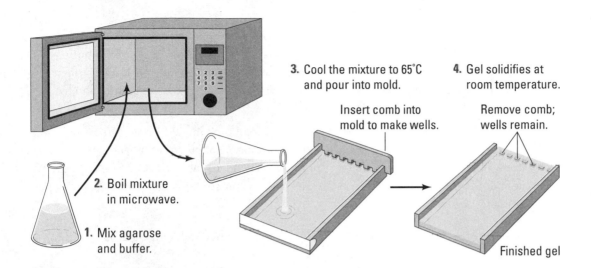

3. Cool the mixture to 65°C and pour into mold.

Insert comb into mold to make wells.

4. Gel solidifies at room temperature.

Remove comb; wells remain.

2. Boil mixture in microwave.

1. Mix agarose and buffer.

Finished gel

Figure 3. Casting an Agarose Gel

Step 3 The gel will become cloudy as it solidifies (15–20 minutes). Do not disturb or touch the gel while it is solidifying!

Step 4 When the agarose has set, carefully remove the ends of the casting tray and place the tray in the electrophoresis gel box so that the comb is at the negative (black) end.

- Why do you place the wells at the negative end of the gel box?

- What is the chemical nature of DNA? Will the DNA fragments migrate toward the positive end of the gel box or toward the negative end?

Step 5 Fill the box with 1x TAE buffer, to a level that just covers the entire surface of the gel.

Step 6 Gently remove the comb, taking care not to rip the wells. Make sure that the sample wells left by the comb are completely submerged in the buffer.

Step 7 The gel is now ready to be loaded with your DNA samples. (If your teacher says that you will load the gel on another lab day, close the electrophoresis box to prevent drying of the gel.)

Loading the Gel

Before loading your gel with samples of DNA, you should practice using the pipette or other loading device. One easy way to do this is to slowly aspire a sample of buffer and expel it into a "pretend well" on a paper towel ("pretend gel"). Your teacher might suggest another method for practicing how to load gels. Keep practicing until you feel comfortable loading and expelling a sample.

Make sure you record the order in which you load the samples. Be sure to use a fresh loading device (either plastic micropipette or other type of pipette) for each sample. Be sure you know how to use the pipette properly. When in doubt, ask your teacher. Take care not to puncture the bottom of the well with the pipette tip when you load your samples.

Step 1 Load 15–20 µL of each sample of DNA into a separate well in the gel, as shown in Figure 4.

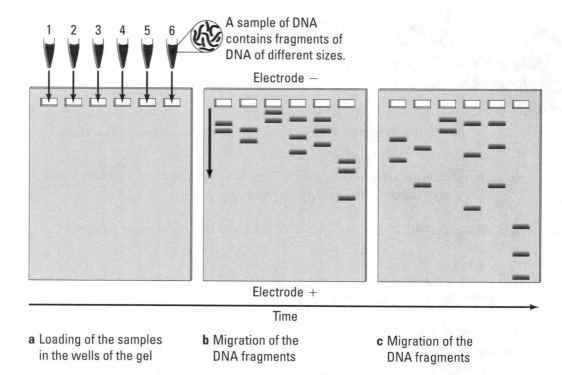

a Loading of the samples in the wells of the gel

b Migration of the DNA fragments

c Migration of the DNA fragments

Figure 4. Loading an Agarose Gel and Migrating DNA Fragments Through Time

Step 2 Slowly draw up the contents of the first sample tube into the pipette.

Step 3 Using two hands, steady the pipette over the well you are going to load.

Step 4 Expel any air in the end of the pipette *before* loading the DNA sample.

Step 5 Dip the pipette tip through the surface of the buffer, position it just inside the well, and slowly expel the mixture. Sucrose in the loading dye weighs down the sample, causing it to sink to the bottom of the well. *Be careful not to puncture the bottom of the well with the pipette tip or reaspirate your sample up into the pipette.*

Step 6 Draw the pipette tip out of the buffer.

Step 7 Using a clean loading device for each sample, load the remaining samples into their wells.

Electrophoresis

Step 1 Close the top of the electrophoresis chamber and then connect the electrical leads to an appropriate power supply, positive (+) electrode to positive (+) electrode (red to red) and negative (-) electrode to negative (-) electrode (black to black). Make sure both electrodes are connected to the same channel of the power supply, just as you would connect leads to jump-start a car battery — red to red and black to black.

   CAUTION: Be sure to keep the power OFF until you connect all leads!

Step 2 Turn on the power supply and set the voltage as directed by your teacher. (It is recommended that you "run the gel" at 50 volts for approximately 2 hours. If you run the gel at a higher voltage for less time, the fragments migrate too quickly through the gel with less separation. Again, ask your teacher for assistance if needed.)

Step 3 Shortly after the current is applied, you should see loading dye moving through the gel toward the positive pole of the electrophoresis apparatus. (**Note:** The purplish-blue band in the loading dye migrates through the gel at the same rate as a DNA fragment approximately 300 base pairs long.)

Step 4 Allow the DNA to electrophorese until the loading dye band is about 1 cm from the end of the gel. Your teacher may monitor the progress of the electrophoresis in your absence if you have to attend another class.

Step 5 Turn off the power supply, disconnect the leads from the power supply, and remove the lid of the electrophoresis chamber.

Step 6 Carefully remove the casting tray and slide the gel into a staining tray labeled with the name of your group.
   - Measure in centimeters the distance that the purplish-blue loading dye has migrated into the gel. Measure from the front edge of the well to the front edge of the dye band (also called the dye front).
   - Be sure to record your data (in centimeters).

Step 7 Take your gel to your teacher for further staining instructions. Again, your teacher might monitor the staining procedure.

■ Analyzing Results

Calculating the Sizes of Restriction Fragment Length Polymorphisms

Mathematical formulas have been developed for describing the relationship between the molecular weight of a DNA fragment and its mobility (i.e., how far it migrates in the gel). In general, DNA fragments, like the ones in your evidence samples, migrate at rates inversely proportional to the $\log_{10}$ of their molecular weights. **For simplicity's sake, base pair length (bp) is substituted for molecular weight when determining the size of DNA fragments.** Thus, the size in base pair length of a DNA fragment can be calculated using the distance the fragment travels through the gel. To calculate the base pair length, a DNA standard, composed of DNA fragments of *known* base pair length, is run on the same gel as the unknown fragments and is then used to create a standard curve. The standard curve, in this case a straight line, is created by graphing the distance each fragment traveled through the gel versus the $\log_{10}$ of its base pair length.

Creating the Standard Curve

As explained above, base pair (bp) length is substituted for molecular weight. Note that in plotting the standard curve, calculating the $\log_{10}$ of the base pair length of each fragment is unnecessary because the base pair size is plotted on the logarithmic axis of semi-log paper. Examine your stained gel on a light box or other surface that helps visualize the bands.

- What observations can you make?

- What quantitative measurements can you make?

1. Examine the "ideal" or mock gel shown in Figure 5 that includes DNA samples that have been cut with three restriction enzymes, *Bam*HI, *Eco*RI, and *Hind*III, to produce RFLPs (fragments). Sample D is DNA that has not been cut with enzyme(s). DNA cut with *Hind*III provides a set of fragments of known size and serves as a standard for comparison.

Ideal Restriction Digest of *Lambda* DNA

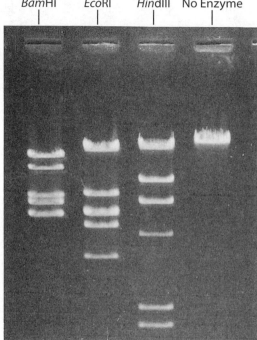

Reprinted with permission from Micklos and Freyer, DNA Science 2e, © 2003 Cold Spring Harbor Laboratory Press.

Figure 5. Ideal Gel

2. Using the ideal gel shown in Figure 5, measure the distance (in cm) that each fragment migrated *from* the origin (the well). (**Hint:** For consistency, measure from the front end of each well to the front edge of each band, i.e., the edge farthest from the well.). Enter the measured distances into Table 1. (See * and ** notes below the table for an explanation for why there are only six bands seen but more fragments.)

Table 1. DNA Fragment Migration Distance

HINDIII		BAMHI		ECORI	
Distance Traveled	BP Length	Distance Traveled	BP Length	Distance Traveled	BP Length
	*27,491				
	*23,130				
	9,416				
	6,557				
	4,361				
	2,322				
	2,027				
	**564				
	**125				

*For this "ideal" gel, assume that these two bands appear as a single band instead of resolving into separate bands.

** These bands do not appear on the ideal gel and likely will not be seen.

3. Plot the standard curve using the data from the DNA sample cut with *Hin*dIII. To do this, your teacher might ask you to graph the data directly using Excel with distance traveled as the (arithmetic) x-axis and the base pair (bp) length as the (logarithmic) y-axis. Based on this graph, why must the data be plotted using the log scale? You might want to plot the data again using semi-log paper.

Connect the data point with a best-fit line. However, you should ignore the point plotted for the 27,491bp/23,130 doublet. When using 0.8% agarose gel, these fragments appear as one. Congratulations! Your best-fit line is the standard curve.

4. Now use the standard curve to calculate the approximate sizes of the *Eco*RI and *Bam*HI fragments. Using a ruler, how can you use the standard curve to calculate the sizes of unknown fragments?

Designing and Conducting Your Investigation

Now that you've learned about the techniques used to create DNA profiles or "fingerprints," it's time to apply the techniques as you investigate the disappearance of Ms. Mason. Your task is to design and conduct a procedure *based on DNA evidence* to determine whose blood is spattered on the classroom floor. The chief investigator (your teacher) will provide you with DNA evidence collected at the crime scene from the blood, Ms. Mason (saliva on her coffee cup), Mr. Gladson (tissue with which he wiped his nose), and Bobby (bubble gum). In addition, you will be given a sample of DNA cut with *Hin*dIII. Remember from your analysis of the "ideal" or mock gel that DNA cut with *Hin*dIII serves as a marker, providing a set of RFLPs of known sizes (standard).

Analyzing Results

Evaluate your crime scene samples to determine whose blood was on the classroom floor. Because this case likely will go to trial, visual analysis (qualitative data) of the DNA profiles is not sufficient to identify a perpetrator. Based on your results, write the conclusion to the scenario to reveal "whodunit" based on motive, means, opportunity, and DNA evidence.

Evaluating Results

1. What are some possible challenges you had in performing your investigation?

2. What are some possible sources of error in the electrophoresis procedure? How can you minimize any potential sources of error?

■ Thinking About Your Results

1. There are important social and ethical implications of DNA analysis. Already, DNA testing can reveal the presence of markers of certain genetic diseases, such as Huntington's. So, who should have access to your genetic profile? Health insurance companies? College admissions offices? Employers? What issues about confidentiality are raised by genetic testing? Who owns your DNA and its information?

2. Suppose a DNA test that predicted your chances of getting a disease, such as cancer, were available. You take the test for cancer, and the results say you have a two in three chance of getting cancer sometime in the next 20 years. Who should have access to this information? Your doctor? Health insurance companies? Employers? Would *you* want to know this information?

3. The Innocence Project (IP) is an international litigation and public policy organization dedicated to exonerating wrongfully convicted individuals through DNA testing. Three-quarters of DNA exoneration cases involve misidentification by witnesses. To date, nearly 300 people previously convicted of serious crimes in the U.S. have been exonerated by DNA testing. However, not everyone is in favor of the IP. One United States Supreme Court justice expressed concern that DNA testing poses risks to the criminal justice system, in which a person is judged by a jury of peers. What social and ethical issues are raised by using DNA evidence to re-examine old court decisions? What other arguments can you make (or find) against using DNA evidence for court cases?

4. With genetic engineering, biotechnicians can clip out beneficial genes from native plants in foreign countries and insert them into their crop plant relatives here in the United States, with great benefits to the latter — to prevent attack by insects, to increase productivity, or to allow the crops to be grown in colder climates. These benefits can be worth billions of dollars, but if the crops are grown in the United States, should countries where the native plants are located benefit from the bioengineering? Who owns the information in DNA? Who can profit from that information? Investigate this controversy on the Internet with examples drawn from different crops grown here in the U.S.

■ Where Can You Go from Here?

The following are suggestions for expanding your study of biotechnology.

1. Do you remember earlier when you read that more than 99% of your DNA is the same as another person's DNA, and that the 1% difference is attributed to small differences in genetic code? Conduct independent research on how these small differences can be detected by molecular biologists. Begin by investigating unique repeat DNA sequences called variable tandem repeats (VNTRs), short tandem repeats (STRs), and single nucleotide polymorphisms (SNPs). Prepare a mini-poster presentation for your classmates illustrating how these small differences can be used to individualize DNA from different organisms, including humans. Are the differences between you and other individuals in the genes themselves? If so, how do you account for the fact that everyone needs the same genes to produce your cell components and your organs, such as your liver and lungs?

2. Often scientists have only a small amount of DNA available for analysis. The polymerase chain reaction (PCR) is another key technique that molecular biologists use to amplify a specific sequence of DNA. Developed by Kary Mullis in 1983, PCR produces millions of copies of a DNA sequence in a few hours, with the original sequence serving as the template for replication. PCR has a variety of applications, including DNA cloning, determining DNA-based phylogeny, diagnosing hereditary diseases, and identifying genetic fingerprints. Ask your teacher if you can learn to perform PCR. PCR usually requires a relatively expensive piece of equipment, a DNA thermocycler; however, you can investigate less expensive methods of PCR.

3. Select an episode of one of your favorite TV crime investigation shows that focuses on DNA as evidence. Compare TV science with *real* science.

INVESTIGATION 10
ENERGY DYNAMICS

What factors govern energy capture, allocation, storage, and transfer between producers and consumers in a terrestrial ecosystem?

■ BACKGROUND

Almost all life on this planet is powered, either directly or indirectly, by sunlight. Energy captured from sunlight drives the production of energy-rich organic compounds during the process of photosynthesis. These organic compounds create biomass. The net amount of energy captured and stored by the producers in a system is the system's net productivity. Gross productivity is a measure of the total energy captured. In terrestrial systems, plants play the role of producers. Plants allocate that biomass (energy) to power their life processes or to store energy. Different plants have different strategies of energy allocation that reflect their role in various ecosystems. For example, annual weedy plants allocate a larger percentage of their biomass production to reproductive processes and seeds than do slower growing perennials. As plants, the producers are consumed or decomposed, and their stored chemical energy powers additional individuals, the consumers, or trophic levels of the biotic community. Biotic systems run on energy much as economic systems run on money. Energy is generally in limited supply in most communities. Energy dynamics in a biotic community is fundamental to understanding ecological interactions.

To model ecosystem energy dynamics, you will estimate the net primary productivity (NPP) of Wisconsin Fast Plants (the producers) growing under lights and the flow of energy from plants to cabbage white butterfly larvae (the consumers) as the larvae eat cabbage-family plants.

The following exercises describe skills and methods for estimating energy flow in a terrestrial ecosystem. Note and record any questions that occur to you as you work through this activity.

Questions might include the following:
- What kinds of things affect plant productivity, the growth of cabbage white butterfly larvae, or the interactions of these organisms?
- How do you keep track of energy as it moves through the biological system? Can the techniques used for tracking energy be improved?
- What is the role of energy in ecosystems?

One or more of these questions will help guide you through the final part of this laboratory, where you are expected to carry out your own research project based on one of your questions.

■ Learning Objectives

- To design and conduct an experiment to investigate a question about energy capture and flow in an ecosystem

- To explain community/ecosystem energy dynamics, including energy flow, NPP, and primary and secondary producers/consumers

- To predict interspecific ecological interactions and their effects

- To use mathematical analyses in energy accounting and community modeling

- To make the explicit connection between biological content and the investigative experience

■ General Safety Precautions

- Cabbage white butterflies (*Pieris rapae*) are listed as a pest species by the USDA. Therefore, no butterflies or larvae raised in the laboratory should be released to the wild.

- Euthanize the butterflies or larvae by freezing them when your investigation is complete. The plants and soil can simply be discarded.

- Disease outbreaks are common in cultured populations of organisms. Although the diseases associated with the organisms in this investigation are not dangerous to humans, it is important to maintain cleanliness in the laboratory and of your experimental equipment to minimize possible impacts on the study caused by disease.

- Long-term culturing for plants or butterflies requires cleanliness. Be sure to clean all culturing chambers and wipe them down with dilute Clorox (and dry completely) before starting another generation of plants or butterflies. Use new materials if you have any doubts.

- Cultures involve artificial light sources and liquids; caution should be exercised to keep the two separate.

■ THE INVESTIGATIONS

■ Getting Started

These questions and tasks are designed to help you understand energy dynamics and prepare for your investigations.

1. The economy of a business or household is somewhat like the energetics of a biological community. A well-run household or business creates a budget based on a careful accounting of money coming in and money going out. Likewise, the energy dynamics of a biological community can be modeled by accounting for the energy coming in and going out through different members of the community. Keeping track of money is relatively straightforward — you count it. You count how much money is coming in and how much is going to various expenses and savings.

How do you keep track of energy in living organisms? It is a challenge. Producers capture light energy and convert it into chemical energy stored in energy-rich molecules. These molecules have mass, so the energy in biological systems can be indirectly measured by mass — biomass. With your lab team, take a moment to brainstorm how you can account for energy use and, in a biological community, transfer it in a manner similar to the ways in which people account for money.

2. This investigation requires you to take care of and maintain healthy populations of living organisms — plants and animals. In fact, before you begin this investigation, you will need to start both plant and animal cultures. Wisconsin Fast Plants and cabbage white butterflies are both easily raised in the classroom or laboratory. Neither takes up much time or equipment, but they both need to be tended regularly. As a lab team, discuss the care and maintenance of the organisms you use in this lab. Prepare a schedule and divide up responsibilities for long-term care and maintenance. (This includes taking care of animal wastes.) Check out online information on care and maintenance of the organisms you and your teacher select for this investigation at *http://fastplants.ning.com/video/2038532:Video:13* and *http://fastplants.ning.com/video/juan-enriquez-wants-to-grow*. See the butterfly life cycle in Figure 1.

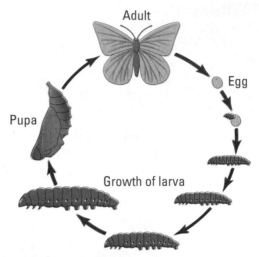

Figure 1. Butterfly Life Cycle

■ Procedures

Estimating Net Primary Productivity (NPP) of Fast Plants

Remember as you work through the first part of this investigation to think about and record questions you ask while working with these organisms and the system.

Primary productivity is a rate — energy captured by photosynthetic organisms in a given area per unit of time. Based on the second law of thermodynamics, when energy is converted from one form to another, some energy will be lost as heat. When light energy is converted to chemical energy in photosynthesis or transferred from one organism (a plant or producer) to its consumer (e.g., an herbivorous insect), some energy will be lost as heat during each transfer.

In terrestrial ecosystems, productivity (or energy capture) is generally estimated by the change in biomass of plants produced over a specific time period. Measuring biomass or changes in biomass is relatively straightforward: simply mass the organism(s) on an appropriate scale and record the mass over various time intervals. The complicating factor is that a large percentage of the mass of a living organism is water — not the energy-rich organic compounds of biomass. Therefore, to determine the biomass at a particular point in time accurately, you must dry the organism. Obviously, this creates a problem if you wish to take multiple measurements on the same living organism. Another issue is that different organic compounds store different amounts of energy; in proteins and carbohydrates it is about 4 kcal/g dry weight and in fats it is 9 kcal/g of dry weight). As you plan your own investigation, take into consideration all the above information.

You and your teacher will select a model organism for this lab depending on time of year, availability, and cost. The following steps assume that you and your lab team are culturing about 30 to 40 Wisconsin Fast Plants as a model organism. Other plants can be used instead, including wild or native plants, but check with your teacher first.

Step 1 In your lab notebook, design and construct a systems diagram to model energy capture and flow through a plant. Use annotations to help explain your reasoning. Before taking any measurements, think about the input and output of energy in a plant. For instance, what do you predict about the quantity of energy the plants take in compared to the quantity of energy that goes out? What do you think are various ways that a plant (or a number of plants) could lose energy, and how could you estimate the amount of energy lost through these various pathways? Enter your predictions in your lab notebook by constructing an annotated system diagram, such as Figure 2, of the flow of energy into and out of a plant.

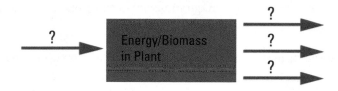

Figure 2. Energy Flow into and out of a Plant

Step 2 Your energy diagram will help you and your lab team design a data collection procedure that helps you measure energy capture and flow in a plant. As a team, design your investigation to sample the biomass of an adequate number of plants early in the life cycle and then again later in the life cycle. Remember, biomass is only the mass of the DRY plant materials, not of the water in the plant. Make sure your procedure accounts for this. Describe this procedure in your lab notebook and then check with your teacher for approval and suggestions. Be sure to record your observations, questions, reflections, and measurements daily in your notebook. In your lab notebook, record information about the size and overall appearance of your Fast Plants.

Step 3 In your notebook, graphically present a comparison of the biomass/energy of plants early in their life cycle versus older plants.

Step 4 Determine the average (mean) grams of biomass added per plant over the period of growth. Each gram of plant biomass represents about 4.35 kcal of energy. Convert grams of biomass/day to NPP (kcal)/day. Show this work in your lab notebook. Explain why this is *net* primary productivity and not *gross* productivity.

Step 5 Explain in your notebook why the mass of dry plants is a better measure of primary productivity and biomass than is the mass of living plants (containing water). What percentage of the living plants is biomass? (Use this calculation in Analyzing and Evaluating Results, Step 4.)

Step 6 Now reconstruct your energy flow diagram with actual data that you have collected in your notebook. Be sure to include an explanation, supported by evidence, as to why you feel your diagram represents energy flow in Fast Plants. Your explanation should also include a description of the uncertainties of your data and your conclusions; put boundaries on your conclusions (as you would insert error bars).

Estimating Energy Flow Between Fast Plants Producers and Cabbage Butterfly Larvae

Don't forget to think of and record questions about these organisms and the system as you work through your investigation.

Step 1 Cabbage white butterfly larvae eat plants from the cabbage family. As with Fast Plants, accounting for energy flow into and out of these butterflies can be inferred from biomass gained and lost. In your lab notebook, develop a system diagram, such as Figure 3, to model energy flow from Fast Plants to cabbage butterfly larvae. Before taking any measurements, predict the input and the output of energy in the butterfly larvae you will be growing. Enter these predictions in your lab notebook.

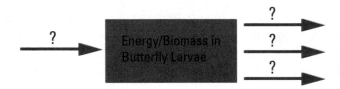

Figure 3. Energy Flow from Fast Plants to Cabbage Butterfly Larvae

Step 2 As butterfly larvae grow toward maturity, they pass through different developmental stages called instars. You will use larvae that are already well along their developmental path through the larval stages (4th or 5th instar). These larvae first grew on young Fast Plants, and they were later transferred to brussels sprouts (another member of the cabbage family) in a Brassica Barn (see Figure 4). For this part of the investigation, you and your lab team need to develop a procedure that will quantify the growth of butterfly larvae over three days. Start with freshly massed brussels sprouts in the Brassica Barn.

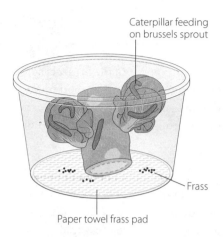

Figure 4. Brassica Barn

Step 3 Create a table in your lab notebook that helps you organize the data collected, including estimates of the energy/biomass flow from plants to butterfly larvae. Develop your procedure keeping in mind your end goal — to measure the biomass consumed by the larvae, the biomass gained by the larvae, and the biomass lost by the larvae. Likely, you'll need to estimate some factors using data from a large sample. Don't forget about the energy in the frass (wastes).

Step 4 Transfer the larvae to another Brassica Barn to finish out their life cycle.

■ Analyzing and Evaluating Results

Convert biomass measurements (grams) to energy units in kilocalories. Work in small groups to determine how best to complete the following tasks. Make sure that all your units are comparable: per time, mass, and energy.

Step 1 For Fast Plants, assume that one gram of dried biomass contains 4.35 kilocalories of energy. This estimate was determined by burning similar plant material in a bomb calorimeter.

Step 2 You were investigating living butterfly larvae, so you could not dry them or their food supply. Assume that the biomass of 4th instar larvae is 40% of the wet mass. (This estimate may be inaccurate, so you should actually measure this quantity using extra butterfly larvae, if possible.) Calculate the biomass of the larvae. For butterfly larvae, use an average value of 5.5 kcal/g of biomass to calculate energy of each larva.

Step 3 To determine the energy content in the larval frass, use 4.76 kcal of energy/g of frass. Calculate the frass lost per individual larva.

Step 4 To determine the energy content of the brussels sprouts eaten by each larva, convert the wet mass of the sprout to dry mass and multiply by 4.35 kcal/g. Use the estimated percentage of biomass (dry mass) in fresh Fast Plants calculated in estimating the Fast Plants' net primary productivity (NPP), Step 5 on page S130, to estimate the biomass of each brussels sprout.

Step 5 These procedures are similar to an energy audit. Because energy is neither created nor destroyed, you must account for all energy in the system. (That is why you need to determine frass mass.) Combine your two earlier energy flow diagrams into one, and now include all the information that you measured. For those energy pathways that you did not explicitly measure, provide an estimated energy quantity. For instance, the amount of light energy in the system is more difficult to estimate. What other parts of the energy flow diagram could you not actually measure?

Step 6 Graph your results. For the plants and for the butterfly larvae, design and construct appropriate graphs of your results. Enter sketches of these graphs in your lab notebook and prepare more finished copies for your mini-poster presentation when you complete this lab. If you use bar graphs for illustrating the means, standard error bars should be included to display the range of the data. In your notebook (and mini-poster presentation), describe the data and their presentation. Follow that with conclusions that you can support with your data about energy capture and flow in this artificial lab community.

■ Designing and Conducting Your Investigation

In the previous procedures, you began to develop your skills by applying methods to the problem of energy capture and flow in an ecosystem. You were encouraged to note and record questions about this system as you worked through the investigation. Now it is time to select one of those questions, propose your hypothesis, design your investigation, and carry it out. Be sure to connect your work to your overall understanding of energy and ecosystems.

The following are questions that could be investigated; however, you should have developed your own question(s) and considered a possible investigation(s).

- Do all plants have the same percentage of biomass?
- Is the percentage of biomass the most important characteristic of a plant in terms of its effect on the growth of an animal?
- How do plants with different life strategies allocate biomass in different organs?
- How much is allocated to reproduction?
- How much energy is allocated to plant defense?
- How much energy does it cost an animal to process different plant sources?

Review and consolidate your questions into a list of possibilities. Consult with your teacher and other students. After choosing your question, hypothesis, and design, submit the plan (proposal) for your investigation to your teacher for approval. Be sure to refer to the rubric provided by your teacher that will be used to evaluate your work. Consider working as a team on a single question to reduce your overall workload.

Step 1 Conduct your investigation or construct and test your mathematical model.

Step 2 Prepare a mini-poster that addresses the requirements outlined in the rubric.

Step 3 Present your mini-poster to your peers and invited guests in class. Encourage your peers to review and critique your work based on the rubric guidelines. Use those reviews to improve your mini-poster after the presentation. Your teacher will use the same rubric, along with your lab notebook, to determine your final grade for this investigation.

INVESTIGATION 11

TRANSPIRATION*

What factors, including environmental variables, affect the rate of transpiration in plants?

■ BACKGROUND

Cells and organisms must exchange matter with the environment to grow, reproduce, and maintain organization, and the availability of resources influences responses and activities. For example, water and macronutrients are used to synthesize new molecules, and, in plants, water is essential for photosynthesis. Organisms have evolved various mechanisms for accumulating sufficient quantities of water, ions, and other nutrients and for keeping them properly balanced to maintain homeostasis.

Plants absorb and transport water, nutrients, and ions from the surrounding soil via osmosis, diffusion, and active transport. Once water and dissolved nutrients have entered the root xylem, they are transported upward to the stems and leaves as part of the process of transpiration, with a subsequent loss of water due to evaporation from the leaf surface. Too much water loss can be detrimental to plants; they can wilt and die.

The transport of water upward from roots to shoots in the xylem is governed by differences in water (or osmotic) potential, with water molecules moving from an area of high water potential (higher free energy, more water) to an area of low water potential (lower free energy, less water). (You may have studied the concept of water potential in more detail when exploring the processes of osmosis and diffusion in Investigation 4 in this manual.) The movement of water through a plant is facilitated by osmosis, root pressure, and the physical and chemical properties of water. Transpiration creates a lower osmotic potential in the leaf, and the TACT (transpiration, adhesion, cohesion, and tension) mechanism describes the forces that move water and dissolved nutrients up the xylem.

---

* Transitioned from the *AP Biology Lab Manual* (2001)

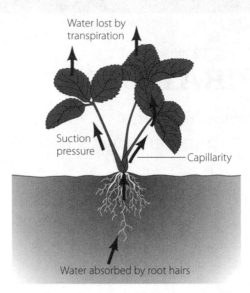

Figure 1. Transpiration Model

During transpiration, water evaporating from the spaces within leaves escapes through small pores called stomata. Although evaporation of water through open stomata is a major route of water loss in plants, the stomata must open to allow for the entry of CO_2 used in photosynthesis. In addition, O_2 produced in photosynthesis exits through open stomata. Consequently, a balance must be maintained between the transport of CO_2 and O_2 and the loss of water. Specialized cells called guard cells help regulate the opening and closing of stomata.

In this laboratory investigation, you will begin by calculating leaf surface area and then determine the average number of stomata per square millimeter. From your data, several questions emerge about the process of transpiration in plants, including the following:

- Do all plants have stomata? Is there any relationship between the number of stomata and the environment in which the plant species evolved?

- Are leaf surface area and the number of stomata related to the rate of transpiration? What might happen to the rate of transpiration if the number of leaves or the size of leaves is reduced?

- Do all parts of a plant transpire?

- Do all plants transpire at the same rate? Is there a relationship between the habitat in which plants evolved and their rate of transpiration?

- What other factors, including environmental variables, might contribute to the rate of transpiration?

- What structural features and/or physiological processes help plants regulate the amount of water lost through transpiration? How do plants maintain the balance between the transport of CO_2 and O_2 and the amount of water lost through transpiration?

You will then design an experiment to investigate one of these questions or a question of your own. As a supplemental activity, you can examine microscopically thin sections of stems, identify xylem and phloem cells, and relate the function of these vascular tissues to observations made about the structure of these cells.

The investigation also provides an opportunity for you to apply and review concepts you have studied previously, including the relationship between cell structure and function; osmosis, diffusion, and active transport; the movement of molecules and ions across cell membranes; the physical and chemical properties of water; photosynthesis; and the exchange of matter between biological systems and the environment.

Learning Objectives

- To investigate the relationship among leaf surface area, number of stomata, and the rate of transpiration
- To design and conduct an experiment to explore other factors, including different environmental variables, on the rate of transpiration
- To investigate the relationship between the structure of vascular tissues (xylem and phloem) and their functions in transporting water and nutrients in plants

General Safety Precautions

If you investigate transpiration rates using a potometer, you should be careful when assembling your equipment and when using a razor blade or scalpel to cut the stem of a plant, cutting to a 45° angle.

When appropriate, you should wear goggles for conducting investigations. Nail polish used in the investigation is toxic by ingestion and inhalation, and you should avoid eye contact. All materials should be disposed of properly as per your teacher's instructions.

THE INVESTIGATIONS

Getting Started

These questions are designed to help you understand concepts related to transpiration in plants before you design and conduct your investigation(s).

1. If a plant cell has a lower water potential than its surrounding environment, make a prediction about the movement of water across the cell membrane. In other words, will the cell gain water or lose water? Explain your answer in the form of a diagram with annotations.

2. In the winter, salt is sometimes spread over icy roads. In the spring, after the ice has melted, grass often dies near these roads. What causes this to happen? Explain your answer in the form of a diagram with annotations.

3. Prepare a thin section of stem from your plant and examine it under the microscope to identify the vascular tissues (xylem and phloem) and the structural differences in their cells. Describe how the observed differences in cellular structure reflect differences in function of the two types of vascular tissue.

4. If you wanted to transplant a tree, would you choose to move the tree in the winter, when it doesn't possess any leaves but it's cold outside, or during the summer, when the tree has leaves and it's warm and sunny? Explain your answer.

■ Procedure

Materials

- Living representative plant species available in your region/season, such as *Impatiens* (a moisture-loving plant), *Coleus,* oleander (more drought tolerant), *Phaseolus vulgaris* (bean seedlings), pea plants, varieties of *Lycopersicon* (tomato), peppers, and ferns

- Calculator, microscope, microscope slides, clear cellophane tape, clear nail polish, and scissors
- Additional supplies that you might need after you choose a method to determine leaf surface area (Step 1 below). Ask your teacher for advice.

Record data and any answers to questions in your lab notebooks, as instructed by your teacher.

Step 1 Form teams of two or three and investigate methods of calculating leaf surface area. (You will need to calculate leaf surface area when you conduct your experiments.) Think about and formulate answers to the following questions as you work through this activity:

    a. How can you calculate the total leaf surface area expressed in cm^2? In mm^2?

    b. How can you estimate the leaf surface area of the entire plant without measuring every leaf?

    c. What predictions and/or hypotheses can you make about the number of stomata per mm^2 and the rate of transpiration?

    d. Is the leaf surface area directly related to the rate of transpiration?

    e. What predictions can you make about the rate of transpiration in plants with smaller or fewer leaves?

    f. Because most leaves have two sides, do you think you have to double your calculation to obtain the surface area of one leaf? Why or why not?

g. Water is transpired through stomata, but carbon dioxide also must pass through stomata into a leaf for photosynthesis to occur. There is evidence that the level of carbon dioxide in the atmosphere has not always been the same over the history of life on Earth. Explain how the presence of a higher or lower concentration of atmospheric carbon dioxide would impact the evolution of stomata density in plants.

h. Based on the data in the following table, is there a relationship between the habitat (in terms of moisture) to which the plants are adapted and the density of stomata in their leaves? What evidence from the data supports your answer?

**Table 1. Average Number of Stomata per Square Millimeter (mm²)
of Leaf Surface Area**

PLANT	IN UPPER EPIDERMIS	IN LOWER EPIDERMIS
Anacharis	0	0
Coleus	0	141
Black Walnut	0	160
Kidney Bean	40	176
Nasturtium	0	130
Sunflower	85	156
Oats	25	23
Corn	70	88
Tomato	12	130
Water Llly	460	0

Step 2 Make a wet mount of a nail polish stomatal peel to view leaf epidermis using the following technique:

a. Obtain a leaf. (The leaf may remain on the plant or be removed.)

b. Paint a solid patch of clear nail polish on the leaf surface being studied. Make a patch of at least one square centimeter.

c. Allow the nail polish to dry completely.

d. Press a piece of clean, clear cellophane tape to the dried nail polish patch. Using clear (not opaque) tape is essential here. You might also try pulling the peel away from the leaf without using any tape and then preparing a wet mount of the peel with a drop of water and a cover slip.

e. Gently peel the nail polish patch from the leaf by pulling a corner of the tape and peeling the nail polish off the leaf. This is the leaf impression that you will examine. (Make only one leaf impression on each side of the leaf, especially if the leaf is going to be left on a live plant.)

f. Tape the peeled impression to a clean microscope slide. Use scissors to trim away any excess tape. Label the slide as appropriate for the specimen being examined and label the side of leaf from which the peel was taken.

g. Examine the leaf impression under a light microscope to at least 400X (or highest magnification). Draw and label what you observe. Can you observe any stomata? Search for areas where there are numerous stomata.

h. Count all the stomata in one microscopic field. Record the number.

i. Repeat counts for at least three other distinct microscopic fields and record the number of stomata.

j. Determine an average number of stomata per microscopic field.

k. From the average number per microscopic field, calculate the number of stomata per 1 mm^2. You can estimate the area of the field of view by placing a transparent plastic ruler along its diameter, measuring the field's diameter, and then calculating area by using πr^2. (Most low-power fields have a diameter between 1.5–2.0 mm.)

l. Trade slides with two other lab teams so you examine three different slides under the microscope using the same procedure described above.

■ Designing and Conducting Your Investigation

The procedure should have raised several questions about factors that relate to the rate of transpiration in plants. Some possible questions are listed below, but you may have others.

- What environmental variables might affect the rate of transpiration?
- Do all parts of a plant transpire?
- Do all plants transpire at the same rate?
- Is there a relationship between the habitat in which plants evolved to their rate of transpiration?

Rate of transpiration can be measured by a variety of methods, including the use of a potometer with or without a gas pressure sensor and computer interface or the use of the whole plant method. These methods are detailed in this investigation, but your teacher may help you substitute another procedure.

If using a gas pressure sensor and computer interface to measure transpiration rate, your teacher likely will provide instructions. If you are unfamiliar with the use of probes with computer interface, it is suggested that you spend about 30 minutes learning how to collect data using the equipment.

Step 1 Design an experiment to investigate one of the aforementioned questions or one of your own questions to determine the effect of an environmental variable(s) on the rate of transpiration in plants. When identifying your design, be sure to address the following questions:

- What is the essential question being addressed?
- What assumptions are made about the questions being addressed?
- Can those assumptions be easily verified?
- Will the measurement(s) provide the necessary data to answer the question under study?
- Did you include a control in your experiment?

Step 2 Make a hypothesis/prediction about which environmental factors will have the greatest effect on transpiration rates. Be sure to explain your hypothesis.

Step 3 Conduct your experiment(s) and record data and any answers to your questions in your lab notebooks or as instructed by your teacher. Write down any additional questions that arose during this study that might lead to *other* investigations that you can conduct.

■ Option 1: Potometer with or Without Gas Pressure Sensor

Materials

- Representative plant species available in your region/season, such as *Impatiens* (a moisture-loving plant), *Coleus*, oleander (more drought toler-ant), *Phaseolus vulgaris* (bean seed-lings), pea plants, varieties of *Lycopersicon* (tomato), peppers, and ferns

- Potometer, which you assemble from clear plastic tubing, a ring stand with clamp, and a 0.1-mL or 1.0-mL pipette, depending on the diameter of the stem of the plant you choose. Your teacher will have several different sizes of plastic tubing available. (The tubing can be filled using a water bottle or plastic syringe *without a needle*.) If using a syringe, attach it to the end of the pipette and pull water into the

potometer. (Why should the tubing be free of air bubbles? Why must the stem be completely immersed in the water?) If using a gas pressure sensor, the tubing is inserted directly into the device, with no pipettes required. (The potometer assembly is illustrated in Figure 2.)

- Fan, heat lamp, water, small plastic bag, spray bottle with water, salt, and other materials provided by your teacher to simulate an environmental variable

- Petroleum jelly to make an airtight seal between the cut end of stem and tubing filled with water (You can also use small clamps to seal without the "goop.")

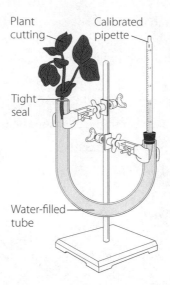

Figure 2. Potometer Assembly

Using a razor blade, carefully cut the plant stem so that its diameter will fit into the piece of plastic tubing in the potometer assembly. Note that it is often helpful to cut the stem while it is submerged under water to prevent air bubbles from being introduced into the xylem. Your teacher will provide additional instructions, if necessary. Please be careful when using the razor blade!

■ Option 2: Whole Plant Method

Materials

- Small potted plant (*Impatiens*, tomato seedling, bean seedling, pea plant, etc.) with many leaves and few flowers
- One-gallon size plastic food storage bag without zipper
- String

Step 1 Saturate the plant with water the day/night before beginning your investigation.

Step 2 Carefully remove a plant from the soil/pot, making sure to retain as much of the root system and keeping soil particles attached to the roots. Wrap the root ball of the plant(s) in a plastic bag and tie the bag around the base so that only the leaves are exposed. (Be sure to remove all flowers and buds.) Do not water your plant any more until you finish your experiment! You can also keep the plant in the plastic pot and place it in the plastic bag.

Step 3 Determine the mass of each plant and then its mass for several days under your environmental condition(s).

Step 4 Record your data in your lab notebook or as instructed by your teacher.

■ Calculations: Determining Surface Area and Transpiration Rates

Step 1 In the first part of this lab, you were asked to investigate methods to calculate leaf surface area and the surface area of all the leaves on a plant or plant cutting (depending on your experimental setup). Your teacher may suggest a particular method. Determine the total surface area of the leaves in cm^2 and record the value.

Step 2 Calculate the rate of transpiration/surface area. If you are using a gas pressure sensor to collect data, you can express these rate values as $kPa/min/cm^2$, where kPa (kilopascal) is a unit of pressure. Record the rate.

Step 3 After the entire class agrees on an appropriate control, subtract the control rate from the experimental value. Record this adjusted rate.

Step 4 Record the adjusted rate for your experimental test on the board to share with other lab groups. Record the class results for each of the environmental variables investigated.

Step 5 Graph the class results to show the effects of different environmental variables on the rate of transpiration. You may need to convert data to scientific notation with all numbers reported to the same power of 10 for graphing purposes.

Step 6 Your teacher may suggest you perform statistical analysis (e.g., a T-test) of your data, comparing results of experimental variable(s) to controls.

■ Analyzing Results

1. How was the rate of transpiration affected by your choice of experimental variable as compared to the control?

2. Think of a way you can effectively communicate your results to other lab groups. By comparing results and conclusions, explain how changes or variables in environmental conditions affect transpiration rates.

3. Based on data collected from different lab groups, which environmental variable(s) resulted in the greatest rate of water loss through transpiration? Explain why this factor might increase water loss when compared to other factors.

4. Why did you need to calculate leaf surface area to determine the rate(s) of transpiration?

5. What structural or physiological adaptations enable plants to control water loss? How might each adaptation affect transpiration?

6. Make a prediction about the number of stomata in a leaf and the rate of transpiration. What type(s) of experiments could you conduct to determine the relationship between the number of stomata and the rate of transpiration?

7. Create a diagram with annotation to explain how the TACT (transpiration, adhesion, cohesion, tension) mechanism enables water and nutrients to travel up a 100-ft. tree. Predict how a significant increase in ambient (environmental) temperature might affect the rate of transpiration in this tree. Explain your prediction in terms of TACT and the role of guard cells in regulating the opening and closing of stomata.

■ Evaluating Results

1. Was your initial hypothesis about the effect of your environmental variable on the rate of transpiration supported by the data you collected? Why or why not?

2. What were some challenges you had in performing your experiment? Did you make any incorrect assumptions about the effect of environmental variables on the rate(s) of transpiration?

3. Were you able to perform without difficulty the mathematical routines required to analyze your data? Which calculations, if any, were challenging or required help from your classmates or teacher?

■ Where Can You Go from Here?

1. Investigate how guard cells control the opening and closing of stomata, including the role of abscisic acid and K^+.

2. Design an experiment to investigate transpiration in two different types of plants — one that is drought tolerant and one that requires a significant amount of water. What predictions can you make about the rate of transpiration in each?

3. If you had to revise the design of your experiment, what suggestions would you make? Why would you make them?

4. If your investigations generated other questions that you might want to research, ask your teacher if you can conduct other experiments.

INVESTIGATION 12
FRUIT FLY BEHAVIOR

What environmental factors trigger a fruit fly response?

■ BACKGROUND

Drosophila melanogaster, the common fruit fly, is an organism that has been studied in the scientific community for more than a century. Thomas Hunt Morgan began using it for genetic studies in 1907. The common fruit fly lives throughout the world and feeds on fruit and the fungi growing on rotting fruit. It is a small fly, and one could question why scientists have spent so much time and effort on this tiny insect. It is about the size of President Roosevelt's nose on a dime, but despite its small size, the fly is packed with many interesting physical and behavioral characteristics. Its genome has been sequenced, its physical characteristics have been charted and mutated, its meiotic processes and development have been investigated, and its behavior has been the source of many experiments. Because of its scientific usefulness, *Drosophila* is a model research organism. Its name is based on observations about the fly; the fly follows circadian rhythms that include sleeping during the dark and emerging as an adult from a pupa in the early morning. This latter behavior gave rise to the name *Drosophila*, which means "lover of dew." The explanation for the species name *melanogaster* should be clear after observing the fly's physical features. It has a black "stomach," or abdomen. No doubt the dew-loving, black-bellied fly will continue to make contributions to the scientific community and to student projects.

We begin our investigation with a few simple questions. What do you know about fruit flies? Have you seen fruit flies outside the lab and, if so, where? Describe where and when you have noted fruit flies.

■ Learning Objectives

- To investigate the relationship between a model organism, *Drosophila*, and its response to different environmental conditions

- To design a controlled experiment to explore environmental factors that either attract or repel *Drosophila* in the laboratory setting

- To analyze data collected in an experiment in order to identify possible patterns and relationships between environmental factors and a living organism

- To work collaboratively with others in the design and analysis of a controlled experiment

- To connect and apply concepts (With the fruit fly as the focal organism, your investigation could pull together many topics, such as genetics, animal behavior, development, plant and animal structures from cells to organs, cell communication, fruit ripening, fermentation, and evolution.)

■ General Safety Precautions

- Do not add substances to the choice chamber unless your teacher has approved them.

- If the substance you add is flammable, such as ethanol, use precaution and do not conduct your experiment near a heat source or flame.

- Many of the substances used in this experiment are food items, but you should not consume any of them.

- Fruit flies are living organisms that should not be released to the environment. After all the investigations are complete, flies should be tapped into a "morgue" through a funnel. The morgue typically is a 150-mL beaker that contains about 50 mL of salad oil or 70% alcohol.

■ THE INVESTIGATIONS

■ Getting Started

This procedure is designed to help you understand how to work with fruit flies. You may start with general information about how to determine the sex of a fruit fly. How do you tell the difference between male and female flies? Is the sex of the fly important to your investigations? Look at the female and male fruit flies in Figure 1. Then look at the fruit flies in Figure 2. Can you identify which ones are female and which ones are male? Focus on the abdomen of the flies to note differences.

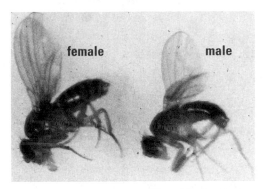

Figure 1. Determining the Sex of Fruit Flies

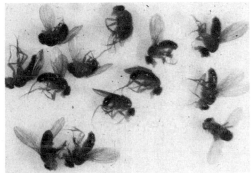

Figure 2. Fruit Flies

Step 1 Using fruit fly cultures, carefully toss 10 to 20 living flies into an empty vial. Be sure to plug the vial as soon as you add the flies. Do not anesthetize the flies before this or any of the behavior experiments.

Step 2 When flies are tossed, they are tapped into an empty vial. Tap a culture vial (push the vial down on a solid surface several times) on the table to move the flies to the bottom of the vial. Quickly remove the foam or cotton top and invert an empty vial over the top of the culture vial. Invert the vials so that the culture vial is on the top and the empty vial is on the bottom, and tap the flies into the empty container by tapping it on a solid surface several times. Be sure to hold the vials tightly to keep them together. You must then separate the vials and cap each separately. Do not try to isolate every fly from the original culture. It is difficult to separate flies, and you may lose a fly or two in the process.

Step 3 After your lab group has the flies in a vial without food, observe the position of the flies in your upright vial.

Step 4 Invert the vial, and observe the position of the flies after 15 seconds and after 30 seconds.

Step 5 What was the flies' response? Did most/all of the flies move in the same general direction? If so, this might be an "orientation movement," which is a movement that is in response to some stimulus. Based on how you manipulated the vial, to what stimulus might the flies be responding? Do you think that they were responding to some chemical change in the vial? Did your observations generate other questions? Explain your answers.

■ Procedure

Animals move in response to many different stimuli. A chemotaxis is a movement in response to the presence of a chemical stimulus. The organism may move toward or away from the chemical stimulus. What benefit would an organism gain by responding to chemicals in their environment? A phototactic response is a movement in response to light. A geotactic response is a movement in response to gravity.

You will investigate fruit fly movement using a choice chamber that exposes the flies to different substances that you insert into the chamber. Because flies are very common in households (in fact, fruit flies live almost everywhere that humans live), think about using foods or condiments that might result in a positive or a negative chemotactic response from the flies. What foods or condiments do you think would attract or repel flies? Why? Do fruit flies exhibit a response to light or to gravity? How can you alter the chamber to investigate those variables?

Step 1 Prepare a choice chamber by labeling both ends with a marker — one end "A" and the other "B" (see Figure 3). Cut the bottom of the bottles, dry the interior thoroughly, and tape them together. Remove any paper labels.

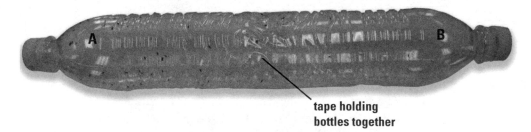

tape holding
bottles together

Figure 3. Choice Chamber

Place a cap on one end of a chamber before adding flies. Insert a small funnel in the open end of the chamber and place the chamber upright on the capped end. Tap 20–30 fruit flies into the choice chamber using the funnel.

Step 2 After transfer, quickly cap the other end of the chamber.

Step 3 Begin your study of the choice of flies by placing a few (5–10) drops of distilled water on two cotton balls, and adhere one moist cotton ball to each end of the chamber. (Do not add too much of any chemical to the cotton; too much liquid will drip down into the chamber and affect the experiment by sticking flies to the bottle.) What is the importance of using distilled water at both ends of the chamber?

Step 4 Lay the chamber down on a white surface or on white paper.

Step 5 Give the flies at least 5 minutes of undisturbed time, and then count (or closely approximate) the number of flies at each end of the chamber. Create a table to record the number of flies you find at each end (A and B) of the chamber.

Step 6 List all of the substances that you will be testing, and predict what you think the flies will prefer based on your knowledge of fruit flies.

Step 7 Begin to test each substance you are including in your investigation. Place a few drops of one substance on a cotton ball. Remove cap A, place the cotton ball in the cap, and replace the cap on the chamber. Place a cotton ball with distilled water on the other end. How might you determine which of the substances stimulate a negative chemotaxis and which stimulate a positive chemotaxis?

Step 8 Lay the chamber down on a light colored surface (or on white paper) and observe the flies.

Step 9 Give the flies at least 5 minutes of undisturbed time, and then count the number of flies at each end of the chamber.

Step 10 Change the caps, and give the fruit flies another substance.

Step 11 Gather data for at least four different substances. Which substances do fruit flies prefer? Which do they avoid?

Step 12 Quantify the results and express them graphically. Complete a chi-square analysis of your results. Using data from the entire class, construct a preference table. Were your hypotheses about the preferences of fruit flies supported or not? Did the flies demonstrate a chemotaxis in relation to any of the substances you chose? Can you think of any reasons for their preferences?

■ Designing and Conducting Your Investigation

Now that you have discovered the preferences for individual substances, design an experiment using the choice chamber to compare the preferences of fruit flies to all test substances or the chemotactic responses of your flies. Create a table that includes the results comparing all of the substances you tested.

The following are questions that you could investigate; however, as you worked through the beginning of this lab, you should have developed your own question and an investigation to answer that question:

- Are all substances equally attractive or repellant to the fruit flies?
- Which substances do fruit flies prefer the most?
- Which substances do fruit flies prefer the least?
- Do preferred substances have any characteristic in common?
- What other factors might affect whether or not the fruit flies moved from one part of your choice chamber to another?
- Do you think that it is the fruit itself that attracts the flies? Should they be called *fruit flies* or something else?
- Some experiments could be designed using fruit fly larvae. Do larvae respond the same way that adults respond? Are there other factors in the environment that affect the choice?
- What factors must be controlled in an experiment about environmental variables and behavior?
- What is the difference among phototaxis, chemotaxis, and geotaxis? Do fruit flies demonstrate all of them?
- Does a phototactic response override a chemotactic response?
- Does the age of the fruit fly change its geotactic response?
- Are there other organisms that respond the same as fruit flies? Are there other organisms that respond differently from fruit flies?

■ Analyzing Results

Look for patterns in fly behavior based on the number and ratio of fruit flies on different ends of your choice chamber. How will you determine which of the substances stimulate the greatest negative chemotactic response and positive chemotactic response? Do you see any patterns about materials or forces to which fruit flies are attracted?

Develop a method for sharing your results and conclusions to classmates — and then share them!

■ Evaluating Results

1. Is there anything that was shared by all of the environmental factors to which the flies were attracted?

2. Is there anything that was shared by all of the environmental factors to which the flies were repelled?

3. How do you explain the behavior of fruit flies in someone's kitchen or in nature based on the information you collected? Do your data explain all fruit fly movements? Explain your answers.

■ Where Can You Go from Here?

One possible extension for this investigation is to identify another organism that behaves similarly to the fruit fly and one that you expect would behave differently. For example, you could substitute ladybugs, houseflies, or mealworms for fruit flies and construct choice chambers using other substances that you think might be attractive to these organisms.

INVESTIGATION 13
ENZYME ACTIVITY*

How do abiotic or biotic factors influence the rates of enzymatic reactions?

■ BACKGROUND

Enzymes are the catalysts of biological systems. They speed up chemical reactions in biological systems by lowering the activation energy, the energy needed for molecules to begin reacting with each other. Enzymes do this by forming an enzyme-substrate complex that reduces energy required for the specific reaction to occur. Enzymes have specific shapes and structures that determine their functions. The enzyme's active site is very selective, allowing only certain substances to bind. If the shape of an enzyme is changed in any way, or the protein denatured, then the binding site also changes, thus disrupting enzymatic functions.

Enzymes are fundamental to the survival of any living system and are organized into a number of groups depending on their specific activities. Two common groups are catabolic enzymes ("*cata*" or "*kata-*" from the Greek "to break down") — for instance, amylase breaks complex starches into simple sugars — and anabolic enzymes ("*a-*" or "*an-*" from the Greek "to build up"). (You may know this second word already from stories about athletes who have been caught using anabolic steroids to build muscle.)

Catabolic enzymes, called proteases, break down proteins and are found in many organisms; one example is bromelain, which comes from pineapple and can break down gelatin. Bromelain often is an ingredient in commercial meat marinades. Papain is an enzyme that comes from papaya and is used in some teeth whiteners to break down the bacterial film on teeth. People who are lactose intolerant cannot digest milk sugar (lactose); however, they can take supplements containing lactase, the enzyme they are missing. All of these enzymes hydrolyze large, complex molecules into their simpler components; bromelain and papain break proteins down to amino acids, while lactase breaks lactose down to simpler sugars.

Anabolic enzymes are equally vital to all living systems. One example is ATP synthase, the enzyme that stores cellular energy in ATP by combining ADP and phosphate. Another example is rubisco, an enzyme involved in the anabolic reactions of building sugar molecules in the Calvin cycle of photosynthesis.

---

* Transitioned from the *AP Biology Lab Manual* (2001)

To begin this investigation, you will focus on the enzyme peroxidase obtained from a turnip, one of numerous sources of this enzyme. Peroxidase is one of several enzymes that break down peroxide, a toxic metabolic waste product of aerobic respiration. Using peroxidase, you will develop essential skills to examine your own questions about enzyme function.

Later, you will have an opportunity to select an enzyme, research its properties and mode of reaction, and then design an experiment to explore its function. The investigation also provides an opportunity for you to apply and review concepts you have studied previously, including the levels of protein structure, energy transfer, abiotic and biotic influences on molecular structure, entropy and enthalpy, and the role of enzymes in maintaining homeostasis.

■ Learning Objectives

- To understand the relationship between enzyme structure and function

- To make some generalizations about enzymes by studying just one enzyme in particular

- To determine which factors can change the rate of an enzyme reaction

- To determine which factors that affect enzyme activity could be biologically important

■ General Safety Precautions

Follow general laboratory safety procedures. Wear proper footwear, safety goggles or glasses, a laboratory coat, and gloves. Use proper pipetting techniques, and use pipette pumps, syringes, or rubber bulbs. Never pipette by mouth! Dispose of any broken glass in the proper container. Since the concentrations of the reactive materials in this laboratory are environmentally friendly (0.1% hydrogen peroxide and 0.3% guaiacol), they can be rinsed down a standard laboratory drain. The concentrations used here are deemed to be safe by all chemical standards, but recall that any compound has the potentiality of being detrimental to living things and the environment. When you develop your individual investigations you must always consider the toxicity of materials used.

Key Vocabulary

Baseline is a universal term for most chemical reactions. In this investigation the term is used to establish a standard for a reaction. Thus, when manipulating components of a reaction (in this case, substrate or enzyme), you have a reference to help understand what occurred in the reaction. The baseline may vary with different scenarios pertinent to the design of the experiment, such as altering the environment in which the reaction occurs. In this scenario, different conditions can be compared, and the effects of changing an environmental variable (e.g., pH) can be determined.

Rate can have more than one applicable definition because this lab has two major options of approach, i.e., using a color palette and/or a spectrophotometer to measure percent of light absorbance. When using a color palette to compare the change in a reaction, you can infer increase, decrease, or no change in the rate; this inference is usually called the **relative rate of the reaction**. When using a spectrophotometer (or other measuring devices) to measure the actual percent change in light absorbance, the rate is usually referred to as **absolute rate of the reaction**. In this case, a specific amount of time can be measured, such as 0.083 absorbance/minute.

THE INVESTIGATIONS

Getting Started

Procedure 1: Developing a Method for Measuring Peroxidase in Plant Material and Determining a Baseline

Peroxide (such as hydrogen peroxide) is a toxic byproduct of aerobic metabolism. Peroxidase is an enzyme that breaks down these peroxides. It is produced by most cells in their peroxisomes.

The general reaction can be depicted as follows:

Enzyme + Substrate --> Enzyme-Substrate Complex --> Enzyme + Product(s) + ΔG

For this investigation the specific reaction is as follows:

Peroxidase + Hydrogen Peroxide --> Complex --> Peroxidase + Water + Oxygen

$$2H_2O_2 \rightarrow 2H_2O + O_2 \text{ (gas)}$$

Notice that the peroxidase is present at the start and end of the reaction. Like all catalysts, enzymes are not consumed by the reactions. To determine the rate of an enzymatic reaction, you must measure a change in the amount of at least one specific substrate or product over time. In a decomposition reaction of peroxide by peroxidase (as noted in the above formula), the easiest molecule to measure would probably be oxygen, a final product. This could be done by measuring the *actual* volume of oxygen gas released or by using an indicator. In this experiment, an indicator for oxygen will be used. The compound guaiacol has a high affinity for oxygen, and in solution, it binds instantly with oxygen to form tetraguaiacol, which is brownish in color. The greater the amount of oxygen gas produced, the darker brown the solution will become.

Qualifying color is a difficult task, but a series of dilutions can be made and then combined on a palette, which can represent the relative changes occurring during the reaction. A color palette/chart ranging from 1 to 10 (Figure 1) is sufficient to compare relative amounts of oxygen produced. Alternatively, the color change can be recorded as a change in absorbency using a variety of available meters, such as a spectrophotometer or a probe system. (Information about the use of spectrophotometers and/or probe systems is found in the Additional Information section of this investigation.)

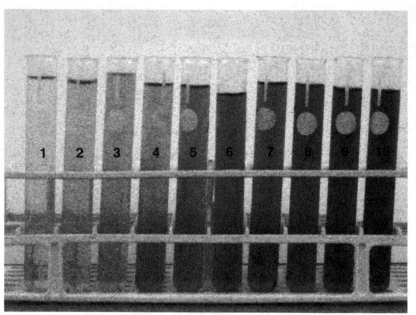

Figure 1. Turnip Peroxidase Color Chart

Materials

- Turnip peroxidase
- 0.1% hydrogen peroxide
- Guaiacol
- Distilled (deionized) water
- 2 test tubes (approximately 16 x 150 mm) and appropriate test tube rack
- Timer
- 1, 5, and 10 mL graduated pipettes, pipette pumps, or syringes (1, 2, 5, and 10 mL)

This investigation is designed to be performed without a spectrophotometer, but your teacher may ask you to use a spectrophotometer or probe system. If so, additional equipment may be required.

Step 1 Using two 16 x 150 mm test tubes, mark one "substrate" and the other tube "enzyme." To the substrate tube, add 7 mL of distilled water, 0.3 mL of 0.1 percent hydrogen peroxide, and 0.2 mL guaiacol for a total volume of 7.5 mL. Cover the test tube with a piece of Parafilm® and gently mix.

Step 2 To the enzyme tube, add 6.0 mL of distilled water and 1.5 mL of peroxidase for a total volume of 7.5 mL. Cover the test tube with a piece of Parafilm and gently mix.

Step 3 Combine the contents of the two tubes (subtrate and enzyme) in another 16 x 150 mL test tube, cover the tube with Parafilm, invert twice to mix, and place the tube in a test tube rack. Immediately begin timing the reaction.

Step 4 Observe the color change for the next 5 minutes. Rotate the tube before each reading. Record the observed color at 0, 1, 2, 3, 4, and 5 minutes. (A cell phone and/or camera are excellent ways to record color change.)

Step 5 Use the color palette/chart (Figure 1) to help you quantify changes in color over time. Graph your data in your laboratory notebook.

Consider the following questions before you proceed to the next experiment:

- You measured the color change at different times. Which time will you use for your later assays? Why? (The time/color change that you select will serve as your baseline for additional investigations.)

- When you use this assay to assess factors that change enzyme activity, which components of the assay will you change? Which will you keep constant?

■ Procedure 2: Determining the Effect of pH on Enzymatic Activity

Numerous variables can be employed to observe the effects on the rate of an enzymatic reaction and possibly the specific fit of the enzyme with the substrate.

- What do you predict will occur if the pH in the reaction changes? How do you justify your prediction?

Materials

- Turnip peroxidase
- 0.1% hydrogen peroxide
- Guaiacol
- Buffers with range of pH
- Distilled (deionized) water
- 12 test tubes (approximately 16 x 150 mm) and appropriate test tube rack

- Timer
- 1, 5, and 10 mL graduated pipettes, pipette pumps, or syringes (1, 2, 5, and 10 mL)
- Spectrophotometer or probe system

Step 1 Using clean 16 x 150 mL test tubes, make six sets of pairs of original substrate and enzyme tubes for a total of 12 tubes or 6 pairs. This time you will substitute a different pH buffer for the distilled water used in the original enzyme tubes. Prepare the tubes as follows and be sure to label them.

- For each substrate tube in a pair, add 7 mL of distilled water, 0.3 mL of hydrogen peroxide, and 0.2 mL of guaiacol for a total volume of 7. 5 mL.

- For each enzyme tube in the pair, add 6.0 mL of a specific pH solution and 1.5 mL of peroxidase for a total volume of 7.5 mL. For example, in the enzyme tube of the first pair, you can substitute 6.0 mL of buffer solution of pH 3 for the distilled water; in the enzyme tube of the second pair, you can substitute 6.0 mL of buffer solution of pH 5 for the distilled water, and so forth.

- Cover each test tube with a piece of Parafilm, and gently mix.

Step 2 Combine the substrate and enzyme tubes for all six pairs (total volume 15.0 mL per pair), cover with Parafilm, gently mix, and place the tubes back in the test tube rack. Immediately begin timing the reactions.

Step 3 Record the observed color for each tube at 0 minutes and again at the time you chose based on your results in Procedure 1. (Again, a cell phone and/or camera are excellent ways to record color change.)

Step 4 Use the palette/color chart (Figure 1) to help you quantify the changes you observe. Graph your data as color intensity versus pH. What conclusions can you draw from your results?

■ Designing and Conducting Your Investigation

You now have the basic information and tools needed to explore enzymes in more depth on your own. In this part of the lab, you will do just that. You will have the chance to develop and test your own hypotheses about enzyme activity. To help you get started, read the following questions, and write your answers in your laboratory notebook.

- In Procedure 1, was the limiting factor of your baseline reaction the enzyme or the substrate? How could you modify the procedure you learned to answer this question?

- What are three or four factors that vary in the environment in which organisms live? Which of those factors do you think could affect enzyme activity? How would you modify your basic assay to test your hypothesis?

Design and conduct an experiment to investigate an answer(s) to one of the questions above or another question that might have been raised as you conducted Procedures 1 and 2. Remember, the primary objective of the investigation is to explore how biotic and abiotic factors influence the rate of enzymatic reactions.

■ Analyzing Results

From the data that you collected from your independent investigation, graph the results. Based on the graph and your observations, compare the effects of biotic and abiotic environmental factors on the rate(s) of enzymatic reactions and explain any differences.

■ Additional Information

If a spectrophotometer is available, the following information is useful.

The use of measuring devices can better quantify your results. Using a spectrophotometer, you can select a specific wavelength to fit the color/pigment expected in an experiment. The change in the amount or concentration of color/pigment may be measured as absorbance (amount of the wavelength trapped by the pigment) or transmittance (amount of the wavelength that is not trapped by the pigment).

For Procedure 1:

1. Turn on your spectrophotometer approximately 10 to 15 minutes prior to starting the investigation so that it will warm up appropriately.

2. To measure the amount of the compound tetraguaiacol, set the wavelength to 470 nm.

3. Set your machine at zero absorbance using a blank containing all the appropriate materials *except* the substrate (i.e., 13.3 mL of distilled water, 0.2 mL of guaiacol, and 1.5 mL of enzyme extract = 15 mL total).

4. Determine the baseline.

A. Using two 16 x 150 mm test tubes, label one "substrate" and the other "enzyme." Substrate tube: 7 mL of distilled water, 0.3 mL of hydrogen peroxide, and 0.2 mL guaiacol (total volume 7.5 mL) Enzyme tube: 6 mL of distilled water and 1.5 mL of peroxidase (total volume 7.5 mL)

B. Combine the materials of the substrate and enzyme tubes. Mix the tubes twice and pour into a cuvette. (When mixing or rotating always cover the opening of the cuvette with Parafilm.)

C. Place the cuvette into the spectrophometer and record absorbance; this is your initial or "0" time reading. Remove the tube. Repeat recording absorbance at 1, 2, 3, 4, and 5 minutes. Be sure to rotate (use Parafilm to cover) the tube and also clean its surface with a scientific cleaning wipe before each reading.

5. Record and graph your data.

For Procedure 2:

Follow steps 1, 2, and 3 above. In step 4, set up as outlined above. Make an initial reading at time "0" and a second reading at the time you chose as optimal based on results obtained in Procedure 1. Record and graph your data.

AP BIOLOGY EQUATIONS AND FORMULAS

Statistical Analysis and Probability

Mean

$$\bar{x} = \frac{1}{n}\sum_{i=1}^{n} x_i$$

Standard Deviation*

$$S = \sqrt{\frac{\sum(x_i - \bar{x})^2}{n-1}}$$

Standard Error of the Mean*

$$SE_{\bar{x}} = \frac{s}{\sqrt{n}}$$

Chi-Square

$$\chi^2 = \sum \frac{(o-e)^2}{e}$$

Chi-Square Table

p value	Degrees of Freedom							
	1	2	3	4	5	6	7	8
0.05	3.84	5.99	7.82	9.49	11.07	12.59	14.07	15.51
0.01	6.64	9.21	11.34	13.28	15.09	16.81	18.48	20.09

$\bar{x}$ = sample mean

n = size of the sample

s = sample standard deviation (i.e., the sample-based estimate of the standard deviation of the population)

o = observed results

e = expected results

Degrees of freedom are equal to the number of distinct possible outcomes minus one.

Laws of Probability

If A and B are mutually exclusive, then:
$$P(A \text{ or } B) = P(A) + P(B)$$
If A and B are independent, then:
$$P(A \text{ and } B) = P(A) \times P(B)$$

Hardy-Weinberg Equations

$p^2 + 2pq + q^2 = 1$ p = frequency of the dominant allele in a population

$p + q = 1$ q = frequency of the recessive allele in a population

Metric Prefixes

Factor	Prefix	Symbol
10^9	giga	G
10^6	mega	M
10^3	kilo	k
10^{-2}	centi	c
10^{-3}	milli	m
10^{-6}	micro	μ
10^{-9}	nano	n
10^{-12}	pico	p

Mode = value that occurs most frequently in a data set

Median = middle value that separates the greater and lesser halves of a data set

Mean = sum of all data points divided by number of data points

Range = value obtained by subtracting the smallest observation (sample minimum) from the greatest (sample maximum)

* For the purposes of the AP Exam, students will not be required to perform calculations using this equation; however, they must understand the underlying concepts and applications.

Rate and Growth

Rate

$$\frac{dY}{dt}$$

Population Growth

$$\frac{dN}{dt} = B - D$$

Exponential Growth

$$\frac{dN}{dt} = r_{max} N$$

Logistic Growth

$$\frac{dN}{dt} = r_{max} N \left(\frac{K - N}{K} \right)$$

Temperature Coefficient Q$_{10}$ [†]

$$Q_{10} = \left(\frac{k_2}{k_1} \right)^{\frac{10}{T_2 - T_1}}$$

Primary Productivity Calculation

$$\frac{mg\ O_2}{L} \times \frac{0.698\ mL}{mg} = \frac{mL\ O_2}{L}$$

$$\frac{mL\ O_2}{L} \times \frac{0.536\ mg\ C\ fixed}{mL\ O_2} = \frac{mg\ C\ fixed}{L}$$

(at standard temperature and pressure)

---

dY = amount of change

dt = change in time

B = birth rate

D = death rate

N = population size

K = carrying capacity

r_{max} = maximum per capita growth rate of population

T_2 = higher temperature

T_1 = lower temperature

k_2 = reaction rate at T_2

k_1 = reaction rate at T_1

Q_{10} = the factor by which the reaction rate increases when the temperature is raised by ten degrees

---

Water Potential (Ψ)

$$\Psi = \Psi_P + \Psi_S$$

Ψ_P = pressure potential

Ψ_S = solute potential

The water potential will be equal to the solute potential of a solution in an open container because the pressure potential of the solution in an open container is zero.

The Solute Potential of a Solution

$$\Psi_S = -iCRT$$

i = ionization constant (this is 1.0 for sucrose because sucrose does not ionize in water)

C = molar concentration

R = pressure constant ($R = 0.0831$ liter bars/mole K)

T = temperature in Kelvin (°C + 273)

Surface Area and Volume

Volume of a Sphere

$V = \frac{4}{3} \pi r^3$

Volume of a Rectangular Solid

$V = lwh$

Volume of a Right Cylinder

$V = \pi r^2 h$

Surface Area of a Sphere

$A = 4\pi r^2$

Surface Area of a Cube

$A = 6s^2$

Surface Area of a Rectangular Solid

$A = \sum$ surface area of each side

---

r = radius

l = length

h = height

w = width

s = length of one side of a cube

A = surface area

V = volume

Σ = sum of all

Dilution (used to create a dilute solution from a concentrated stock solution)

$$C_i V_i = C_f V_f$$

i = initial (starting) C = concentration of solute

f = final (desired) V = volume of solution

Gibbs Free Energy

$$\Delta G = \Delta H - T\Delta S$$

ΔG = change in Gibbs free energy

ΔS = change in entropy

ΔH = change in enthalpy

T = absolute temperature (in Kelvin)

$$pH^* = - \log_{10} [H^+]$$

---

* For the purposes of the AP Exam, students will not be required to perform calculations using this equation; however, they must understand the underlying concepts and applications.

† For use with labs only (optional).

CONSTRUCTING LINE GRAPHS*

Suppose we are studying some chemical reaction in which a substance, *A*, is being used up. We begin with a large quantity (100 mg) of *A*, and we measure in some way how much *A* is left after different times. The results of such an experiment might be presented pictorially like this:

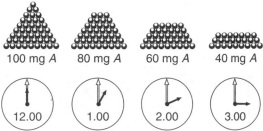

Figure A.1

This is the kind of picture graph that you often see in newspapers. This information can be presented much more simply on a graph — a line graph is permissible — because our experience tells us that when *A* is disappearing in a chemical reaction, it is disappearing more or less smoothly and will not suddenly reappear. In other words, the progress of a chemical reaction is a continuous process, and because time is a continuous process it is permissible to relate the two kinds of information to one another on a line graph. The procedure for constructing the line graph is shown in Figure A.2.

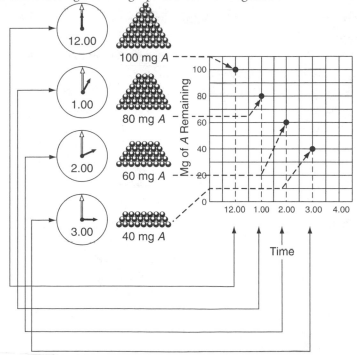

Figure A.2

---

* Based on a handout by Dr. Mary Stiller, Purdue University.

It should be clear from the diagram that each point corresponds both to a particular measurement of the amount of *A* remaining and to the particular time at which that amount remained. (A heavy dot is made opposite both of these two related quantities.) When all the measurements have been recorded in this way, we connect the dots with a line, shown in Figure A.3. (Figures A.21–A.23 explain when to connect the data points.)

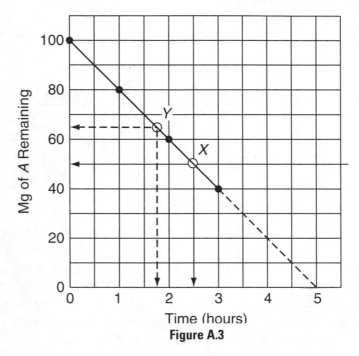

Figure A.3

It should be clear by looking at our graph that the only measurements we actually made are those indicated by the dots. However, because the information on both scales of the graph is assumed to be continuous, we can use the graph to find out how much *A* would have been found if we had made our measurements at some other time, say 2.5 hours. We merely locate the line that corresponds to 2.5 hours on our time scale and follow it up until it crosses our line graph at the point X; then we look opposite X to the "Mg of *A* Remaining" scale, and read off 50 mg. We conclude, then, that if we had made a measurement at 2.5 hours, we would have found 50 mg of *A* left. In a similar way, we can find out from our graph at what time a given amount of *A*, say 65 mg, would be left. We have merely to find the line that represents 65 mg on the vertical scale and follow it across until it cuts the line graph at point Y. Then we see 1.75 hours on the "Time" scale opposite Y. This tells us that had we wished to stop the reaction with 65 mg of *A* remaining, we would have had to do so after 1.75 hours.

You will notice that part of the graph has been drawn with a broken line. In making a line graph we are properly allowed to connect only the points representing our actual measurements. It is possible that measurements made after 3 hours will give points that will fall on the broken-line extension of the graph, but this is not necessarily so. In fact, the reaction may begin to slow up perceptibly, so that much less *A* is used up in the fourth hour than in the third hour. Not having made any measurements during the fourth hour, we cannot tell, and we confess our ignorance quite openly by means of the broken line. The broken line portion of the graph is called an **extrapolation**, because it goes beyond our actual experience with this particular reaction. Between any two of our measured points it seems fairly safe to assume that the reaction is proceeding steadily, and this is called an **interpolation**. Interpolations can only be made between measured points on a graph; beyond the measured points we must extrapolate. We know that the amount of *A* remaining after 4 hours is somewhere between 0 and 40 mg. The amount indicated by the broken line on the graph, 20 mg, is only a logical guess.

Unfortunately, it sometimes happens that even professionals take this sort of limitation of line graphs for granted and do not confess, by means of a broken line, the places where they are just guessing. Therefore, it is up to readers of the graph to notice where the last actual measurement was made and use their own judgment about the extrapolated part. Perhaps the extrapolated part fits quite well with the reader's own experience of this or a similar reaction, and he or she is quite willing to go along with the author's extrapolation. On the other hand, the reader may be interested only in the early part of the graph and be indifferent to what the author does with the rest of it. It may also be that the reader knows that the graph begins to flatten out after 3 hours and so disagrees with the author. The point is that we, the readers, must be aware of what part of the graph is extrapolated, that is, predicted, from the shape of the graph up to the time when the measurements were stopped. Hence, you must clearly indicate on a line graph the points that you actually measured. Regardless of what predictions or conclusions you want to make about the graph, you *must* give the reader the liberty of disagreeing with you. Therefore, it is very improper to construct a line graph consisting of an unbroken line without indicating the experimentally determined points.

■ BASIC REQUIREMENTS FOR A GOOD GRAPH

The following procedure applies primarily to graphs of experimental data that are going to be presented for critical evaluation. It does not apply to the kind of rough sketch that we often use for purposes of illustration.

Every graph presented for serious consideration should have a good **title** that tells what the graph is about. Notice that we need more than just a title; we need a *good* title. Before we try to make a good title, let us look at an example and try to decide what kind of title is a useful one. Look at Figure A.4.

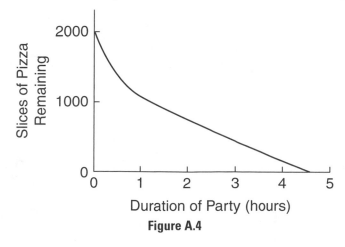

Figure A.4

If you like pizza, it might be very useful to know when this party is being held. Without a title, you cannot tell even whether the graph refers to any particular party at all. It might represent average figures for all the parties held last year, or it might represent the expected figures for a party that is going to be held tonight. Let us suppose that these data refer to a study party given by AP Biology students on March 9. Here, then, are some possible titles:

(a) The APs Have a Party

(b) Pizza Rules! Enjoy it with AP

(c) An AP Biofeast!

None of those titles is especially useful or informative because none of them tells what the graph is all about. Now look at these two titles:

(d) Anticipated Consumption of Slices of Pizza at the AP Biology Party, March 9

(e) Anticipated Consumption of Slices of Pizza at the AP Biology Party, March 9, 2011, 7:00 p.m.–11:00 p.m.

You should be able to see that only title (e) is helpful and useful. It enables you to tell, by glancing at the calendar, whether or not you can attend the party, and it helps make that graph fall a little more steeply. The point we are driving at is that a *good* title is one that tells exactly what information the author is trying to present with the graph. Although brevity is desirable, it should not substitute for completeness and clarity.

Now that you are clear on titles, look at the graph in Figure A.5. Its title tells you that here is some potentially useful information. The graph suggests that, at least for 2011, there was an upper limit to the amount of time people could usefully spend in studying for an exam, and you might wonder, for example, how long you would have had to study to make a perfect score.

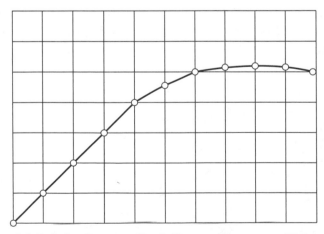

Figure A.5: Relation Between Study Time and Score on a Biology Exam in 2011

Unfortunately, however, you cannot tell, because the graph has no labels of numbers or units the scales. Even though this graph has a descriptive and intriguing title, it is of no use to us at all without these very important parts. Obviously, before we can take full advantage of the information that the graph is trying to present, we need to have some additional details.

In Figure A.6 the additional information has been supplied, information that seems to make the graph more useful to us in preparing for the exam.

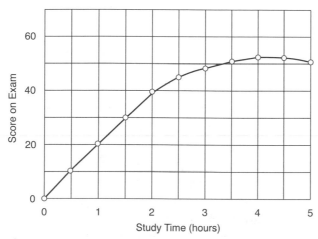

Figure A.6: Relation Between Study Time and Soore on a Biology Exam in 2011

This additional information includes scales, or **axes**, that are carefully marked with numbers, and labels and units that are neatly presented. Obviously, one cannot label all the points along the axes; that would make the numbers crowd together and look sloppy. The units should be marked at intervals that correspond more or less to the intervals between the experimental points. The small marks, called **index marks**, can be drawn in if the experimental points are very widely spaced. Most elegantly, a **frame** is put around the whole graph, and index marks are placed all around. This makes it easy to lay a ruler across the graph when interpolating between the experimental points. The diagram in Figure A.7 summarizes some features of a good graph.

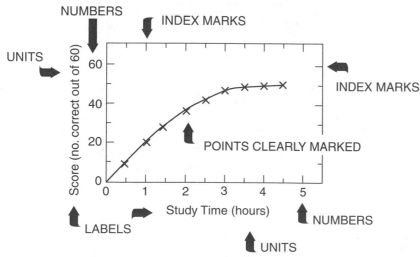

Figure A.7: Relation Between Study Time and Score on a Biology Exam in 2011

■ STEEPNESS OR SLOPE OF A LINE GRAPH

Look at the graph in Figure A.8 for the disappearance of *A* in a chemical reaction. Such a graph, in which the amount of some quantity is shown on the vertical scale, or **ordinate**, with time shown on the horizontal scale, or **abscissa**, is frequently called a "progress graph" or "progressive curve," because it shows how some process progresses in time. This graph may also be called a "time course" for the process because it shows the extent to which the process has occurred at different times.

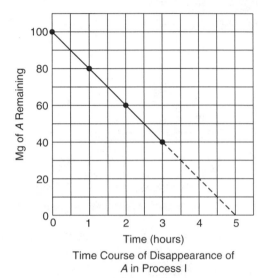

Time Course of Disappearance of
A in Process I

Figure A.8

Let us call the process represented by the graph "Process I" and consider another reaction, "Process II," in which *A* is also consumed. Suppose that we start Process II also with 100 mg of *A*, and that after 1, 2, and 3 hours there are 90, 80, and 70 mg, respectively, left. The progress curve for Process II is displayed in Figure A.9.

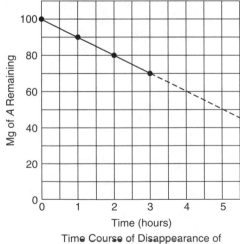

Time Course of Disappearance of
A in Process II

Figure A.9

Now, suppose we want to compare the graphs for the two processes. Because they have exactly the same scales, we can put both lines on the same graph, as shown in Figure A.10. Notice, however, that now in addition to the labels on the scales, we need labels on the two lines to distinguish between the two processes.

Look at the 1-hour mark on the time scale of the graph. Opposite this put an X on the line for Process I and a Y on the line for Process II. Then, opposite X on the ordinate you should be able to see that 80 mg of *A* are left in Process I; opposite Y you can see that 90 mg of *A* are left in Process II. Apparently, Process I has used up 20 mg of *A* and Process II has used up only 10 mg in the same amount of time. Obviously, Process I is faster, and the line graph for Process I is steeper than the graph for Process II.

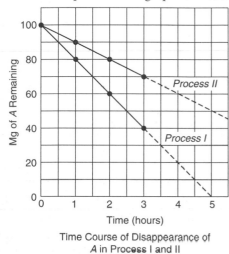

Time Course of Disappearance of
A in Process I and II

Figure A.10

The rate for Process I is 20 mg *A* used/hr, while the rate for Process II is 10 mg *A* used/hr.

We have seen that a steeper line graph means a faster reaction when the progress curves for two reactions are plotted on the same scale. (Obviously, if the progress curves are plotted on different scales, we cannot compare the steepness of the line directly, but have to calculate what the slope would be if the two curves were plotted on the same scale.)

Suppose, now, that we make a new kind of graph, one that will show the steepness, or slope, of the progress curve. Because the **slope** of the progress curve is a measure of the speed of velocity, or **rate** of the reaction or process, such a graph is frequently called a "rate graph" or "rate curve." The diagram in Figure A.11 shows how a rate curve can be made for Process I.

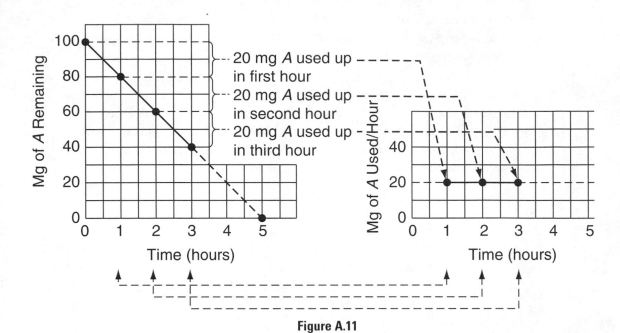

Figure A.11

Notice that the time scale of this rate graph is exactly like the time scale of the progress curve from which it was derived, but that the ordinate is different. The ordinate of the progress curve shows milligrams of *A* remaining; the ordinate of the rate curve shows milligrams of *A* used per hour. Obviously, a rate graph must always show rate on one of its scales, and it is ordinarily the vertical one that is used. This is because the rate of a reaction or process is what mathematicians call a **dependent variable**. Time is the **independent variable** in this experiment; it is independent of changes in the dependent variable (the rate of reaction), and it is the variable that is shown on the horizontal axis. Regardless of whether the process is the increase in height or weight of a plant, or the using up or producing of something in a reaction, the rate graph for the process must always show *amount of something per unit time* on one of its axes. One very common type of rate graph is the one shown in Figure A.11, with a rate on the ordinate and the time on the abscissa. Other kinds of rate graphs may have temperature or molarity on the abscissa. The rate of growth of a plant, for example, depends on how many factors that we might wish to vary, and so we can have as many different kinds of rate graphs for that process as there are independent variables.

Let us emphasize: a progress curve always shows amount of reaction on the vertical scale and time on the horizontal scale. The corresponding rate curve *may* show time or some other variable on the horizontal scale, but it *always* shows rate, or amount of reaction per unit time, on the vertical scale. This point is very important. When we look at a rate curve that has time on the horizontal scale, we must visualize the progress curve from which the rate curve was derived. When we look at a rate curve that has any other variable except time on the horizontal scale, we shall see that each point on the rate curve represents a separate progress curve.

In the same way as for Process I, a rate curve can be made for Process II. Plotted on the same graph, the two should look something like the diagram in Figure A.12.

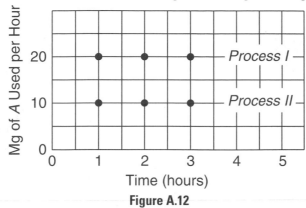

Figure A.12

There are two things to notice in this example. First, the curve for Process I lies higher than that for Process II. This is in accord with the facts as we have seen them, namely, that Process I is faster and so has a greater slope or higher value for the steepness. Second, notice that both curves are perfectly flat. Naturally, because the progress curves for the two processes were both perfectly straight lines, having everywhere the *same* slope, the rate of steepness graph must show exactly the same thing, that is, that the rate or steepness is everywhere the same.

On the other hand, consider the graph in Figure A.13, which represents the disappearance of A in yet another reaction, Process III.

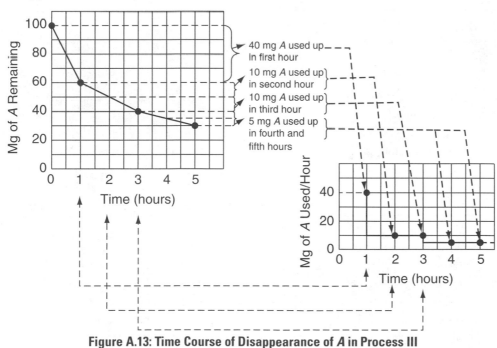

Figure A.13: Time Course of Disappearance of *A* in Process III

You can see that Process III differs from Processes I and II in that the progress curve for III is not a perfectly straight line. It is steepest at the beginning, becomes less steep after

1 hour, and again after 3 hours. Obviously, because the rate of the process is changing with time, the corresponding rate curve will not be perfectly flat. The rate has to start out high, then drop at 1 hour and at 3 hours, and you can see in the graph on the right that this is exactly what it does. In fact, the rate curve looks like steps because whenever the slope of the progress curve decreases, the rate curve must show a drop to a lower value. Conversely, if the progress curve for a process should get steeper, as sometimes happens (the reaction goes faster after it gets "warmed up"), the rate curve must show a corresponding increase to a higher value.

Until now we have been able to read the steepness, or slope, of the progress curve directly from the scales of the graph because the progress curves we have been studying were either perfectly straight lines or else made up of straight-line segments. In most real situations, however, we cannot do this because the slope of the progress curve does not change sharply at a given time, but, gradually, over a period of time. You probably remember how to measure the slope of a curved line, but let us review the process anyway. (See Figure A.14.)

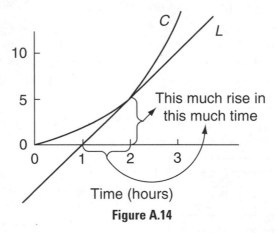

Figure A.14

Suppose we want to measure the slope, or steepness, of the curved line C at time 2 hours. We can see that the curve rises 5 units total in the 2 hours, so that the average slope is 2.5 units per hour. However, it is easy to see from the graph that this average is very misleading; the progress curve is almost flat at the beginning (i.e., has 0 slope) and then accelerates rapidly, so that the line curves upward. If we want to find the true slope at 2 hours, we must draw line L in such a way that L has the same slope as C at the 2-hour point. Then we can see that L rises about 5 units between 1 and 2 hours, just twice the average slope for the first 2 hours.

We have seen that a perfectly flat curve, like that for Process I or II, means that the corresponding progress curve is a perfectly straight line having the same slope at all points. Conversely, a progress curve that changes in slope, like that of Process III, will give a rate curve that looks like steps. You should be able to figure out that the "steps" on the rate curve will be sharp and square if the progress curve has an abrupt change in slope, and more rounded off if the progress curve changes slope gradually. In any case, in regions where the rate curve is perfectly flat it is clear that the progress curve must have constant steepness, or slope. However, if the progress curve itself gets perfectly flat, then that portion of the progress curve has 0 slope; in other words, the reaction has stopped. This kind of situation is pictured in Figure A.15 where the rate and progress curves for another reaction, call it Process IV, are shown.

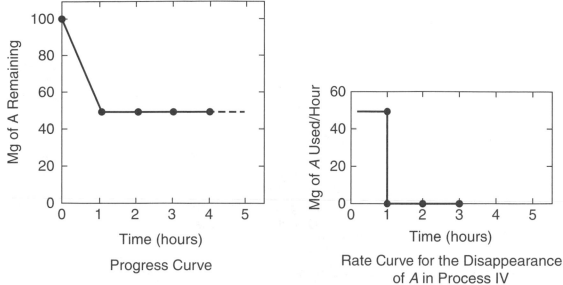

Figure A.15

In the progress curve on the left, we can see that after the first hour the reaction stopped. From the graph we can see that after 1 hour there were 50 mg of A remaining; after 2 hours there were still 50 mg remaining; and there are still 50 mg remaining even at 4 hours. Obviously, Process IV stopped when one-half of A had been used up. Now look at the rate curve on the right. It is perfectly flat for the first hour because the slope of the progress curve was constant during that time. After the first hour the rate curve is also perfectly flat but it has dropped down to 0, indicating that although the progress curve has constant slope, the slope is actually 0. Obviously, flatness in a rate curve and flatness in a progress curve mean different things. Flatness in the progress curve for a reaction means that the reaction has stopped; flatness in the rate curve means that the reaction is going on at a constant rate. You can see, then, that we have to be able to glance at a graph and tell whether it is a rate curve or a progress curve in order to be able to interpret what the shape of the curve is trying to tell us.

Now let us take one more example of this kind of rate curve. The graph in Figure A.16 shows the progress in the growth of a pea plant. First, we can see that the slope is not the same everywhere. In fact, there is an interval where the slope increases very gradually from 0. By 1 week or so the slope has reached its maximum value and is steady until about 3 weeks. Thereafter, the slope begins to decrease again, as the curve bends over, and eventually, at about 4.5 weeks, as the curve gets perfectly flat, the slope, or steepness, tends to be 0 again.

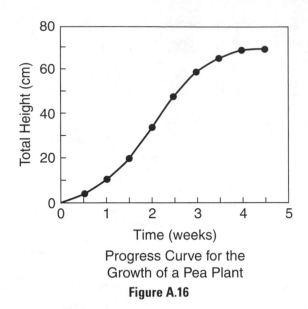

Progress Curve for the
Growth of a Pea Plant

Figure A.16

Suppose, now, that we try to imagine what the rate curve for the growth of this pea plant will look like. If you read through the preceding paragraph, you will have a rough description of it. In fact, it will look like the graph in Figure A.17.

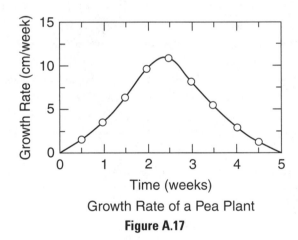

Growth Rate of a Pea Plant

Figure A.17

Notice from the two graphs that where the steepness of the progress curve gets larger, the corresponding rate curve turns upward. Similarly, when the slope of the progress curve decreases again, the rate curve turns downward. A rate curve that is turning up means, therefore, that the process is speeding up; a flat rate curve means that the process is going at a constant rate; and a rate curve that is turning down means that the process is slowing down. When the rate curve hits the x-axis, it means that the reaction has stopped.

Probably 80 percent of the graphs you will encounter in biology are either rate curves or progress curves. You will have noticed from the preceding discussion that biologists tend to use the words "graph" and "curve" interchangeably. Technically, of course, the entire picture, including the abscissa, ordinate, labels, numbers, units, index marks, and title, together with the line graph portrayed, is the "graph," while the line graph itself is called the "curve." You will notice, too, that biologists call a line graph a "curve," even though the line itself may be perfectly straight.

To summarize, remember that a progress curve is made from measurements at different times during the progress of a reaction that is continuous with time. A graph that shows how much or to what extent a reaction has occurred at different times is a progress or time-course curve. In contrast, a rate curve is a picture of the steepness of one or more progress curves, and any graph that has rate on one of its scales is a rate curve.

So far we have been considering only rate graphs that have time on the abscissa; we could call these **time-rate** curves. As we have seen, a time-rate curve can be made from any progress curve. Next, we are going to consider rate curves that do not have time as the abscissa. As you shall see, such curves are made by combining data from several progress curves, each representing the time course of the reaction under a different set of conditions.

■ OTHER KINDS OF RATE GRAPHS

Let us look at and try to analyze the graph in Figure A.18. Obviously, it is a progress curve because it shows an amount of something on the ordinate and time on the abscissa. There are several different curves all plotted on the same graph, and each is labeled with a different temperature. The title indicates that this graph is trying to tell us how Process I behaves at different temperatures.

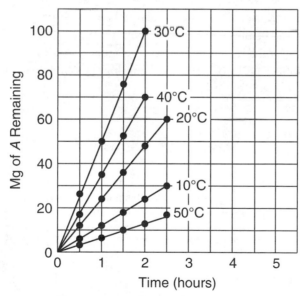

Temperature Dependence of Process I

Figure A.18

Before we try to construct the rate curve for this graph, we should try to imagine how this experiment was carried out. It seems clear that the experiment must have started with several different batches of *A* and that each reaction mixture was kept at a different temperature. Then, every half-hour, the amount of *A* remaining was measured and the amount consumed was calculated. The results might have been plotted in five separate progress curves, as shown in Figure A.19.

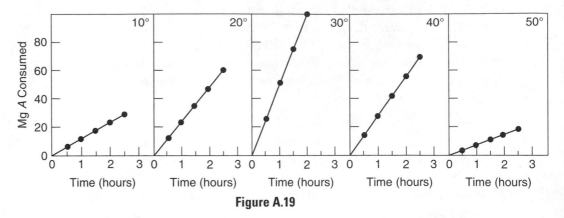

Figure A.19

When all these progress curves are plotted on the same graph, as was done in Figure A.18, we have what is called a "family" of curves. If we look at the slopes of the various members of the family of curves for Process I, we see that the steepest slope does not correspond to the highest temperature. In fact, the curve for 30° is the steepest, whereas the curve for 50° is the least steep; the curve for 10°, the lowest temperature, has an intermediate slope. By analyzing and comparing the slopes of the family of curves in this way we can get a reasonably good notion of the effect of temperature on Process I, but this effect could be shown much more clearly in a rate graph that has temperature as the abscissa. Such a graph would show us at a glance how the rate varies with temperature and, of course, would be preferable, as the whole point in making a graph is to present information simply and clearly. The diagram in Figure A.20 shows how a **rate-temperature** graph would be constructed from this family of curves for Process I.

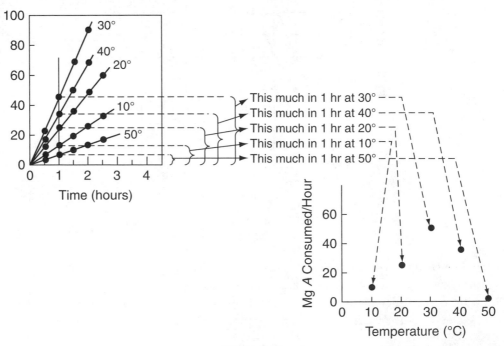

Figure A.20

Having found, as shown in Figure A.20, the five points for our rate graph, we are faced with the question of whether or not it is legitimate to connect these points with a smooth line. We recognize, of course, that both temperature and rate are continuous processes. Between any two given temperatures or rates there are an infinite number of temperatures or rates. The question here, however, is the following: If we do draw a smooth line through our five points, will that line pass through the infinite number of other rates that we could have measured if we had chosen some other temperature? Let us go ahead and draw the line, as shown in Figure A.21

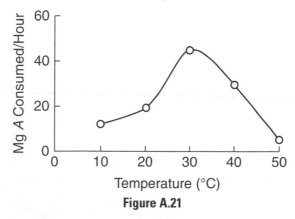

Figure A.21

As we have drawn it, the curve indicates that the rate at 29° and at 31° would be slightly lower than at 30°, and this may not be true. In order to determine the true shape of the curve in the region of the maximum rate we would have to make progress curves at smaller temperature intervals, say, every two degrees. However, it is extremely unlikely that the true shape of the curve is anything like the two possibilities shown on the diagrams in Figure A.22. All our experience tells us that if a reaction depends on temperature, then that dependence will be a smooth curve, without sharp bends. In fact, if in an experiment we should observe behavior of the type shown in Figure A.22, we would immediately begin to suspect that something is wrong with our thermostat! Thus, although it may be that the shape of the rate-temperature curve for Process I is somewhat different from the way we drew it in Figure A.21, we can be reasonably certain that it is not radically different.

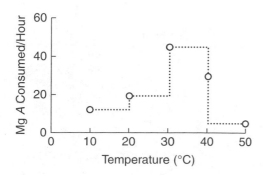 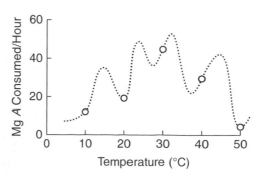

Figure A.22

In addition, we may also tend to be suspicious of a graph if we see a sharp peak, unless the experimental points were taken very close together. For example, common sense would tell us to be careful about accepting the rate curve shown in Figure A.23.

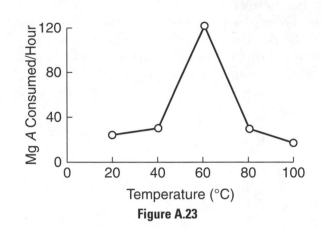

Figure A.23

Obviously, most of the shape is given to the profile by the one measurement at 60°. In biology, as in everything else, mistakes can be made, so the experimenter would have to check the validity of that measurement very carefully. The easiest way to do that would be to make more measurements slightly above and slightly below 60° to see whether these would fall on the line the experimenter has drawn. Alternatively, the experimenter could play it safe and draw only a bar graph for these spaced temperatures. Another useful dodge would be to connect the points with a smooth but broken line rather than a continuous line. As always, the broken line would suggest the tentative and provisional nature of the curve as drawn.

CUTAWAY
CARS

Clive Gifford
Designed by Robert Walster

Additional illustrations by: Sean Wilkinson, John Scorey, Robert Walster

Usborne Publishing wish to thank the following for their help with this part of the book:

Citroën Ltd., Castrol International, Ford Motor Company Limited, Goodyear, Honda, Land Rover, Lotus, MIRA, Michelin Tyre PLC, Peugeot, Porsche Cars Great Britain Ltd., SAAB Automobile AB, Toyota, Volkswagen, Volvo

Contents

Early cars 2

Modern cars 4

Safety 6

Rally car 8

The engine 10

The transmission 12

Grand Prix racing car 14

Aerodynamics 16

Vintage racing car 18

Suspension and steering 20

Brakes and tires 22

Sports car 24

Electrical system 26

Off-road car 28

The future 30

Glossary 31

Cars: Facts 32

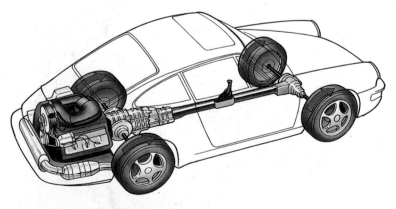

Words in *italic* type

Words in this section which appear in *italic* type and are followed by a small star (for example, *friction**) can be found in the glossary on page 31.

Early cars

The first vehicle to move on land without the help of a horse or other animal was Nicolas-Joseph Cugnot's steam tractor. Built in 1769, it could only run for 15 minutes at a time and its top speed was just 3.6km/h (2.2mph), slower than you can walk.

Cugnot's steam tractor

This is its steam boiler.

This luxury car is a Delaunay-Belleville F6. It was first built in 1908 and was popular with nobles and aristocrats in Europe.

This canvas top opens out to protect the passengers sitting in the back seats.

These wheels were originally designed for cannons. They are made of wood and have spokes like bicycle wheels.

Here you can see the back axle, a rod which joins the back wheels together.

Most of the car's body is made of wood and is either painted or varnished. Car bodies today are usually made of steel.

The first big step in making cars more like they are today came with the invention of a new type of engine powered by a gas. It was called the internal combustion engine and you can learn more about it on pages 10-11.

This Benz Velo was built in 1898.

One of the first cars to be powered by this new engine was built by Karl Benz in 1885 (see page 32). Within ten years, his factory was building many cars for sale. One model, the Benz Velo, was the first car to sell in large numbers.

As more companies started to build cars, improvements such as proper brakes and lights for driving at night were added. More powerful engines combined with better car design made cars much faster and this resulted in many more accidents. Governments brought in laws about cars and speed for the first time.

In Britain, until 1896, a person waving a red flag as a warning had to walk in front of a car. This kept speeds down to under 6.5km/h (4mph).

More reliable

The first motor vehicles were not reliable and broke down all the time. As cars became more popular, car builders concentrated on improving them so that they ran better. Rolls Royce built their first luxury car, the Silver Ghost, in 1906. To demonstrate its reliability, a team of drivers drove it non-stop for 24,120km (14,988 miles). In all this time, the car only had to stop once for repairs.

This windshield folds down.

This engine is much larger but less than half as powerful as the engine in an ordinary family car today.

The headlight is powered by gas. Headlights on today's cars are powered by electricity.

This can is used to carry extra fuel. It is strapped firmly into place.

Most early cars need a strong turn of this starting handle to start their engine up. A modern car uses electricity to start its engine.

Delaunay-Belleville were famous for making steam boilers for trains and ships. In fact, the shape of this engine cover is rather like a steam boiler.

Modern cars

An ordinary Volkswagen Golf

One hundred years after the first motor vehicles, modern cars look a lot different. Yet, the way they work is, in fact, very similar. For example, most cars still rely on an internal combustion engine to power them. Today's cars are more complicated than earlier models. They are made up of hundreds of parts all joined together to form what car engineers call systems.

A Golf used for rally racing

From design to production

It takes many years to design and build a modern car. First, the company researches what customers want and finds out what are the latest technical developments. They then start to choose some of the basic features they wish to include in the new car.

A car starts its life as drawings on a designer's desk. Changes are suggested by many people in the company. Everything from the seat color to the size of the wheels is discussed.

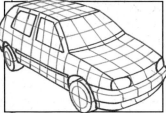

Engineers use Computer Aided Design (or C.A.D.) to determine the size and shape of the car and all its parts. Then, detailed plans and models of the car are made.

The models are tested in wind tunnels (see page 17) to see how they react to air moving over them. Many changes are made to the car's shape and testing lasts a long time.

Many other tests are done before the car can be produced in large numbers to sell to the public. Some of the most important testing is for safety (see pages 6-7).

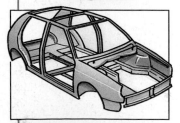

The parts of the car are made in several different factories. Some parts are even made by other companies. The car is then put together on a production line in a factory.

Eventually, cars come off the production line, are given a final test and are ready to be sold. The time between the original design and the first sales can be up to five years.

Volkswagen Golf

The Volkswagen Golf is a popular family car. It is relatively small and compact but can carry up to five people and travel at speeds over 160km/h (100mph).

Wing mirror

This metal rod is the dipstick. It allows you to check how much oil is in the engine.

Engine

This is an air filter. It prevents dirt and dust from getting into the engine.

Headlight

This is the car's radiator. It helps cool the engine down.

Behind the radiator you can see the fan. This also helps to keep the engine cool.

Chassis and monocoque

The car's main parts used to be held in place by a frame called a *chassis**. Family cars today usually have a chassis combined with the body of the car. This is called a monocoque.

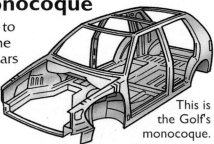

This is the Golf's monocoque.

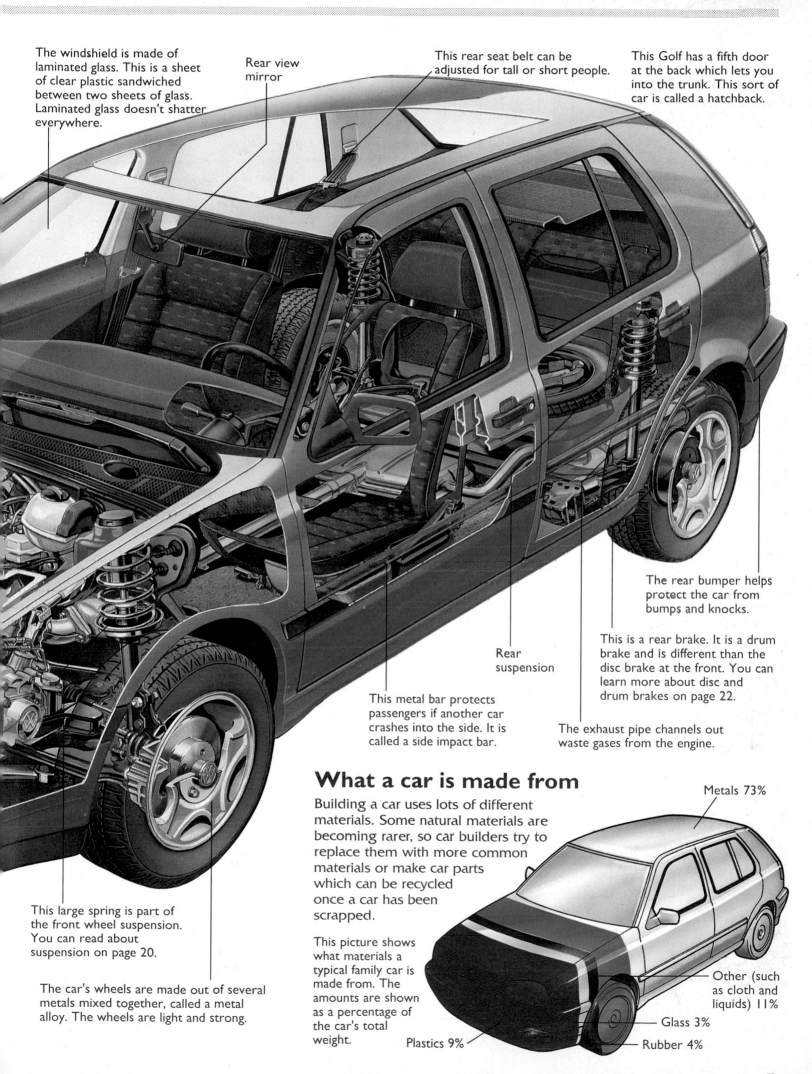

The windshield is made of laminated glass. This is a sheet of clear plastic sandwiched between two sheets of glass. Laminated glass doesn't shatter everywhere.

Rear view mirror

This rear seat belt can be adjusted for tall or short people.

This Golf has a fifth door at the back which lets you into the trunk. This sort of car is called a hatchback.

The rear bumper helps protect the car from bumps and knocks.

This is a rear brake. It is a drum brake and is different than the disc brake at the front. You can learn more about disc and drum brakes on page 22.

Rear suspension

This metal bar protects passengers if another car crashes into the side. It is called a side impact bar.

The exhaust pipe channels out waste gases from the engine.

This large spring is part of the front wheel suspension. You can read about suspension on page 20.

The car's wheels are made out of several metals mixed together, called a metal alloy. The wheels are light and strong.

What a car is made from

Building a car uses lots of different materials. Some natural materials are becoming rarer, so car builders try to replace them with more common materials or make car parts which can be recycled once a car has been scrapped.

This picture shows what materials a typical family car is made from. The amounts are shown as a percentage of the car's total weight.

Metals 73%

Other (such as cloth and liquids) 11%

Glass 3%

Rubber 4%

Plastics 9%

5

Safety

Modern cars are designed to help the driver avoid accidents. The latest brakes, steering and tires all give drivers more control of their car than ever before. These are called active safety features.

If there is an accident, a car's passive safety features protect the driver and passengers. The picture below shows some of the common passive safety features of a modern car in a crash test.

Dummies are used instead of people when a car is crash tested. Their movements and any damage they suffer is recorded using high speed photography and sensors linked to computers.

Crash test dummy

This is a steering wheel air bag (see how it works below).

To stop the driver's head from hitting the steering wheel, the steering column, to which the wheel is attached, can be made to collapse like a telescope.

This headrest stops the head from jolting sharply back. This action is called whiplash and can cause severe back and neck damage.

The seat is firmly attached to the floor. It cannot slide back and trap the legs of a passenger in the back seat.

Seat belts hold people firmly in their seats. Many modern seat belts are fitted with powerful springs called pre-tensioners. They pull the belt tighter if there's a crash.

Submarining is when people are forced forward and under their seat belts by a crash. Modern seats are designed to stop this.

The front of the car body will crumple as the car hits something solid.

Steering wheel air bag

As a car hits something it starts to slow down and stop but the people inside the car keep moving. Many people in crashes are hurt by hitting their heads on the steering wheel or dashboard. An air bag should prevent this.

An air bag must inflate very quickly and stay blown-up until after the driver's head has hit it. This is done by igniting chemicals which create large amounts of gases. These gases inflate the bag in an instant. Some cars have air bags to protect the front passenger as well.

Gases inflate air bag.

Inflating chemical is stored here.

Igniter burns chemicals to create gases.

Switches inside the car set off the chemicals in the air bag when the car crashes at over 33km/h (20mph).

The chemicals react and inflate the bag. A large cushion for the driver's chest and head is created.

The bag inflates in 40 milliseconds. That's less than a third of the time it takes you to blink your eye.

Body strength

Crashes create energy which has to go somewhere. Early car bodies were rigid. These protected against the direct impact of a crash only for the energy to travel through the car and throw people around.

A modern car still has a rigid body, called the passenger cell or cage, which will not break even if the car rolls over. Much of the rest of the car's body is designed to collapse when it is hit. The collapsing parts are called crumple zones and they absorb lots of energy from the crash. The remaining energy is directed around the car body but away from the driver and passengers.

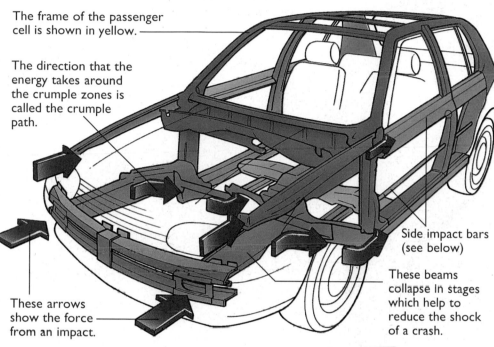

The frame of the passenger cell is shown in yellow.

The direction that the energy takes around the crumple zones is called the crumple path.

These arrows show the force from an impact.

Side impact bars (see below)

These beams collapse in stages which help to reduce the shock of a crash.

Side impact bars

Many accidents involve side-on crashes where one car punches a hole through another's door. Although some companies are starting to use side air bags, the most common way to protect people is to put strong rods of steel, called side impact bars, inside the door frame.

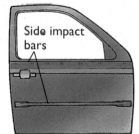

Side impact bars

Computer simulation

Some car companies use powerful computers to improve car safety. They build a model of the car in the computer which is accurate right down to the last detail.

Although this takes a long time to do, it allows every part of the car to be crash tested in the computer. Engineers can alter the size or the strength of a piece of the car at the touch of a few buttons, and see the effect more quickly than building a proper part which has to be checked in a real car crash test.

This is a computer test of the air bag opening.

The tests can take as long as 30 hours to complete but provide the safety team with lots of important information.

Crash testing

Crash tests have to cover all the different possible types of crashes. Engineers record what happens to a car in each crash by using photography and electronic instruments, both inside and outside of the car. They can then tell what changes may be needed to improve the car's design.

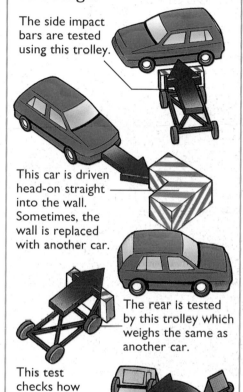

The side impact bars are tested using this trolley.

This car is driven head-on straight into the wall. Sometimes, the wall is replaced with another car.

The rear is tested by this trolley which weighs the same as another car.

This test checks how secure the passenger cage is when the car rolls over.

This is an overhead view of a crash test to the front of a car.

Rally car

Rally cars race in difficult conditions: through deserts, over icy roads and on bumpy dirt tracks, for example. They have to be tough to take the battering they receive. Most rally cars are specially modified versions of normal family cars.

Ford Escort RS Cosworth

This car has won a lot of competitions. It is based on a high speed version of the Ford Escort. It has many features added including a strengthened body, tougher, lighter wheels and a bigger, more powerful engine.

This is a standard Ford Escort.

Wings

This large flap is called a wing. It helps the car grip the road and makes it easier to drive. You can learn more about how it works on page 14.

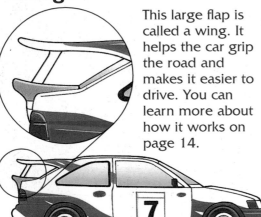

Rear wing

This car is fitted with studded tires, used for driving on ice and snow.

This is the car's exhaust pipe. Its unusual flat shape stops it from hitting bumps in the ground.

These seats are specially shaped to hold the driver and co-driver. They are called bucket seats.

The co-driver sits here. He or she plots the car's route around the rally course.

Driver protection

Rally cars crash and roll over more often than family cars. In a rally car, the driver and co-driver are protected by a strong frame of steel tubes fitted to the inside of the car body. This frame is called a roll cage.

The driver and co-driver are held firmly in their seats by a set of five straps called a racing harness. These straps go around the waist, over the shoulders and between the legs. They all fasten together at the front.

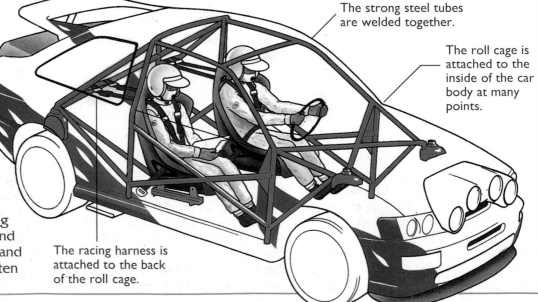

The strong steel tubes are welded together.

The roll cage is attached to the inside of the car body at many points.

The racing harness is attached to the back of the roll cage.

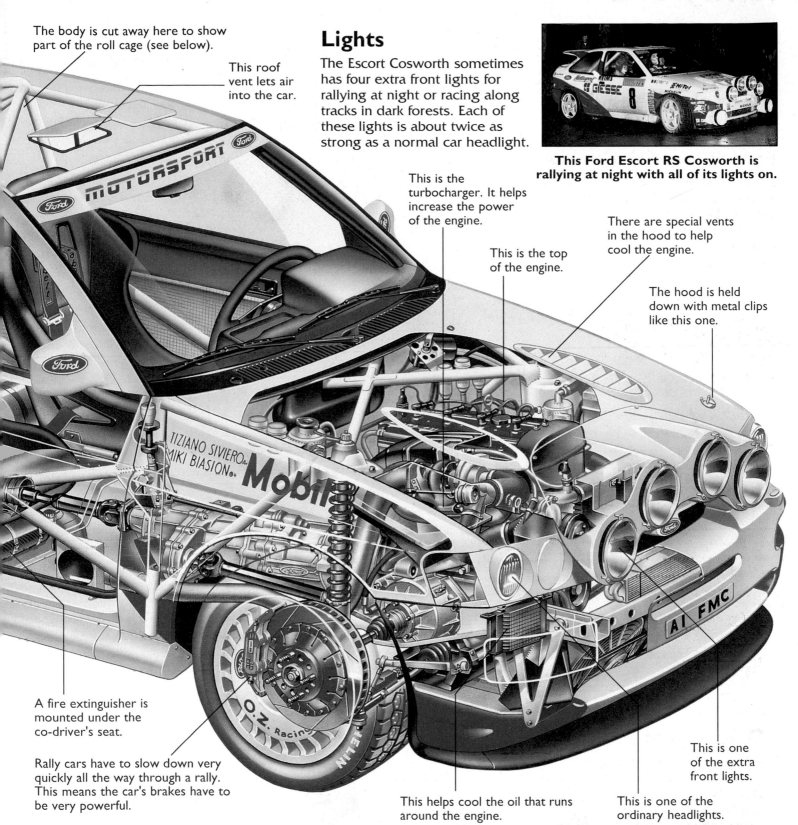

The body is cut away here to show part of the roll cage (see below).

This roof vent lets air into the car.

Lights

The Escort Cosworth sometimes has four extra front lights for rallying at night or racing along tracks in dark forests. Each of these lights is about twice as strong as a normal car headlight.

This Ford Escort RS Cosworth is rallying at night with all of its lights on.

This is the turbocharger. It helps increase the power of the engine.

This is the top of the engine.

There are special vents in the hood to help cool the engine.

The hood is held down with metal clips like this one.

A fire extinguisher is mounted under the co-driver's seat.

Rally cars have to slow down very quickly all the way through a rally. This means the car's brakes have to be very powerful.

This helps cool the oil that runs around the engine.

This is one of the ordinary headlights.

This is one of the extra front lights.

Rally racing

Rally courses are a mixture of roads and dirt tracks. The course is divided into separate sections known as Special Stages. One stage may be along twisting and turning mountain roads, another on mud tracks through dark forests. The cars follow the same route but start one after another. Each car is timed over the different stages by officials called marshals. The winner is the car which has the fastest overall time.

Cars at the bigger rallies are supported by teams of dozens of people and many vehicles. These can include motorcycles to carry messages, trucks holding spare parts, a medical van and, sometimes, even a helicopter.

This car, without extra lights, is racing along a twisting mountain road.

The engine

Most cars are powered by a type of engine called an internal combustion, or I.C., engine. It is called this because it produces power by combusting, or burning, a mixture of fuel and air inside a chamber called a cylinder.

How an I.C. engine works

Here are the names of many of the important parts at the heart of an I.C. engine.

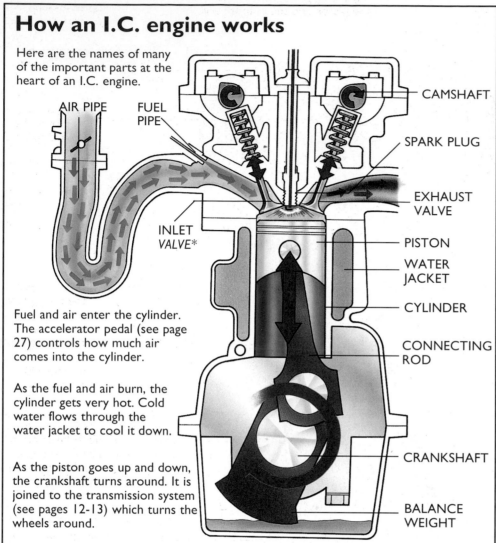

AIR PIPE

FUEL PIPE

INLET VALVE*

CAMSHAFT

SPARK PLUG

EXHAUST VALVE

PISTON

WATER JACKET

CYLINDER

CONNECTING ROD

CRANKSHAFT

BALANCE WEIGHT

Fuel and air enter the cylinder. The accelerator pedal (see page 27) controls how much air comes into the cylinder.

As the fuel and air burn, the cylinder gets very hot. Cold water flows through the water jacket to cool it down.

As the piston goes up and down, the crankshaft turns around. It is joined to the transmission system (see pages 12-13) which turns the wheels around.

The actions that create power in the cylinder are called the combustion cycle. Most car engines have a cycle of four strokes. This means that the piston moves up twice and down twice in one complete cycle.

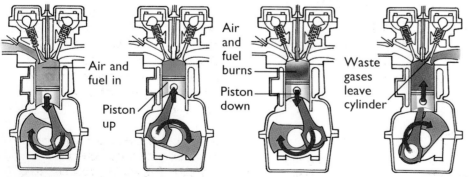

Air and fuel in

Piston up

Air and fuel burns

Piston down

Waste gases leave cylinder

1. At the cycle's start, the piston moves down and the inlet valve opens. The fuel and air mixture is sucked into the cylinder.

2. The piston moves up the cylinder. This compresses and heats up the fuel and air. The spark plug ignites the mixture.

3. The mixture burns, creating gases which expand quickly. These push the piston down. This stroke produces the engine's power.

4. The exhaust valve opens and the waste gases are pushed out of the cylinder by the rising piston. The engine then starts another complete cycle.

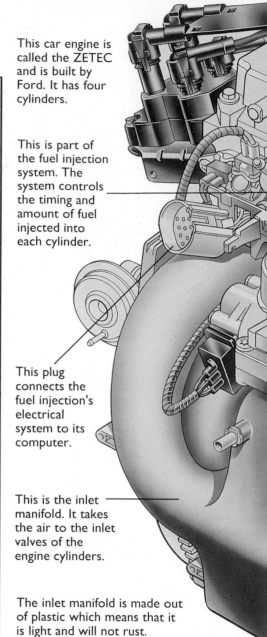

This car engine is called the ZETEC and is built by Ford. It has four cylinders.

This is part of the fuel injection system. The system controls the timing and amount of fuel injected into each cylinder.

This plug connects the fuel injection's electrical system to its computer.

This is the inlet manifold. It takes the air to the inlet valves of the engine cylinders.

The inlet manifold is made out of plastic which means that it is light and will not rust.

How many cylinders?

A modern car engine has more than one cylinder. A small engine may have four while engines used in powerful racing or sports cars can have as many as twelve. They can be arranged in different patterns.

This engine's four cylinders are arranged in line.

This engine's eight cylinders are arranged in a V pattern.

This combination is called a flat six.

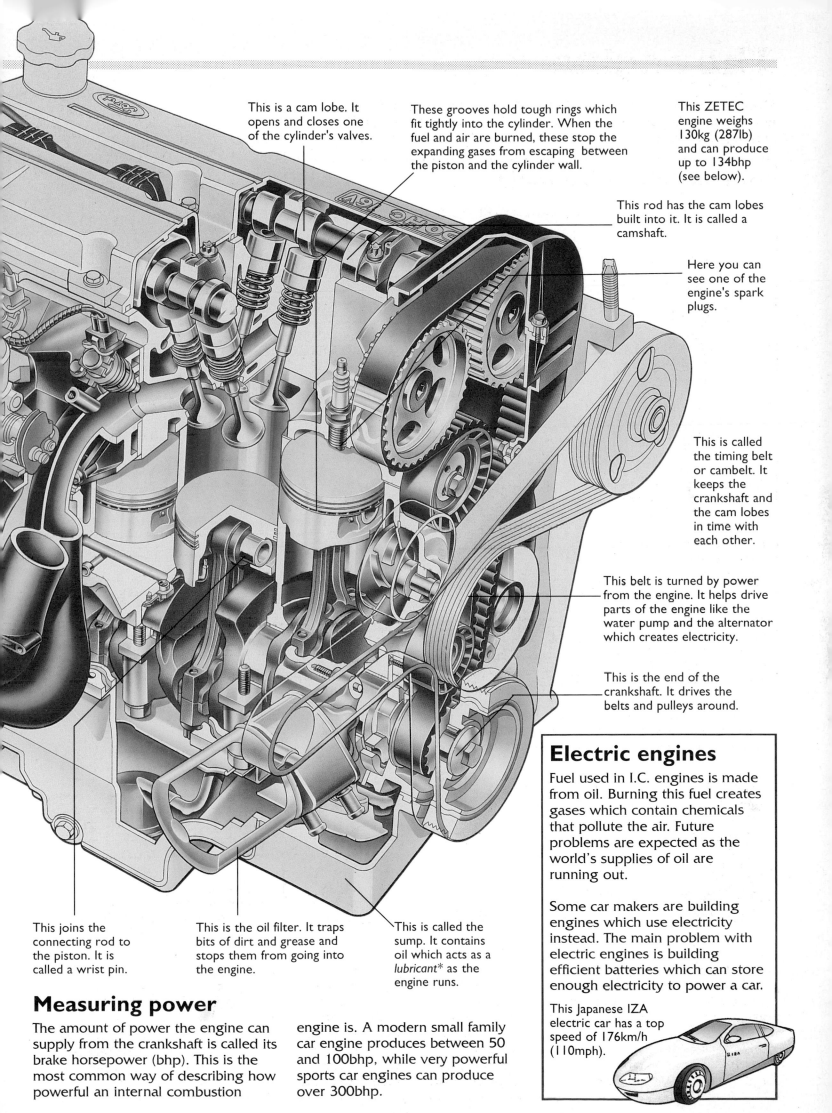

This is a cam lobe. It opens and closes one of the cylinder's valves.

These grooves hold tough rings which fit tightly into the cylinder. When the fuel and air are burned, these stop the expanding gases from escaping between the piston and the cylinder wall.

This ZETEC engine weighs 130kg (287lb) and can produce up to 134bhp (see below).

This rod has the cam lobes built into it. It is called a camshaft.

Here you can see one of the engine's spark plugs.

This is called the timing belt or cambelt. It keeps the crankshaft and the cam lobes in time with each other.

This belt is turned by power from the engine. It helps drive parts of the engine like the water pump and the alternator which creates electricity.

This is the end of the crankshaft. It drives the belts and pulleys around.

This joins the connecting rod to the piston. It is called a wrist pin.

This is the oil filter. It traps bits of dirt and grease and stops them from going into the engine.

This is called the sump. It contains oil which acts as a *lubricant** as the engine runs.

Measuring power

The amount of power the engine can supply from the crankshaft is called its brake horsepower (bhp). This is the most common way of describing how powerful an internal combustion engine is. A modern small family car engine produces between 50 and 100bhp, while very powerful sports car engines can produce over 300bhp.

Electric engines

Fuel used in I.C. engines is made from oil. Burning this fuel creates gases which contain chemicals that pollute the air. Future problems are expected as the world's supplies of oil are running out.

Some car makers are building engines which use electricity instead. The main problem with electric engines is building efficient batteries which can store enough electricity to power a car.

This Japanese IZA electric car has a top speed of 176km/h (110mph).

11

The transmission

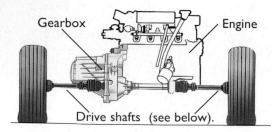

Gearbox   Engine

Drive shafts (see below).

The transmission system sends power from the engine to the wheels. The first transmissions were like bicycle chains, but in today's cars they are made up of many parts. A modern transmission passes the power from the engine through a gearbox, which gives the driver a chance to select different speeds.

The power is then taken to whichever wheels push the car forward. Twenty years ago, most cars were powered by their rear wheels but today more and more cars have a transmission system which drives the front wheel like the one shown below. Some cars are even driven by all four wheels (see page 24).

Gearbox

The heart of a transmission system is the gearbox. This system, made by Saab, has a gearbox with five forward gears and one reverse. Here you can see the names of some of its parts. The explanations on these two pages tell you how it all works.

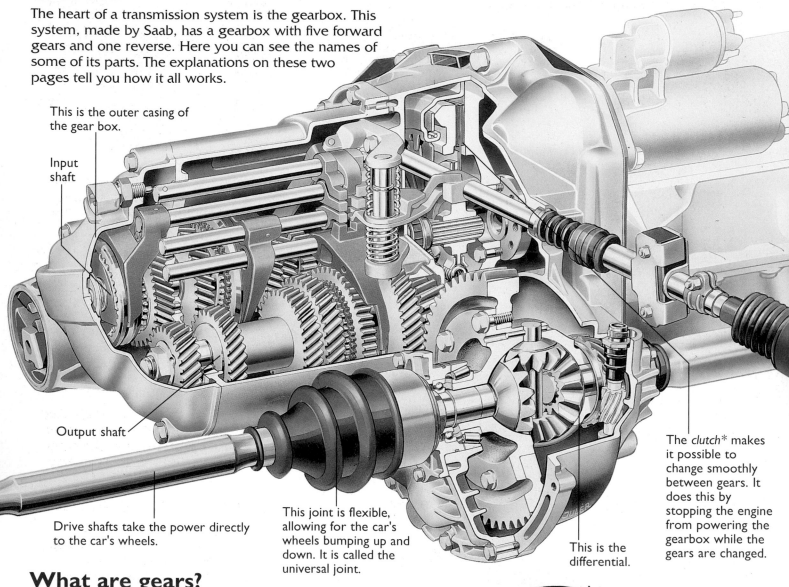

This is the outer casing of the gear box.

Input shaft

Output shaft

Drive shafts take the power directly to the car's wheels.

This joint is flexible, allowing for the car's wheels bumping up and down. It is called the universal joint.

This is the differential.

The *clutch** makes it possible to change smoothly between gears. It does this by stopping the engine from powering the gearbox while the gears are changed.

What are gears?

The gears found in a car gearbox are called cogs and are like wheels with teeth. The teeth allow gears to interlock, or mesh. When the gears mesh together, turning one gear around makes the other turn, but in the other direction.

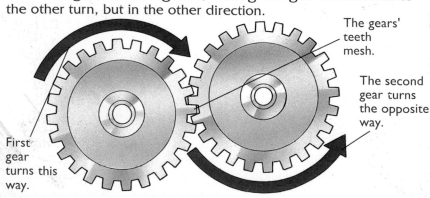

The gears' teeth mesh.

The second gear turns the opposite way.

First gear turns this way.

The small gear turns four times for each turn of the large.

Large gear four times bigger than small gear.

Large gear turns with four times more torque (see below) than the small gear.

If the gears are different sizes, the smaller one turns faster but the slower, bigger gear turns with greater power. Turning power is called *torque** by engineers and mechanics.

How the gearbox works

A car's gearbox contains many gear cogs which together provide the car with four, five or six different speeds. A car needs these because driving requires different combinations of speed and force at different times. For example, driving up a steep hill needs more force than speed while cruising along a motorway needs more speed than force. The lower gears in a gearbox provide greater force and the higher gears more speed.

Input shaft is powered directly by the engine.

Output shaft takes power to the wheels.

Here you can see the gears and shafts in a typical gearbox.

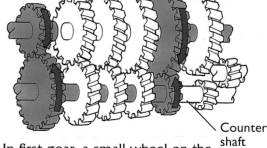

Counter shaft

Gears on the counter shaft drive gears on the output shaft.

On top of the gear stick is this pattern showing where each gear is.

Gear stick

Gear shift rod

Counter shaft

In first gear, a small wheel on the counter shaft and a large wheel on the output shaft connect. The car moves slowly but with much power.

In second gear, the two gear cogs have less difference in size. This gear turns more quickly but with less power. This helps the car pull away with ease.

In the highest gear, the cogs on the input and output shafts are linked so that they turn at the same rate. This top gear allows the car to go at its fastest.

Output shaft turns opposite way to usual.

Idler gear

In reverse, an extra gear, called an idler gear, slips in between the normal input and output gears. The output shaft and the car's wheels turn the opposite way.

What is the differential?

The differential is a complicated set of gears between the two drive shafts of whichever wheels power the car. The differential adjusts the speed at which the two wheels turn when the car goes around a corner. The outer wheel has to travel farther around a corner than the inner one. The differential's gears make the outer wheel turn faster than the inner one.

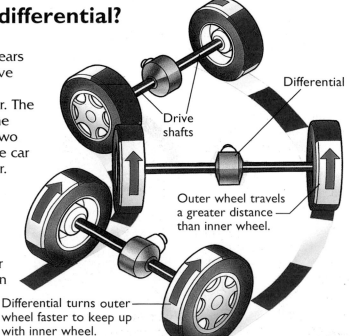

Differential

Drive shafts

Outer wheel travels a greater distance than inner wheel.

Differential turns outer wheel faster to keep up with inner wheel.

Automatic gearbox

Changing from one gear to another constantly can be tiring. One solution is an automatic gearbox that selects the engine gears for you. Automatic transmissions tend to use more fuel and the driver still has to make some choices by selecting with the gear stick.

P is for when the car is parked.

D is for drive, the main forward gear.

R is reverse gear.

Grand Prix racing car

Grand Prix racing is the most famous type of racing. With their powerful engines and light, specially-designed bodies, Grand Prix cars can travel at speeds of up to 320km/h (200mph). Grand Prix cars are often the first to use new technology. Some of the advanced features which prove useful for normal road drivers are eventually seen on ordinary family cars.

This antenna sends radio signals from the driver to his racing team headquarters by the track.

Front wing (see below).

Rear view mirror

The wheel is cut away so that you can see the front brake.

This is the one spring and shock absorber for the front two wheels. It is called a monoshock.

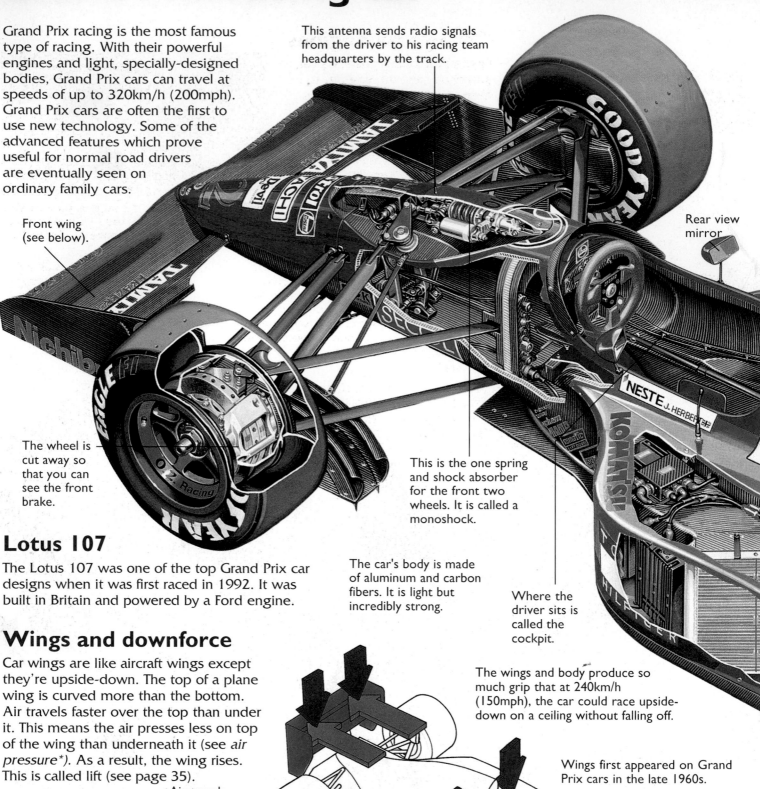

Lotus 107

The Lotus 107 was one of the top Grand Prix car designs when it was first raced in 1992. It was built in Britain and powered by a Ford engine.

The car's body is made of aluminum and carbon fibers. It is light but incredibly strong.

Where the driver sits is called the cockpit.

Wings and downforce

Car wings are like aircraft wings except they're upside-down. The top of a plane wing is curved more than the bottom. Air travels faster over the top than under it. This means the air presses less on top of the wing than underneath it (see *air pressure**). As a result, the wing rises. This is called lift (see page 35).

Air travels over wing.

Wing rises upward.

The wings and body produce so much grip that at 240km/h (150mph), the car could race upside-down on a ceiling without falling off.

Wings first appeared on Grand Prix cars in the late 1960s.

The shape of the car's body also helps produce downforce.

Car wings do the opposite to plane wings. Instead of producing lift, they help the car stick to the ground. The force that makes a car grip the track is called downforce. It helps the car grip without slowing it down too much and gives the driver more control when turning.

Downforce is measured as a weight. A Grand Prix car weighs around 500kg (1100lb) but the downforce created by the back and front wings can be as much as three times that.

14

Grand Prix engines

Grand Prix racing pushes a car, and especially the engine, to its absolute limits. Most engines are completely rebuilt after each race. The mechanics study the telemetrics, which are the performance details of the car recorded on computer during the race. They then rebuild and modify the engine according to the results.

This is the Lotus 107 raced by British driver, Johnny Herbert.

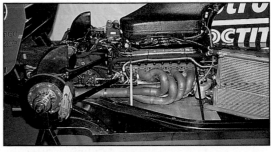

This Ford Cosworth HB engine powers the Lotus 107 and is protected by an advanced lubricant made by its sponsor, Castrol.

This tank holds 210 litres (46 gallons) of racing fuel. It is designed not to puncture, even in a crash.

This is the name of the car's chief sponsor. Sponsors are companies who help to pay for the car to be built and raced in return for publicity. Castrol also uses racing cars to try out new products for use in future road cars.

These are called slick tires and are used in dry weather racing. They have almost no tread (see page 23) which means more of the tire touches the track. Wet weather tires have more tread.

This part of the body is called a side fairing or pod.

Here is the air filter.

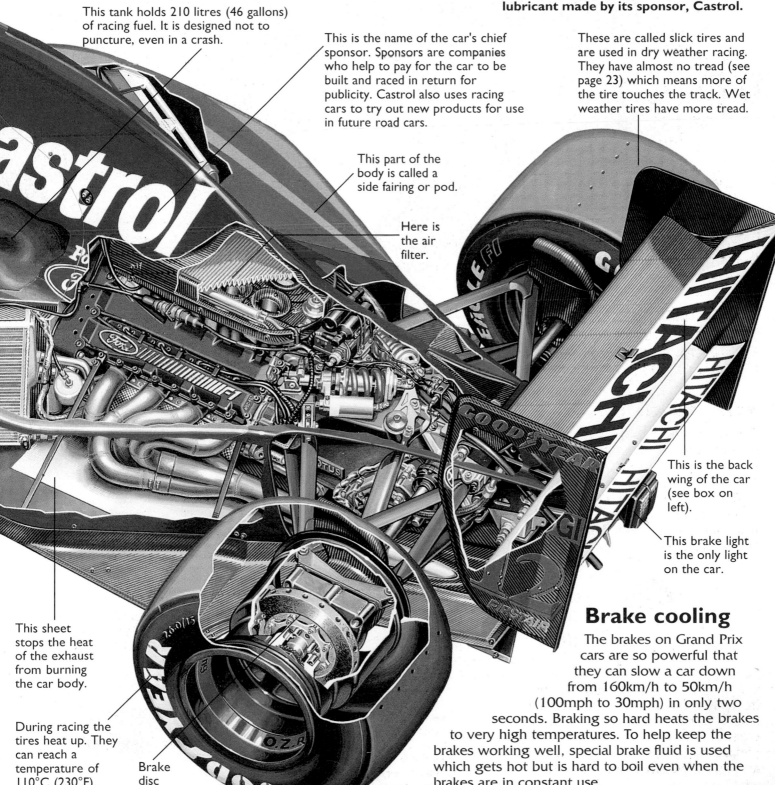

This sheet stops the heat of the exhaust from burning the car body.

During racing the tires heat up. They can reach a temperature of 110°C (230°F).

Brake disc

This is the back wing of the car (see box on left).

This brake light is the only light on the car.

Brake cooling

The brakes on Grand Prix cars are so powerful that they can slow a car down from 160km/h to 50km/h (100mph to 30mph) in only two seconds. Braking so hard heats the brakes to very high temperatures. To help keep the brakes working well, special brake fluid is used which gets hot but is hard to boil even when the brakes are in constant use.

Aerodynamics

To understand aerodynamics, you need to know about *friction**. Friction is the scientific name for when two things rub together. You can feel the effects of friction if you rub your hands together.

The tighter you press your hands together the more effort it takes to move them. After a short while, your hands start to warm up. If you kept rubbing them for a long time, the friction would cause wear and you would get blisters.

Friction wastes power, creates heat and, over time, wears down the surfaces of objects rubbing together. Reducing friction means that cars can move faster and with less effort.

Without friction, a car wouldn't go at all. Friction between wheels and the ground allows the wheels to grip the ground and push the car forward. A car's brakes also rely on friction to slow the wheels down.

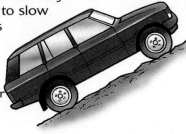

The tires grip even when the car moves up a steep slope.

The friction of air

When air and a moving object rub together they create friction. Today's cars are designed to cause less air friction than cars in the past. Their particular shapes and some of their features were developed by the use of aerodynamics.

Aerodynamics is the study of how a moving object travels through the air. It was first developed to look at how aircraft fly but is now used on motor vehicles as well.

Modern cars have smooth, rounded shapes (known as *streamlined**) which air passes over easily. This reduces the amount of friction from the air.

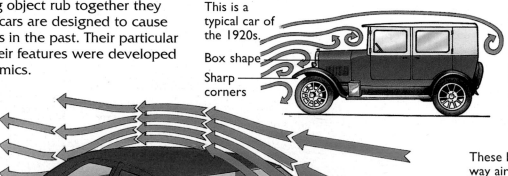

This is a typical car of the 1920s.

Box shape

Sharp corners

Air hits the front of the car flat on. The air cannot easily pass over and around the car so it creates lots of air friction.

These lines show the way air flows, or travels, over the car.

Streamlined features on cars

Wheel arches fit closely around the wheel.

Door handles fit flush into the car body.

The lights are molded into the body of the car.

The windshield is angled back.

The wing mirrors are rounded and smooth.

Drag coefficient

The drag coefficient, or Cd, is a measure of how much air friction a particular car will encounter. Less air friction means the car uses less fuel. Drag coefficients have gotten smaller as cars have become more streamlined. A family car in the 1960s had a drag coefficient of around 0.5 or 0.45. In today's family car, it is around 0.3.

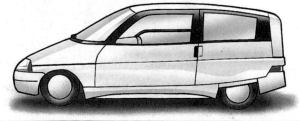

This Vesta 2 research car, built by Renault, has a drag coefficient of only 0.19.

Reducing friction

In a car, the surfaces of moving parts that rub together are made as smooth as possible to reduce friction. A liquid is far smoother than the surfaces of the car parts. A thin layer of liquid, usually oil, placed between the moving parts will produce a smoother surface and less friction. A liquid used in this way is called a *lubricant**.

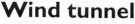

Thin layer of oil between two moving surfaces.

Metal

The oil is much smoother than the metal.

A rolling movement creates less friction than a sliding one. You can see this for yourself. First slide a book across a table. Then put some marbles underneath it and push it across the table again. The marbles roll rather than slide and this rolling creates less friction which means the book moves more easily. In some car parts, steel balls do the same job as the marbles.

These steel balls are called ball bearings.

Wind tunnel

One of the most important tools used in aerodynamics is a wind tunnel. It allows scientists to measure and record exactly how air travels around a car at different speeds. A modern wind tunnel can also mimic extreme weather to see how parts of the car react. For example, strong jets of water can mimic very heavy rain to see if the car has any tiny leaks.

This powerful fan can be adjusted to provide different strengths of wind.

Water can be injected into the air, to simulate rain or fog.

These lights are used to imitate the sun.

The speed of the air flowing around the tunnel can reach up to 150km/h (94mph).

The temperature of the air can be altered by this large heater.

The car is placed on rollers which can turn at different driving speeds.

Computers monitor how the car is performing.

Cameras record the testing so that it can be watched over and over again.

These slats direct the air around the tunnel.

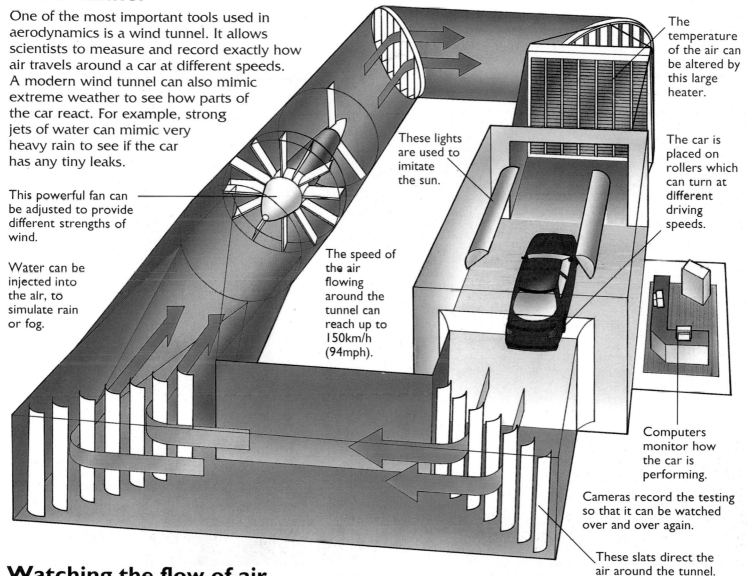

Watching the flow of air

Air is invisible, but its journey over and around a car needs to be watched and recorded. So, engineers have had to invent special techniques to see the air.

This man is injecting white gas into the air just before it flows around the car. Engineers can then see how the air travels.

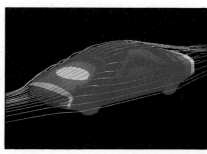

This computer is imitating the flow of air over a model car. Computers have greatly helped to improve cars' aerodynamics.

Vintage racing car

Almost as soon as cars were invented, they were raced against each other. The first official race was in France in 1895. In the early part of the twentieth century, cars built solely for racing first appeared. They competed in famous races such as the Mille Miglia in Italy and the 24 hour race in Le Mans in France. Many of the original cars have been restored and can be found in museums or even racing on tracks at vintage car rallies.

Bentley 4½ Litre

This famous vintage racing car was first built in 1930. Earlier versions of the car raced throughout the 1920s and won Le Mans every year between 1927 and 1930.

The name 4½ Litre refers to the *volume** of the engine's cylinders all added together. This measure is called cubic capacity and is measured in cubic centimeters or cc.

This is a Bentley 4½ Litre from the National Motor Museum in Beaulieu, England.

Le Mans today

The Le Mans race still takes place today but the cars racing in the competition have changed greatly since cars like the Bentley 4½ Litre raced there. For example, the first winning Bentley in 1927 raced at an average speed of 98km/h (61mph). The 1993 winner (shown right) raced at an average speed of 214km/h (132mph).

Modern light materials and a smaller but more powerful engine means that the Peugeot weighs just over a third of the weight of the Bentley so it goes faster. The Peugeot's top speed is over 400km/h (250mph). That is twice as fast as the Bentley.

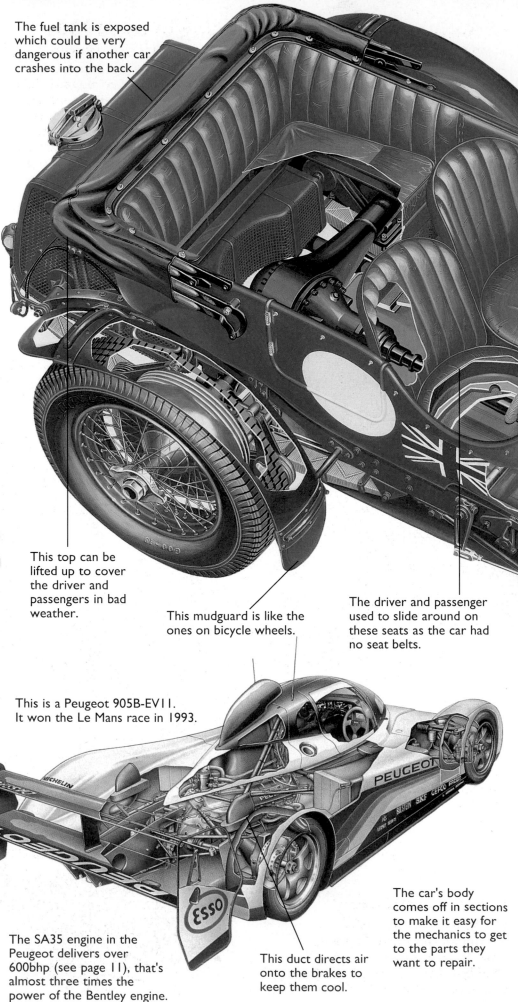

The fuel tank is exposed which could be very dangerous if another car crashes into the back.

This top can be lifted up to cover the driver and passengers in bad weather.

This mudguard is like the ones on bicycle wheels.

The driver and passenger used to slide around on these seats as the car had no seat belts.

This is a Peugeot 905B-EV11. It won the Le Mans race in 1993.

The SA35 engine in the Peugeot delivers over 600bhp (see page 11), that's almost three times the power of the Bentley engine.

This duct directs air onto the brakes to keep them cool.

The car's body comes off in sections to make it easy for the mechanics to get to the parts they want to repair.

This small piece of glass acts as a windshield for the passenger in the front seat. It is called an aeroscreen, because a similar screen was first used on aircraft.

The driver can flip up this wire mesh screen to protect himself from stones thrown up by cars in front.

Racing in the 1930s

Bentleys were just one of the famous makes of cars that raced in the 1930s. Others included Bugatti, Alfa Romeo and Mercedes-Benz. Racing cars of this time were usually open-topped. To keep warm, clean and dry, drivers wrapped themselves up in many layers of clothes and often a final covering of leather coats, hats, gloves and goggles.

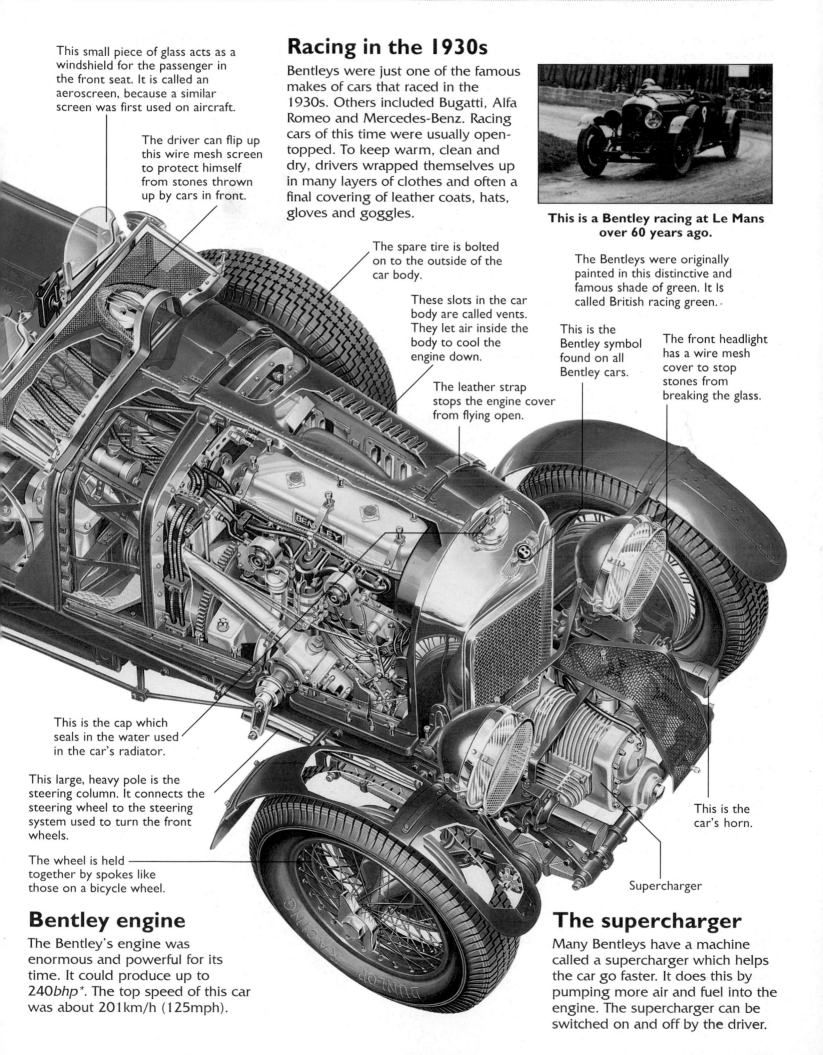

This is a Bentley racing at Le Mans over 60 years ago.

The spare tire is bolted on to the outside of the car body.

These slots in the car body are called vents. They let air inside the body to cool the engine down.

The leather strap stops the engine cover from flying open.

The Bentleys were originally painted in this distinctive and famous shade of green. It Is called British racing green.

This is the Bentley symbol found on all Bentley cars.

The front headlight has a wire mesh cover to stop stones from breaking the glass.

This is the cap which seals in the water used in the car's radiator.

This large, heavy pole is the steering column. It connects the steering wheel to the steering system used to turn the front wheels.

The wheel is held together by spokes like those on a bicycle wheel.

This is the car's horn.

Supercharger

Bentley engine

The Bentley's engine was enormous and powerful for its time. It could produce up to 240*bhp**. The top speed of this car was about 201km/h (125mph).

The supercharger

Many Bentleys have a machine called a supercharger which helps the car go faster. It does this by pumping more air and fuel into the engine. The supercharger can be switched on and off by the driver.

Suspension

A car's suspension makes traveling much more comfortable. The car's wheels bounce up and down over holes and bumps in the road. The suspension system stops the whole car from bouncing around uncontrollably. The suspension also helps the wheels to stay in touch with the ground as much as possible. This improves the car's handling which is how drivers describe how easy a car is to control. There are several types of suspension. Many use a spring like the one shown on the right.

Spring

Shock absorber (see below)

Riding on springs

When a car goes over a bump, the spring compresses, squashing up to absorb the energy of the bump; but it must eventually return to its normal position. A spring expands as quickly as it compresses. It expands past its normal size then is pulled back.

Normal size   Compressed   Expanded   Compressed

Springs rise and fall many times before they get back to normal size. A car body fitted only with springs would bounce up and down for quite some time. The solution is to fit each spring with a device called a shock absorber.

Car body with just springs for suspension.

Car body rises and falls for a long time.

Active suspension

This modern system of suspension uses *hydraulic** cylinders instead of springs and shock absorbers. The height of each wheel is controlled by the cylinders which are connected to a central computer in the car. Active suspension greatly improves a car's handling.

When accelerating, active suspension stops the front wheels from rising off the ground.

When braking sharply, active suspension stops the front of a car from dipping down.

When cornering sharply the inner wheels tend to rise. Active suspension helps keep them on the ground.

You can see the springs and shock absorbers connected to each wheel on this picture.

Car suspension springs have to be strong to cushion the weight of a loaded car as it goes over a bump.

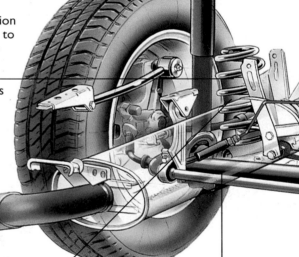

The suspension springs are joined to this car separately from the shock absorbers.

This is the rear *axle**.

How a shock absorber works

A shock absorber slows the rise of the spring. The most common type of shock absorber uses a piston joined to the spring and a cylinder of oil. This is called a hydraulic shock absorber. It works by using special openings called *valves**. Oil travels through these valves faster when the piston moves down the cylinder than when it moves up. This means that the spring can compress quickly but expands slowly.

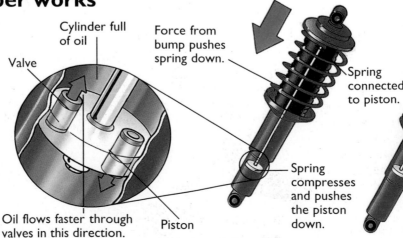

Cylinder full of oil

Valve

Oil flows faster through valves in this direction.

Force from bump pushes spring down.

Spring connected to piston.

Piston

Spring compresses and pushes the piston down.

As spring rises, it pulls the piston back up the cylinder.

Valves and oil slow the spring's rise.

20

Steering

Turning a car's steering wheel seems quite easy but your effort has to be increased so that you can turn the heavy car with its wheels gripping the ground strongly. Many cars use a system of two interlocking *gears** called a rack and pinion. At the end of the steering wheel column is the pinion. This interlocks with a sliding, toothed rail called the rack.

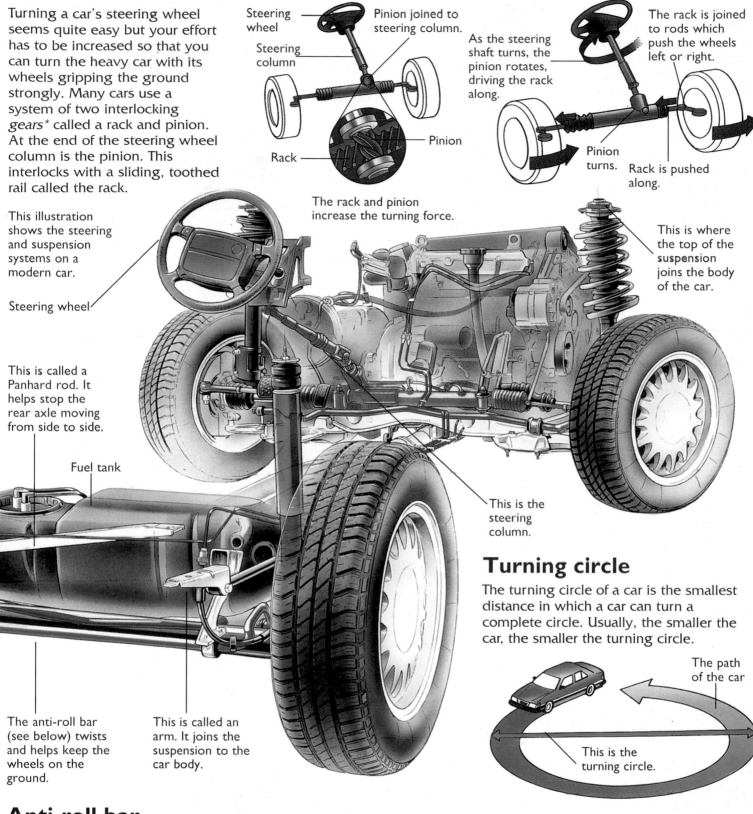

Steering wheel

Steering column

Pinion joined to steering column.

Pinion

Rack

As the steering shaft turns, the pinion rotates, driving the rack along.

The rack is joined to rods which push the wheels left or right.

Pinion turns.

Rack is pushed along.

The rack and pinion increase the turning force.

This illustration shows the steering and suspension systems on a modern car.

Steering wheel

This is where the top of the **suspension** joins the body of the car.

This is called a Panhard rod. It helps stop the rear axle moving from side to side.

Fuel tank

This is the steering column.

The anti-roll bar (see below) twists and helps keep the wheels on the ground.

This is called an arm. It joins the suspension to the car body.

Turning circle

The turning circle of a car is the smallest distance in which a car can turn a complete circle. Usually, the smaller the car, the smaller the turning circle.

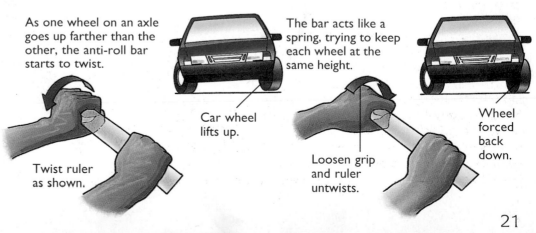

The path of the car

This is the turning circle.

Anti-roll bar

An anti-roll bar is a steel rod connected to the frame of the car. It helps prevent a car from leaning over on tight, fast corners or after hitting a large bump in the road. It does this by stopping the wheel from rising too high in the air. On the right you can see how it works by imitating its movement with a long, plastic ruler.

As one wheel on an axle goes up farther than the other, the anti-roll bar starts to twist.

Twist ruler as shown.

The bar acts like a spring, trying to keep each wheel at the same height.

Car wheel lifts up.

Loosen grip and ruler untwists.

Wheel forced back down.

Brakes

Braking is all about stopping wheels that are spinning very fast. A modern car has a brake on each wheel and these all work at the same time when you press the brake lever. There are two main types of brake, disc and drum brakes. Both types use a *hydraulic** system. You can find out about hydraulic systems in planes on page 38.

Hydraulic system

Modern brakes are powered by a liquid put under pressure, called a *hydraulic** system. With the help of the car engine, the liquid is forced through pipes and cylinders to make the brakes move.

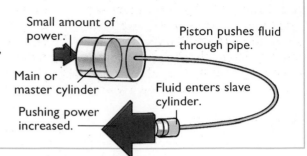

Small amount of power.

Piston pushes fluid through pipe.

Main or master cylinder

Fluid enters slave cylinder.

Pushing power increased.

Disc brakes

Disc brakes are similar to brakes on a bicycle. Bicycle brakes have a lever called a caliper which opens and closes. On the ends of the caliper are brake pads which press hard onto the rim of the bicycle wheel. The *friction**, or rubbing, created by the pads slows the wheel down. When a car disc brake works, hydraulic fluid forces the caliper to close onto a disc joined to the car wheel.

Here you can see where a disc brake fits inside a wheel.

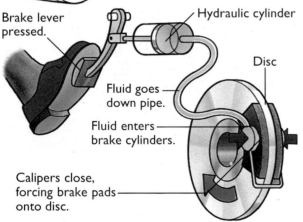

Brake lever pressed.

Hydraulic cylinder

Fluid goes down pipe.

Fluid enters brake cylinders.

Disc

Calipers close, forcing brake pads onto disc.

Here is a car disc brake.

Brake caliper

This clip holds the brake pads in place.

This is one of the brake cylinders.

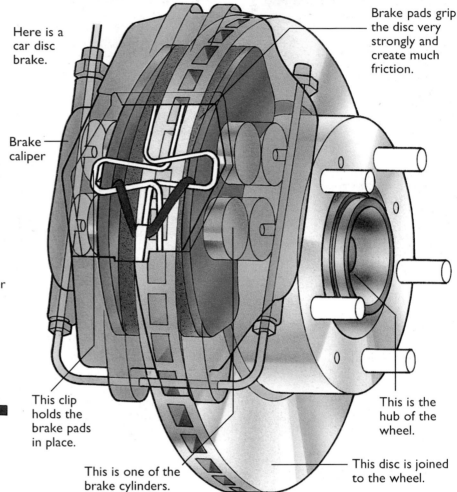

Brake pads grip the disc very strongly and create much friction.

This is the hub of the wheel.

This disc is joined to the wheel.

Drum brakes

Drum brakes are so-called because they have a metal drum attached to the car wheel instead of a disc.

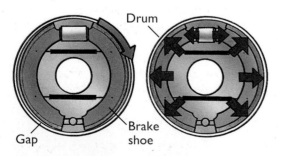

Drum

Gap

Brake shoe

Brake pads fit on curved brake shoes which sit inside the drum. There is a gap between the shoes and drum.

When the driver brakes, a hydraulic system pushes the shoes out to touch the drum. This slows the wheel down.

The inside of a drum brake.

Brake shoe

Powerful springs push the shoes away from the drum when the brake is released.

This hydraulic cylinder pushes the brake shoe onto the drum.

ABS braking

Sometimes, if brakes are pressed too hard, they can lock and stop the wheels from spinning. If the wheels are not going around, the driver cannot steer and may skid and hit something. ABS, or anti-locking brake system, has sensors on the wheels linked to a computer. This can adjust the brake pressure up to 10 or 12 times a second. This means the brakes are put on and off a fraction all the time; enough to allow the driver to brake and steer safely around hazards.

Tires

Modern tyres are complicated car parts, designed by computers and tested as thoroughly as, and sometimes more than, other parts of the car. So much work goes into designing and making them because they are vital to a car's safety and performance. Tires are the only part of the car that touch the ground. They must be able to grip the road enough to move the car along efficiently and allow the driver to control the car easily both in a straight line or when turning.

This is a modern car tire, made by Michelin. It is made up of many different layers called plies.

Types of tire

There are many different types of tires for different vehicles and driving conditions.

The first tires were made of solid rubber. This tire from a Bugatti car of the 1930s is filled with air like a modern one but is not as wide.

This tire is made for rallying across heavy mud or sand. It has a very deep, chunky tread, a lot like tires used on tractors.

This tire is very wide and has almost no tread. It is used by Grand Prix cars when the track is completely dry. If it rains, the tire must be swapped for one with more tread.

Radial tires*, like this one, have plies running at right angles to the side walls.

The top surface of a tire is marked with a pattern of grooves called the tread.

The tread clears water, mud, dirt and snow out from between the tire and the road.

This layer is called the undertread. It is made of tough rubber.

Tire rubber is a mixture of natural rubber which can stand a lot of heat and man-made rubber which is more hard wearing.

This part of the tire is made from thin steel wires all woven together. It makes the tire stronger.

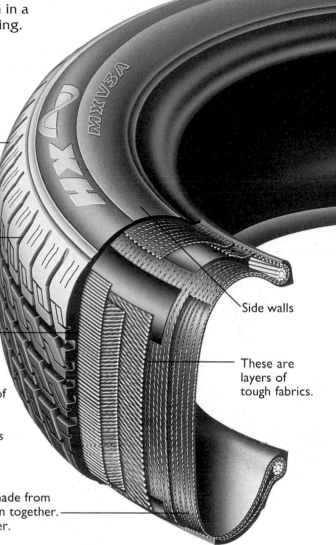

Side walls

These are layers of tough fabrics.

Grip in wet weather

If the grooves in the tread of a tire are too narrow or too shallow, they cannot do their job properly. Instead of spraying water out from under the tire so it can grip the road, a slippery film of water forms between the tire and the road. The car can lose its grip and go out of control. This is called hydroplaning. Modern tread is designed to avoid this.

This new Goodyear tire has a large channel down its middle to remove more water than an ordinary road tire.

Complicated tread pattern

This special photo shows water being directed out from under the tire.

The part of the tire you can see above is the footprint. That is the part which touches the ground at any one time.

Getting rid of tires

Millions of worn down tires go for scrap every year. Because each tire is made from a range of different materials, they are hard to recycle. Some tires are burned but many are buried underground where they can create pollution or help fuel dangerous underground fires.

There are other, less harmful ways to dispose of scrap tires. For example, some can be given a new layer of tread in a complicated process called retreading or recapping.

These parts of the car bumper are made from scrap tires.

Sports car

Sports cars are the quickest cars on the road. They can start off very fast and steer precisely and accurately. They are great fun to drive, but are often small inside and extremely expensive to buy. Some drivers race their sports cars on tracks. Famous sports car makers include Ferrari, Lotus, Chevrolet and Jaguar.

Porsche 911 Carrera 4

First built in 1963, the Porsche 911 is one of the best-known sports cars. It has raced at Le Mans and won the Monte Carlo rally. Over 250,000 have been built. This Carrera 4 model is one of the latest of many versions of the 911.

Here's the spare wheel.

The 911 has been changed many times. However, it still looks similar to this early model.

This fan cools the oil used in the engine.

Rounded design

Dr. Ferdinand Porsche designed one of the world's most popular cars many years before the Porsche company built the 911. The two cars have a rounded shape. Can you guess what the other car is? Turn to page 32 for the answer.

This car has its fuel tank at the front.

This drive shaft takes power from the engine to the car's wheels.

Four wheel drive

In most cars the engine feeds power either to the back or front pair of wheels. The wheels that do not receive power are pushed or pulled by the others. In a four wheel drive car, all four wheels receive power straight from the engine. This helps the car grip the road better and makes it easier for the driver to control it in bad weather.

The engine's power can be varied between the back and front wheels, depending on which can grip the road better. In normal driving, the back wheels get 70% and the front wheels, 30%.

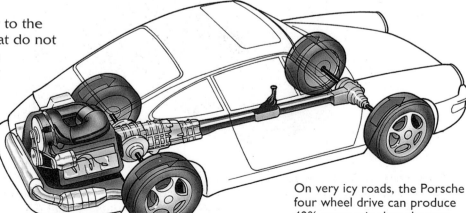

On very icy roads, the Porsche four wheel drive can produce 40% more grip than the two wheel drive version of the car.

Acceleration

Acceleration is how fast a car can increase its speed. Sports cars must have good acceleration. This is often measured as how quickly a car can go from standing still to 100km/h (62mph). The 911 Carrera 4 can do this in 5.7 seconds.

This Porsche 959 can accelerate from 0 to 100km/h (62mph) in just 3.9 seconds.

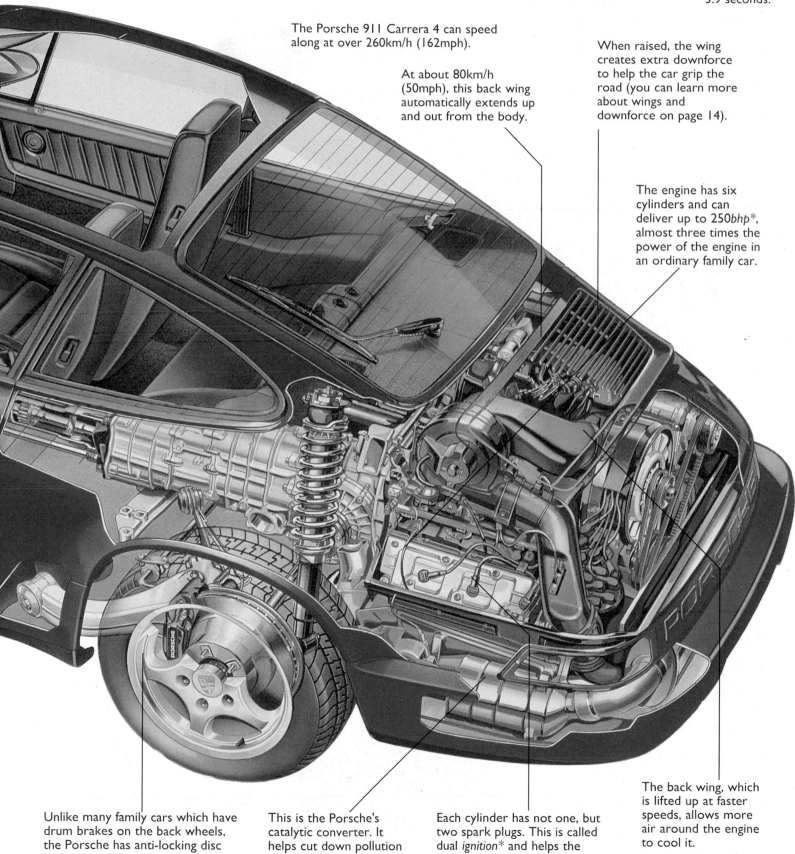

The Porsche 911 Carrera 4 can speed along at over 260km/h (162mph).

At about 80km/h (50mph), this back wing automatically extends up and out from the body.

When raised, the wing creates extra downforce to help the car grip the road (you can learn more about wings and downforce on page 14).

The engine has six cylinders and can deliver up to 250bhp*, almost three times the power of the engine in an ordinary family car.

Unlike many family cars which have drum brakes on the back wheels, the Porsche has anti-locking disc brakes on all four wheels.

This is the Porsche's catalytic converter. It helps cut down pollution from the engine.

Each cylinder has not one, but two spark plugs. This is called dual *ignition** and helps the engine run more smoothly.

The back wing, which is lifted up at faster speeds, allows more air around the engine to cool it.

25

Electrical system

A modern car would not work without its electrical system. Electricity is needed to start the car, to make the spark plugs burn the air and fuel mixture in the engine and to power the lights, windshield wipers and other electrical parts of the car.

Ignition key

Ignition switch

The battery stores electricity to power the electrical system when the engine is still.

Power from the car battery is stepped up, or increased, by this device called a coil.

This is the distributor. It helps time the engine (see right).

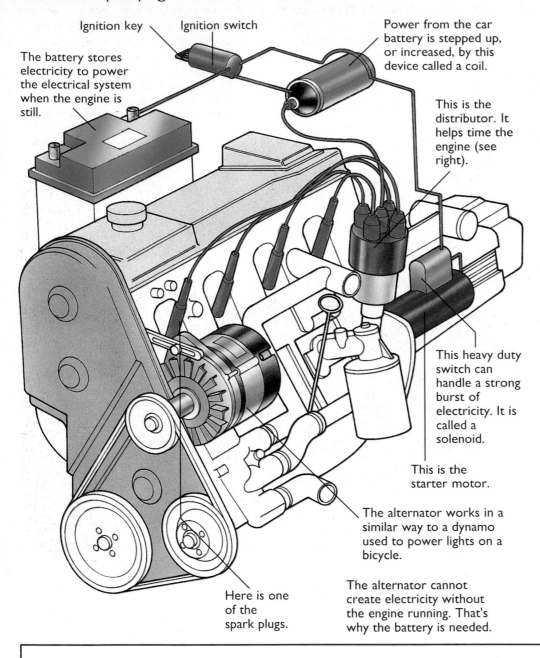

This heavy duty switch can handle a strong burst of electricity. It is called a solenoid.

This is the starter motor.

The alternator works in a similar way to a dynamo used to power lights on a bicycle.

Here is one of the spark plugs.

The alternator cannot create electricity without the engine running. That's why the battery is needed.

Starting the engine

Turning the ignition key releases electricity from the battery, which passes through the solenoid switch to the starter motor.

The starter motor turns the engine's flywheel making the pistons move up and down the cylinders. At the same time, more electricity is passed to the coil.

The coil increases the electricity's voltage. The electricity is then fed to the distributor which times the electricity reaching the spark plugs.

As the engine runs, it turns the alternator. The alternator uses this movement to create electricity, which it feeds to the battery and uses to run the electrical system.

The spark plugs start producing sparks which ignite the air and fuel mixture in the cylinder.

Lights

Lights are needed for driving in fog, bad weather conditions and at night. All modern cars have many different lights but they were considered luxury accessories until the 1930s. The first lights were powered by gas like old street lamps but today, all car lights are powered by electricity.

An indicator light tells other car drivers which way the car is turning.

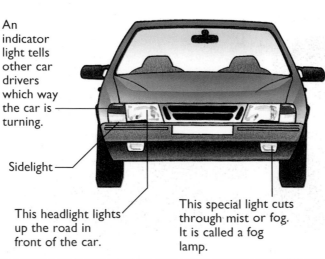

Sidelight

This headlight lights up the road in front of the car.

This special light cuts through mist or fog. It is called a fog lamp.

These brake lights tell drivers behind that the car is slowing down.

Some new cars have extra brake lights in the rear window.

Reversing light

Rear indicator lights

Timing the engine

The power from the coil has to reach the spark plugs at precisely the right time. If it doesn't, then the engine will run very poorly. Getting the timing right is the job of the distributor.

At the middle of the distributor is an arm which turns at a speed decided by how fast the engine is working. Each time the arm gets close to a metal point, it completes an electrical circuit which passes electricity on to the spark plug.

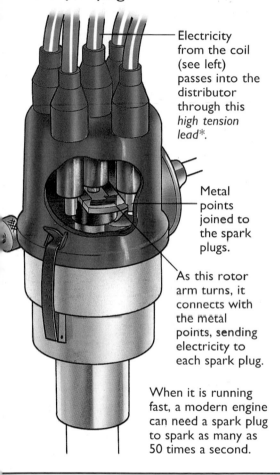

Electricity from the coil (see left) passes into the distributor through this *high tension lead**.

Metal points joined to the spark plugs.

As this rotor arm turns, it connects with the metal points, **sending electricity to each spark plug.**

When it is running fast, a modern engine can need a spark plug to spark as many as 50 times a second.

The car's instruments

The dashboard is the panel in front of the driver and it holds many of the instruments and controls used to drive a car. Some cars now have a screen which displays maps of where the car is heading. The screen is joined to a navigation computer which can offer suggested routes between two places. Nearly all cars have heaters and air fans to keep the driver and passengers at a comfortable temperature.

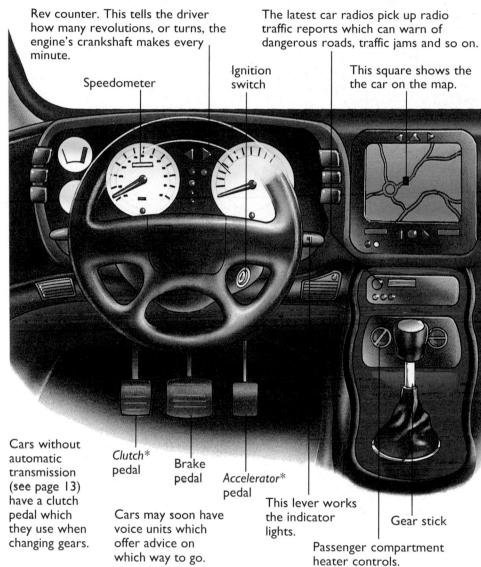

Rev counter. This tells the driver how many revolutions, or turns, the engine's crankshaft makes every minute.

The latest car radios pick up radio traffic reports which can warn of dangerous roads, traffic jams and so on.

Speedometer

Ignition switch

This square shows the the car on the map.

Cars without automatic transmission (see page 13) have a clutch pedal which they use when changing gears.

Clutch* pedal

Brake pedal

Accelerator* pedal

Cars may soon have voice units which offer advice on which way to go.

This lever works the indicator lights.

Gear stick

Passenger compartment heater controls.

Dimming headlights

Most countries have rules about the number, type and position of lights on a car. One of the most important rules is about dimming headlights. Full headlights are used when there are no other vehicles on the road. Bright headlights pointing straight ahead, however, can dazzle the driver of a car coming the other way. To prevent this, modern headlights are designed to dim their beam down onto the road at the flick of a switch.

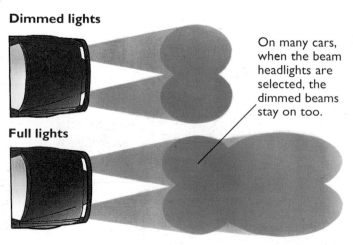

Dimmed lights

Full lights

On many cars, when the beam headlights are selected, the dimmed beams stay on too.

This sports car has odd pop up lights. Do you know why? (see page 32 for the answer).

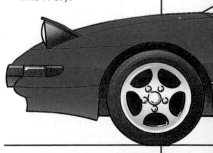

Off-road car

Cars are sometimes needed off roads to drive over rough ground. Off-road cars are as happy on the road as they are over grassland or on a bumpy dirt track.

Range Rover LSE

The Range Rover is a very popular off-road vehicle made by the Land Rover company. The LSE version shown here has a top speed of 180km/h (112mph) and weighs 2150kg (4740lb) when it is empty.

The engine can produce up to 200*bhp**. It has eight cylinders arranged in a V-shaped pattern called a V8.

The roof is specially strengthened just in case the car rolls over.

Most off-road vehicles, including the Range Rover, have four wheel drive. See page 24 to learn more about it.

This Range Rover has an automatic gearbox.

This steel loop can be used as a towbar if the car gets really stuck somewhere and needs to be pulled out.

This air suspension unit replaces the coiled spring in a normal suspension system (see right).

This is the shock absorber for the front left wheel.

This piece of bodywork is called the wheel arch.

The Range Rover in action

The police use the car for traffic control.

Off-road vehicles like the Range Rover are used for all sorts of jobs. Many police forces in Great Britain and abroad have Range Rovers. It is used as an ambulance and fire-fighting vehicle in some isolated areas. Farmers and forestry workers use the Range Rover for traveling through deep, muddy streams and over very rough ground.

Range Rovers can cross deep streams.

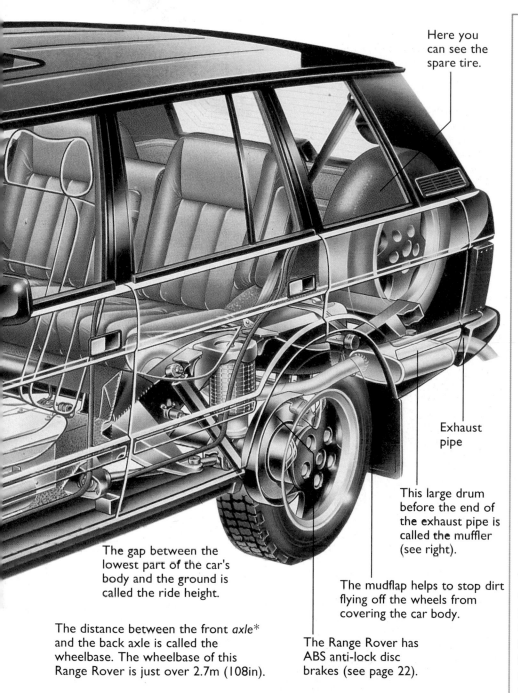

Here you can see the spare tire.

Exhaust pipe

This large drum before the end of the exhaust pipe is called the muffler (see right).

The mudflap helps to stop dirt flying off the wheels from covering the car body.

The Range Rover has ABS anti-lock disc brakes (see page 22).

The gap between the lowest part of the car's body and the ground is called the ride height.

The distance between the front *axle** and the back axle is called the wheelbase. The wheelbase of this Range Rover is just over 2.7m (108in).

Air suspension

The Range Rover's suspension system uses powerful shock absorbers and anti-roll bars, but it doesn't use normal springs (see page 20). Instead, *pneumatic** cylinders, full of pressurized air, are used to cushion the car body and absorb much of the energy from a bump or rut.

The suspension units on each wheel are independent. This means that each wheel can adjust its positioning as the car travels over uneven surfaces. Electronic sensors linked to a computer inside the car can adjust the gap between the car body and the wheels.

To clear obstructions, the body can rise up off the wheels.

For loading and unloading, the car body drops low over the wheels.

When going fast, the car lowers to improve its aerodynamics (see pages 16-17).

The exhaust system

The waste gases from the engine are piped out of the car by the exhaust system. As they leave the engine they are very hot and at a high pressure which would make a lot of noise if they went straight into the air. The exhaust system forces the gases on a long journey through pipes and a special device called a muffler. By the time the gases leave the exhaust system they are much cooler and quieter.

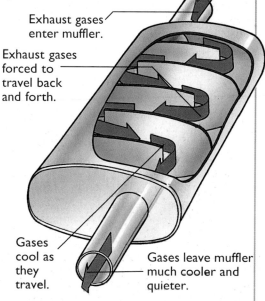

Exhaust gases enter muffler.

Exhaust gases forced to travel back and forth.

Gases cool as they travel.

Gases leave muffler much cooler and quieter.

Catalytic converter

The waste gases from the exhaust contain many substances which pollute the air. All cars now use unleaded gasoline as lead is a serious pollutant. All cars are now fitted with a catalytic converter. This changes some of the waste gases that pass through it into other, less harmful chemicals. For example, dangerous nitrogen oxides are converted into harmless nitrogen and water.

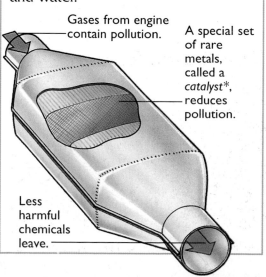

Gases from engine contain pollution.

A special set of rare metals, called a *catalyst**, reduces pollution.

Less harmful chemicals leave.

The future

Cars in the future will still need brakes, steering, suspension and all the other systems shown in this book. With the exception of a few top sports cars, future cars will not go much faster. But they are expected to be safer, easier to drive and less harmful to the environment. Here is a possible car of tomorrow with some of the futuristic features that it may include.

This car would be built using highly advanced robots and computers. These would cut down the amount of materials wasted in building a car.

Complex electronics mean that the engine uses less fuel and produces less pollution. If a car uses 10% less fuel, it will use about 1500 litres (330 gallons) less in its whole lifetime.

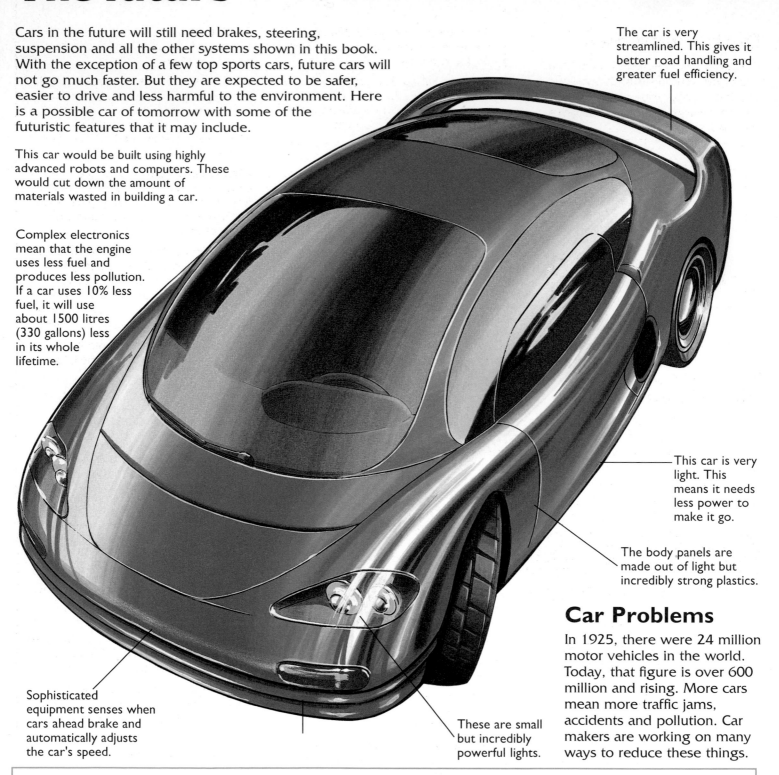

The car is very streamlined. This gives it better road handling and greater fuel efficiency.

This car is very light. This means it needs less power to make it go.

The body panels are made out of light but incredibly strong plastics.

Sophisticated equipment senses when cars ahead brake and automatically adjusts the car's speed.

These are small but incredibly powerful lights.

Car Problems

In 1925, there were 24 million motor vehicles in the world. Today, that figure is over 600 million and rising. More cars mean more traffic jams, accidents and pollution. Car makers are working on many ways to reduce these things.

Safety

Safety researchers will find new ways to protect passengers in a crash. In fact, experts expect to find many new ways to prevent accidents in the first place.
Sensors will be able to scan the road ahead much better than a driver's eyes, especially in the dark and fog. Information from the cameras will appear on instruments called Head Up Displays (HUDs). The driver can see these without bending his head to look. At the moment, HUDs are only found in modern fighter jets. You can find out about these on page 57.

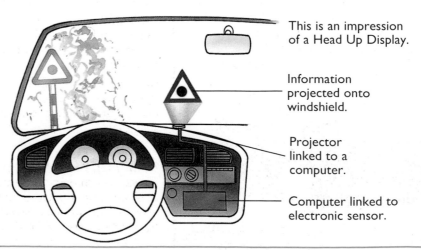

This is an impression of a Head Up Display.

Information projected onto windshield.

Projector linked to a computer.

Computer linked to electronic sensor.

Design your own

Virtual reality machines, which can show you exactly how it would look and feel inside your car, may allow you to design the interior to your own taste before the car is built.

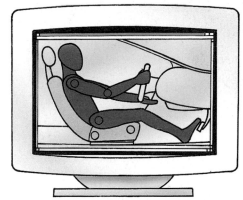

This dummy on the computer screen is testing the driver's seat. The dummy can be altered to the size of each car buyer.

Electric power

Electric cars, such as the one on page 11, are likely to become more common. Many will use a powerful battery which can be recharged, but some may be solar-powered like this three-wheeled car. It was built in Japan and called the Honda Dream.

Solar panels

It averaged a speed of 85km/h (53mph) when it won an Australian race for solar cars.

City driving

Special small cars for crowded towns and cities will become popular. Below is a city car being built by Ford. In the years ahead, similar-shaped cars may be powered by a small electric motor, have solar panels on their roof and be able to park themselves automatically without any help from the driver.

This is Ford's prototype of a city car, the Ka.

Glossary

Accelerator. The pedal that controls the speed of the engine and, so, the speed of the car.

Aerodynamics. The science of how gases, such as air, move over an object. Aerodynamics affects the way cars are designed and built.

Air pressure. The force with which air pushes against an object. Air pressure is increased by pushing air into a small space. This is called compressing.

Alternator. A device which generates electricity from the engine's movement.

Axle. The bar or rod on which the car's wheels turn.

Brake horsepower (bhp). One common measure of the power produced by an engine. It is used by many car manufacturers in their advertisements.

Cam. A small, usually oval, wheel which helps to convert turning movement into up and down movement.

Catalyst. A substance which changes how other chemicals react. A catalyst in a car's exhaust system is used to lower pollution.

Chassis. The framework of the car, usually made of steel. Most of the car's main parts, such as the engine and body panels, are attached to it.

Clutch. Operated by a pedal, it disconnects the gearbox from the engine long enough for the gear to be changed smoothly.

Crank. Something that helps to convert up and down movement into turning movement.

Cross ply tires. Tires with their plies running diagonally across in overlapping layers.

Distributor. A part of the engine which makes the spark plugs produce a spark at precisely the right time.

Differential. A set of gears that allow the car's wheels to turn at different speeds when the vehicle goes around a corner.

Fan belt. A belt which is powered by the engine and helps power the alternator and the engine cooling fan.

Firing order. The order in which the spark plugs produce sparks.

Fossil fuel. Fuels formed by dead plants and animals squashed together over millions of years in the same way that fossils are created. Coal and oil are examples of fossil fuels.

Friction. The resistance found when one surface moves and rubs against another surface.

Gears. Devices with grooves or teeth on their edges that mesh, or link, with each other. When they are powered they can turn each other around. Many gears are toothed wheels like those that drive a bicycle chain.

High tension lead. A thick lead which carries high voltage electricity to and from certain parts of the engine, such as between the distributor and the spark plugs.

Hydraulics. Using a liquid to transmit power from one place to another. A car's brake system uses hydraulics. Early hydraulic machines used water but most today use oil or other liquids that do not freeze as easily as water.

Ignition. Setting light to and burning the fuel and air mixture in the engine's cylinders.

Lubricant. A slippery liquid, such as oil, used to cover surfaces that rub together. The lubricant helps reduce friction. The process of using a liquid in this way is called lubrication.

Parking brake. A hand-operated lever usually connected to the back brakes. It holds a car still when parked.

Pneumatic. Using a compressed gas, usually air, to fill a container or transmit power.

Radial tires. Tires which have their layers or plies running across the tires at a right angle to the rim of the wheel.

Streamlining. To shape a car's body so that it can move through the air as smoothly as possible.

Tachometer. It shows the engine's speed in the form of how many times the crankshaft turns around every minute.

Torque. The turning force from an engine.

Tuning. Adjusting the car's engine so that it performs at its best.

Valve. A device that acts like a door, opening, closing and controlling the flow of a liquid or gas through a pipe or tube.

Volume. The measurement of how much space an object takes up.

Wheel spin. When the car's tires cannot grip the road properly. This often happens when the road is slippery or icy or when the tires are in very poor condition.

Cars: Facts

SOME MOTORING FIRSTS

1769 The earliest vehicle related to the motorcar was a **steam carriage** built by Nicholas Cugnot, a French officer. It was not very successful or efficient. The carriage had to be stopped every 15 minutes to build up the steam again (see page 2).

1803 The British engineer, Richard Trevithick, built the **first steam passenger vehicle** carrying eight passengers.

1859 An **internal combustion engine** that used natural gas as fuel was built by a Belgian, Jean-Joseph Lenoir.

1864 Siegfried Markus invented a motorized cart that used **gasoline vapor**. His electrical system solved the problem of **ignition** (see page 26).

1876 German engineer, Nikolaus Otto, designed an engine which used the **four stroke engine cycle** (see page 10).

1885 The first car to run successfully with a **gasoline engine** was built by German engineer, Karl Benz. This incorporated the internal combustion engine (see page 10).

1888 John Dunlop, from Ireland, made the **first *pneumatic** tire** (a hollow tire filled with air). This was the main British contribution to the development of the motor car, but these tires were first used in France.

1895 The **first motor car race** took place in France (see page 18). The course ran from Paris to Bordeaux and back.

1896 The **first four cylinder car engine** was built by René Panhard and Emile Levassor in France. This had the basic layout that has been used by many cars ever since.

1898 The **first fully enclosed car**, a Renault, was produced in France.

1902 The French government tried to make motorists use **alcohol fuel** manufactured from potatoes.

1903 **Registration plates** were introduced in Britain.

1904 The land speed record of **100mph** was officially reached for the first time.

1905 **Car bumpers** were patented.

1906 The **first car racing track** was built at Brooklands in England.

1912 A car with an **electric self-starter** was introduced by Cadillac.

In **1913** Ford built the **first motor car assembly line**. The first car to be made was the **Ford Model T**. Until 1908, all cars had been handmade and were very expensive. But mass production greatly reduced the cost and time involved in making cars, enabling many more people to buy a car for the first time.

1916 **Mechanical windshield wipers** were introduced.

1919 **Traffic lights** first appeared in the USA. Britain introduced them in **1928**.

1922 Ford became the **first firm to build over a million cars in one year**. This was matched by Volkswagen in **1962** and by British Leyland in **1968**.

1927 The Bugatti Royale, the **largest production car of all time**, was built in Italy. It was over 6.7m (22ft) long, with a 2m (7ft) bonnet, and a 4.3m (14ft 2 in) wheelbase. The 13-litre engine was so powerful that gears were not really needed.

1934 In France, Citroen introduced **front-wheel drive and unit construction** (with body and chassis in one unit). The **first drive-in movie theater** also opened in New Jersey, USA.

1935 The **first person to exceed 300mph** on land was Malcom Campbell in the *Bluebird*.

1936 The **first diesel-engined private car**, a Mercedes-Benz, was built.

1959 The **BMC Mini**, designed by Sir Alec Issigonis, first sold for about £496 ($744). A total of 5.26 million were produced, giving Britain the lead in the world's small car market.

1971 An electric moon buggy was the **first car to be driven in Space**. Astronauts drove it on the Moon and left it there when they returned.

1983 The **world speed record** was broken by Richard Noble in *Thrust 2*. He sped across the Nevada Desert at **633 miles an hour**.

1992 Martin Brundle achieved the **highest speed ever reached by a standard production car** at the Nardo test track in Italy. He drove at a speed of 349.21km/h (217.1mph) in a Jaguar XJ220.

AMAZING CARS

*An **orange bubble car** was built in the 1970s by a fruit company to use as a publicity stunt to advertise their oranges.

***Two cars in one**. One inventor joined two "half cars" together, to provide an engine and controls at both ends. If two drivers worked very carefully together they could drive the car sideways.

*A **swan car** was built in 1912 by the Brooke Car Company. The car was in the shape of a swan at the front and was made purely for fun.

*The **longest car** in the world is over 30m (100ft) long. It was designed by Jay Ohrberg from the USA. This limousine has 26 wheels, a swimming pool and a water bed.

***Waterproof cars** are called Amphicars. They were built in the 1960s to travel on land and water.

*Several inventors have experimented with **flying cars**. One flying car was made especially for the James Bond film, *The Man With the Golden Gun*.

*The **most expensive British standard car** is the XJ220 Jaguar quoted at £402, 418 ($6, 018, 627).

FASCINATING FIGURES

Top 5 car producers

Japan	9,753,000 cars per year
USA	5,440,000
Germany	4,700,000
France	3,188,000
Spain	1,750,000

Did You Know?

*In six years, an average car travels nearly 97,000km (60, 276 miles). Each wheel will have turned 54 million times.
*The number of vehicles built in the world in 1994 was 49, 967, 594, of which 36, 070, 238 were cars.

ANSWERS TO QUESTIONS

Page 24 Dr Ferdinand Porsche designed the famous Volkswagen Beetle before he designed the Porsche 911.

Page 27 The sports car's headlights pop up so that they are high enough off the ground to give a good beam and be clearly seen by other cars. When the lights are not being used, they pop down into the body making the car more *streamlined**.

CUTAWAY
PLANES

Clive Gifford

Designed by Steve Page

Illustrated by: Mark Franklin, Sean Wilkinson, Ian Cleaver,
Robert Walster, and artists from the School of Illustration,
Bournemouth and Poole College of Art and Design.

Usborne Publishing wish to thank the following for their help with this part of the book:

Airbus Industrie · Aircraft Research Association · Air International · Trevor Alner · British Aerospace Flying College Ltd. · Les Coombs · CSE Aviation · David Ditcher · Evans and Sutherland Computer Corporation · Flight Refuelling Ltd. · Helmet Integrated Systems · Hughes Corporation · Irvin GB Ltd. · Stephen Lake · Anthony Lawrence · Lord Corporation · Magellan Systems · Martin Baker Aircraft Company Ltd. · Martin Cross · Lockheed Martin Corporation · Michael Leek · Michelin · National Aerospace Laboratory (NLR) · Quadrant Picture Library · Stuart Priest · Richard Goode Aerobatic Displays · RFD Ltd. · Rolls-Royce Commercial Aero Engines Limited · Chris Sargent · SAS Flight Academy · Sextant Avionique · SFIM Industries · Clive Thomas · Thomson Training & Simulation · Steve Upson · Westland Aerospace

Contents

Introduction.........................34

Controlling a plane.........................36

Cockpits.........................38

Airliners.........................40

Engines.........................42

Aircraft construction.........................44

Aerodynamics and fuel.. 46

Learning to fly.........................48

Take-off and landing........ 50

VSTOL planes.........................52

Safety......................... 54

Modern military planes 56

Navigation............................. 58

Stealth planes.........................60

The future............................. 62

Glossary.........................63

Planes: Facts......................... 64

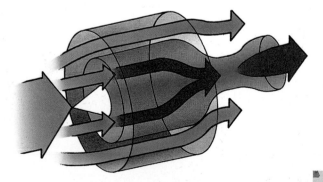

Words in *italic* type

Words in this section which appear in *italic* type and are followed by a small star (for example, *friction**) can be found in the glossary on page 63.

Introduction

The first successful flights people ever made were with the help of balloons filled with gases to make them lighter than air. It was not until 1903 that two Americans, the Wright Brothers, found a way to fly a craft that was heavier than air. In the time since the Wright Brothers' first flight, many advances and inventions have made modern planes look very different from early ones.

BAe Hawk 200

This is a single-seat jet fighter designed by computer with many of the latest advances in aircraft design. Its top speed is almost 1,045km/h (650mph) and when it is empty it weighs only a little more than four family cars.

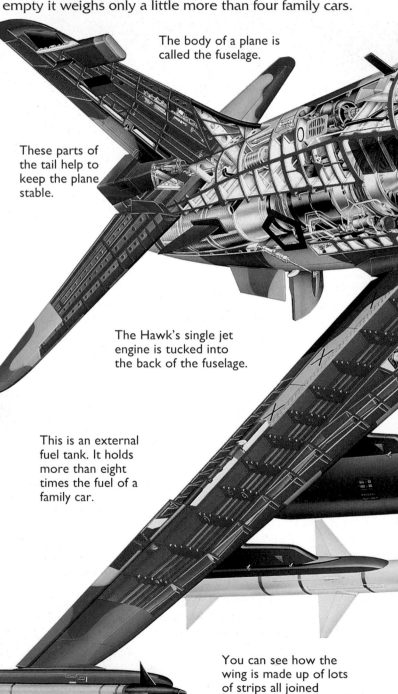

The body of a plane is called the fuselage.

These parts of the tail help to keep the plane stable.

The Hawk's single jet engine is tucked into the back of the fuselage.

This is an external fuel tank. It holds more than eight times the fuel of a family car.

You can see how the wing is made up of lots of strips all joined together. This makes the wing strong but much lighter than if it were made out of solid metal.

The Hawk 200's wingtips each hold a weapon called a Sidewinder missile.

The back edge of a wing is called the trailing edge.

The place where the pilot sits and flies the plane is called the cockpit.

A plane's wings are measured from one wingtip to the other. This is called the wingspan. The Hawk 200's wingspan is 9.9m (33ft).

The front edge of a wing is called the leading edge.

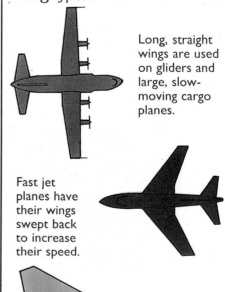

This is a two seater version of the Hawk, used by British display team, the Red Arrows.

The nose of the Hawk contains advanced radar equipment.

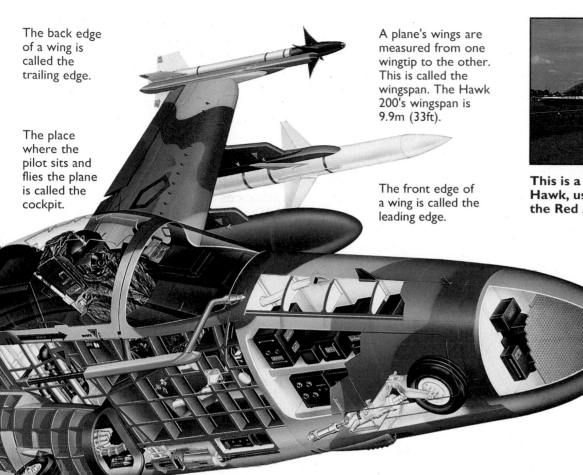

This nosewheel and the wheels at the back are together called the landing gear.

This is an air intake. It channels air into the plane's jet engine. You can learn how a jet engine works on pages 42-43.

These boxes contain complicated electronics which help fly the aircraft. They are called avionics.

Wings

Wings are vital to planes. They provide the lift which takes the aircraft off the ground and into the air. They do this because of their specially curved shape.

As the engines pull the plane through the air, the leading edge of the wing divides the air, forcing some under it and some over. Both the top and bottom surfaces of the wing are curved but the top curves more steeply. The air moving over the wing, therefore has farther to go to catch up with the air moving underneath.

Slower-moving air presses more on the bottom of the wing than the faster moving air passing over the top of it. This stronger *air pressure** under the wing lifts it up. You can learn about car wings on page 8 and boat wings on page 85.

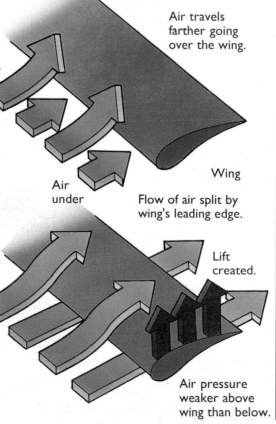

Air travels farther going over the wing.

Air under

Wing

Flow of air split by wing's leading edge.

Lift created.

Air pressure weaker above wing than below.

Wing types

There are many different wing shapes and sizes. Each type is best for a particular kind of plane. Here are three common wing types.

Long, straight wings are used on gliders and large, slow-moving cargo planes.

Fast jet planes have their wings swept back to increase their speed.

Triangular wings, called delta wings, help some military jets, travel even faster.

Controlling a plane

On the previous pages you saw how wings create lift. Lift is one of the *four forces of flight**. The others are thrust, drag and gravity. You can think of these four forces in pairs. For a plane to fly, lift must be greater than gravity, and thrust must be greater than drag.

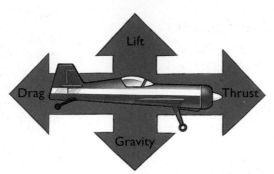

An aircraft uses its engines to create thrust and its wings to create lift. Modern planes are carefully designed to have less drag (see pages 46-47).

Control surfaces

Once in the air, a plane must be controlled otherwise it will crash. The plane must be kept balanced but also be able to change direction.

Changing direction is done by moving hinged parts of the wing, called ailerons, and hinged parts of the tail called the elevators and rudder. Together, these are known as control surfaces. Control surfaces change the direction of some of the air flowing around the plane. The change in the airflow changes the way the plane moves.

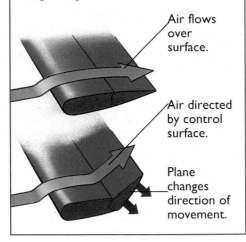

Air flows over surface.

Air directed by control surface.

Plane changes direction of movement.

This cutaway picture of a Slingsby Firefly shows the control surfaces and how they are linked to the controls in the cockpit.

The large hinged flap on both wings is called an aileron. It controls the rolling movement of the plane (see below left).

Small planes not used by the military are called light aircraft.

Rudder control cables

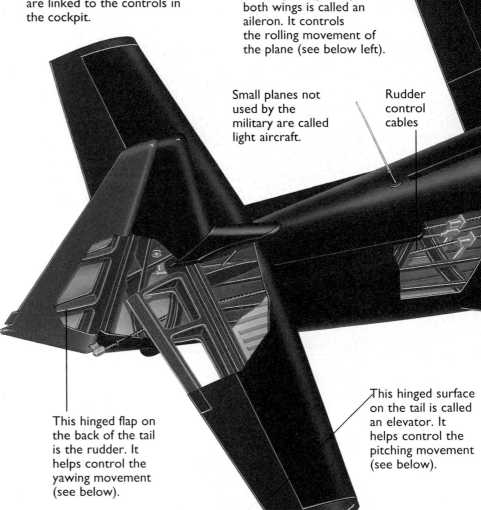

This hinged flap on the back of the tail is the rudder. It helps control the yawing movement (see below).

This hinged surface on the tail is called an elevator. It helps control the pitching movement (see below).

Roll

Roll is when you move the wings up and down using the ailerons. For example, turning the left aileron down will push the left wing up, pushing the right wing down.

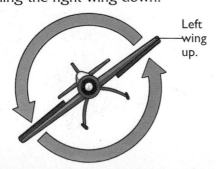

Left wing up.

Pitch

Pitch is when you move the fuselage up and down using the elevators. For example, turning the elevators down, lifts the tail up, causing the plane to dive down.

Nose points down.

Yaw

Yaw is when the plane moves from side to side. It is controlled by using the rudder. For example, turning the rudder left, will turn the plane's nose to the left.

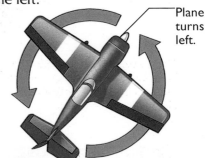

Plane turns left.

The Slingsby Firefly is made of modern materials. The rudder, for example, is made of plastic reinforced, or strengthened, with fine strands of glass.

This control column works two sets of control surfaces. Pushing it to the right and left moves the ailerons. Pushing it back and forth moves the elevators.

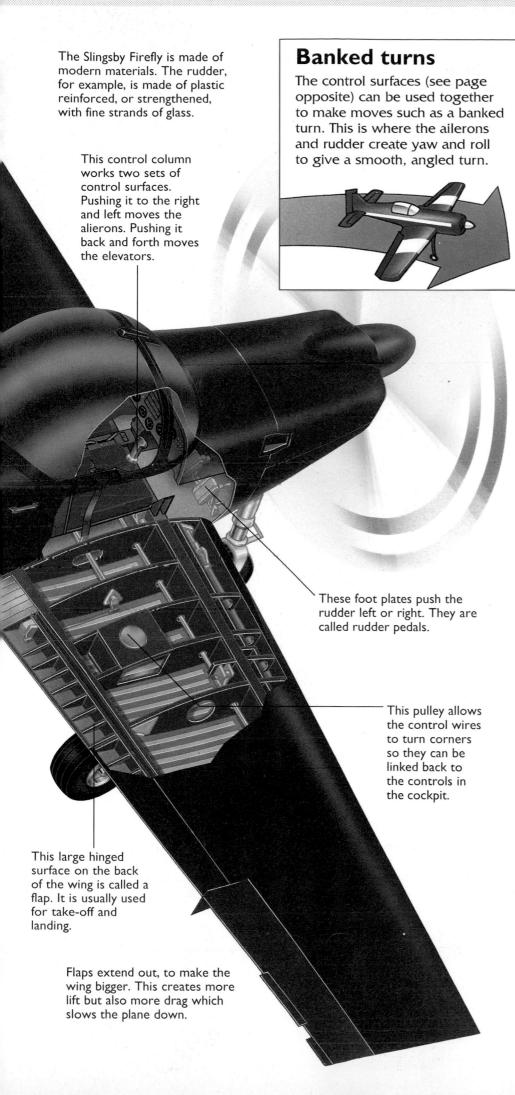

These foot plates push the rudder left or right. They are called rudder pedals.

This pulley allows the control wires to turn corners so they can be linked back to the controls in the cockpit.

This large hinged surface on the back of the wing is called a flap. It is usually used for take-off and landing.

Flaps extend out, to make the wing bigger. This creates more lift but also more drag which slows the plane down.

Banked turns

The control surfaces (see page opposite) can be used together to make moves such as a banked turn. This is where the ailerons and rudder create yaw and roll to give a smooth, angled turn.

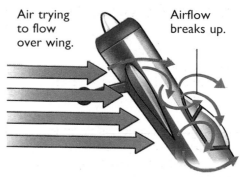

Stalling

When a plane climbs, it is angled up and the air flows less smoothly over the wings. If an aircraft tries to climb too steeply without enough power, there is not enough speed for the air to flow over the wings and create lift. The flow of air breaks up and the aircraft begins to fall out of the sky. This is called *stalling**.

Air trying to flow over wing.

Airflow breaks up.

Pilots are taught how not to stall and how to recover if they do, but it can still be dangerous if the plane is near the ground. Modern planes have a complex set of sensors to help prevent stalling which is called a stall warning system.

Other surfaces

In addition to elevators, ailerons and a rudder, most modern planes have other control surfaces such as spoilers and slats. Slats do a similar job to flaps (see labels just to the left). They extend forward from the front, or leading edge, of the wing. Spoilers are large panels built into the wing which can lift up and 'spoil' the flow of air over the wing. They create less lift and more drag. They are used either to increase the effect of the ailerons or as air brakes (see page 51) to slow the aircraft down.

This airliner wing has its control surfaces arranged for just before landing.

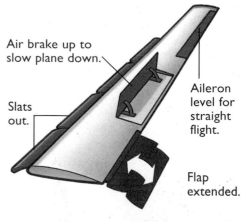

Air brake up to slow plane down.

Slats out.

Aileron level for straight flight.

Flap extended.

Cockpits

The cockpit is where the pilot sits and controls the aircraft. Instruments show how various parts of the plane are performing while navigation systems such as radar (see page 58) and the artificial horizon help keep it on the correct route.

The Optica's cockpit gives a clear view all the way around. It is ideal for aerial observation and photography.

Early cockpits

Early cockpits were often very uncomfortable. Many were open-air and left the pilot and any passengers unprotected from the weather.

A modern aircraft cockpit is full of controls and instruments, but the cockpits of the first planes were empty in comparison. You can see how simple an early aircraft's cockpit is by looking at the one in a 1933 De Havilland Leopard Moth (see right).

The Leopard Moth did have an enclosed cockpit.

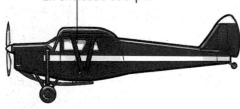

There were 133 De Havilland Leopard Moths built in the 1930s.

From cockpit to wing

In gliders and light aircraft, the cockpit controls are linked directly to the *control surfaces** by a system of cables and pulleys.

In bigger aircraft, they have *hydraulic** systems instead of mechanical cables. Hydraulic power is created by putting a liquid under great pressure, as the diagram on the right shows. A liquid which doesn't freeze, even in very cold weather, is used to fill the cylinders and pipes of a hydraulic system.

Artificial Horizon

The artificial horizon tells the pilot if the plane is flying level. A gyroscope (see page 58) keeps a line on the dial exactly parallel with the horizon of the Earth. This line is the artificial horizon. When the aircraft tips one way or the other, the markings that show the plane's wings dip to either side of the horizon line.

For example, when the aircraft does a banked turn (see page 37) the horizon line appears to tilt. In fact, it remains parallel with the horizon of the Earth and the rest of the plane (including the wings on the dial) tilt around it.

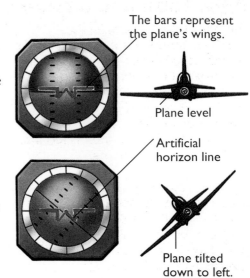

The bars represent the plane's wings.

Plane level

Artificial horizon line

Plane tilted down to left.

Thermometer

Altimeter (see right).

This is the plane's airspeed indicator (see right).

Control column

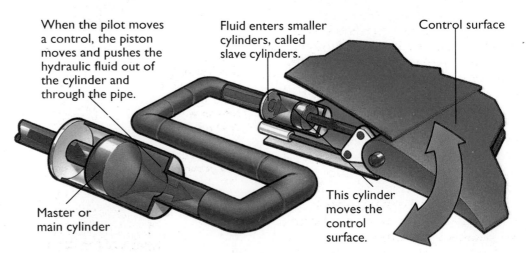

When the pilot moves a control, the piston moves and pushes the hydraulic fluid out of the cylinder and through the pipe.

Fluid enters smaller cylinders, called slave cylinders.

Control surface

Master or main cylinder

This cylinder moves the control surface.

Pitot tube and airspeed indicator

The pitot tube is a small tube mounted on the wing or body of the aircraft. It measures two types of *air pressure**: the pressure of the air around it, called static air pressure, and the pressure of the air rushing at it as the plane flies, called ram pressure. This information is fed into the aircraft's instruments.

A plane's speed through the air is shown by the airspeed indicator, or ASI. The relationship between the two air pressure readings from the pitot tube is changed by the ASI into the airspeed of the aircraft.

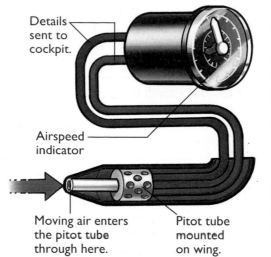

Details sent to cockpit.

Airspeed indicator

Moving air enters the pitot tube through here.

Pitot tube mounted on wing.

Altimeter

The altimeter tells the pilot the altitude, or height above ground, of the plane. Some altimeters use radar (see page 58) but others use the static pressure reading from the pitot tube. *Air pressure** gets less the higher you fly, so the altimeter can calculate the plane's height from the surrounding air pressure.

This sealed capsule of air helps the altimeter make its reading.

The throttles control the speed of the engines.

Fly by wire joystick (see below).

Pilot's seat

Co-pilot's seat

Modern cockpits

As aircraft became more advanced, the numbers of controls and instruments increased and cockpits became much more complicated.

Advanced airliners such as the Boeing 777 and Airbus A340 have their cockpits, called flight decks, specially designed to be simpler and better laid out than before. The cockpit of the A340 (shown on the left) has computer screens which display different types of information, instead of rows of individual instruments.

Here is a test model of the A340 airliner on the ground at the Farnborough Airshow in England.

Fly-by-wire

In the very latest aircraft, some hydraulic systems are replaced with an advanced system called fly-by-wire. With fly-by-wire, electric wires run from a computer to a mixture of electric motors and small hydraulic systems called *actuators** in the wings and tail. When the pilot moves the controls, signals from the computer instruct the motors and hydraulics to move the control surfaces. Fly-by-wire is very precise, much lighter and easier to repair than hydraulics and works well with the plane's flight computers.

Many cockpits which have fly-by-wire replace the control column with this type of small joystick placed to one side of the pilot.

The General Dynamics F16 Fighting Falcon was one of the first military jets to feature fly-by-wire controls.

39

Airliners

Airliners are planes that carry large numbers of passengers. The earliest airliners carried just a few people and were cold and noisy. These planes could only travel long distances by making small hops from place to place.

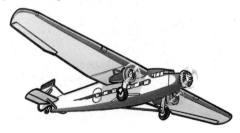

This Ford Tri-motor had a maximum range of just over 800km (500 miles). Some of today's airliners can fly 20 times as far without having to refuel.

Airbus A340-300 and -200

The A340 is the latest in a line of airliners built by several European companies working together under the name Airbus Industrie. There are two versions of the A340. The -300 (shown below) has a long *range** but the -200 can travel even farther. The -200's fuselage is 4m (13ft) shorter and the plane has fewer seats but more fuel. In 1993, an Airbus A340-200 flew around the world stopping only once, in New Zealand, to refuel. The whole journey took just over 48 hours.

Here's an Airbus A340-300 test aircraft in flight.

Airliner fuselages must be incredibly strong to withstand the pressure of high altitude flight and protect the passengers and crew inside.

This is one of the A340's eight passenger exits.

Here is the inner shell of the airliner's fuselage.

Pressurization

As a plane flies higher and higher, the air around it gets thinner. At the altitudes a modern jet airliner flies, there is not enough air for the passengers to breathe. What they do is to keep the airliner's airtight fuselage filled with *pressurized** air that the passengers and crew can breathe normally.

The top floor or deck holds the passengers. It is called the cabin.

Here you can see the complicated structure of the wing.

On the ground the pressure of the air inside the plane is the same as the air outside it.

These air brakes are positioned up to slow the airliner down. You can learn more about air brakes on page 51.

| At great heights, the air has less pressure and is much thinner. | In flight, the air inside the plane is kept to a similar pressure to the air on the ground. |

Wing rib

Because of concerns about the environment, new airliners' engines have to be cleaner and quieter than before.

Fan blades

40

Passenger configurations

The number of seats, what type they are and the way they are arranged inside an airliner is called the passenger configuration. Cheaper seats are squeezed together so airliners can carry more people, but business or luxury seats have more room. A plane's passenger configuration can be changed easily.

Here you can see the numbers of seats across the plane's body in different classes.

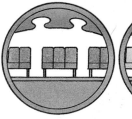

Six seats across in first or luxury class.

Seven seats across in business class.

Eight seats across in economy class.

This wingtip angled up is called a winglet. It helps make the A340 more stable.

These are the business class seats.

Luxury or first class seats.

The lower floor is the luggage or cargo hold.

You can see the A340's flight deck on page 39.

All the other staff in the plane, apart from the pilot, are called aircrew.

Sitting comfortably

Airlines are always trying to make their passengers more comfortable. New ideas include seats that convert into beds so that the passenger can sleep and individual video screens in front of each passenger.

Computer

A business class seat of the future may have its own computer and fax machine.

Loading and unloading

All airliners carry some cargo, from the passenger's suitcases to mail and packages. When they land, many airliners have to unload the passengers, crew and cargo and also be checked, filled with fuel and then loaded again for another journey. This is called turning around an aircraft and it involves many people working together.

Inside the airport, Load Controllers decide the airliner's load, how it is placed around the plane and how much fuel the plane will need.

Cleaners clean the inside of the plane.

Cargo trucks carry baggage to and from the aircraft.

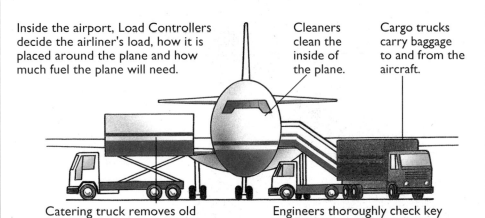

Catering truck removes old meals and loads new ones.

Engineers thoroughly check key parts of the aircraft for problems.

Cargo planes

Some airliners have been rebuilt to carry just cargo. The latest large cargo carrier is a new version of the Airbus A300 airliner, called the A300-600ST. It can carry enormous pieces of machinery or rocket and plane parts up to a weight of 45 metric tonnes (50 tons).

The A300-600ST's fuselage is over 7.2m (24ft) across.

Engines

All aircraft need one or more engines to push them forward. Many use piston engines to drive propellers. Fast military planes and airliners use jet, or gas turbine engines.

Piston engines

The first piston engines were built for cars in the 1880s. Aircraft piston engines work in a similar way to those in cars (see pages 10-11). Instead of driving wheels around though, they spin a propeller at very high speeds. This propeller pulls the aircraft through the air. An aircraft engine is powered by a mixture of fuel and air injected into the engine's cylinders, where it is *ignited** and burned.

This diagram shows how the pistons move inside the cylinders of a piston engine.

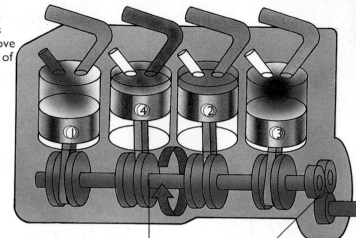

1. Air and fuel are injected into the cylinder.

2. The piston moves up the cylinder, squeezing air and fuel together.

3. The mixture is burned to create gases which push the piston down the cylinder.

4. The piston moves up the cylinder and pushes out waste gases.

Crank converts up and down movement of piston into a turning movement.

Crank passes turning power via the gears to the propeller shaft.

Gas turbine engines

A gas turbine engine burns fuel and air, a little like a piston engine. Instead of moving a piston up and down, though, it drives a series of fan blades, called a turbine, around at high speeds. Gas turbine engines were first used to power aircraft in World War Two. There are many different types of gas turbine engine. The most common is the turbofan engine. These are found on modern jet airliners, military cargo transporters and many other types of jet aircraft.

Rolls Royce RB211-535

This is a powerful turbofan engine built by the British company, Rolls Royce. The power of an engine is measured in pounds or kN. The RB211-535 produces 192kN (43,100lb) of thrust, more power than is produced by 50 family cars. It is found on modern airliners such as the Russian Tupolev Tu204.

This Boeing 757 is powered by two RB211-535 engines.

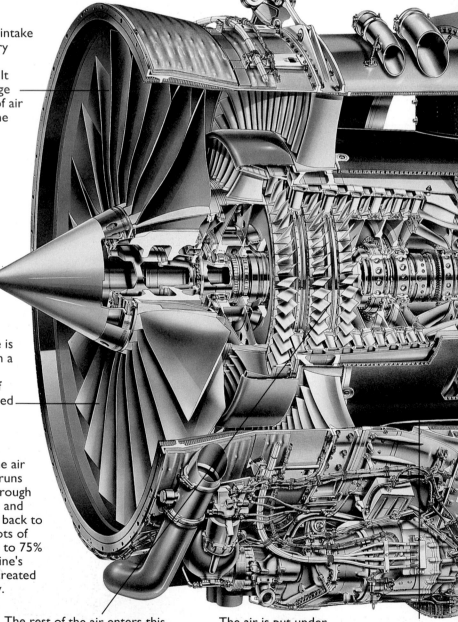

This large intake fan is a very efficient propeller. It pushes huge amounts of air through the engine.

The fan is just over 2m (74in) across.

Each blade is made from a complex mixture of metals called an alloy.

Most of the air sucked in runs straight through the engine and out of the back to produce lots of thrust. Up to 75% of the engine's power is created in this way.

The rest of the air enters this compression chamber where it is squeezed together by small sets of fans called compressor blades.

The air is put under enormous pressure, over 30 times as much as normal.

This is the engine's bypass duct.

Propellers

Propellers are made up of between two and five blades. These are shaped to cut through the air and push it back. Pushing the air back, pulls the aircraft forward. The angle of each blade is called the pitch.

Many propellers have variable pitch. This means that they can change the angle of their blades for different flying jobs. For example, a steep climb needs more pulling power while level cruising needs less.

Propeller blades

Propeller spins around very fast.

Propeller nosecone

Propellers 'screw' forward through the air, like a screw going into wood.

Propellers can have different numbers of blades. This 12-bladed propeller is on a Russian Antonov An76 research aircraft.

Turbojets and props

Turbojets are the simplest type of gas turbine engine. Thrust only comes from the hot gases being pushed out of the back of the engine. Turbojets produce very high speeds but tend to be noisy and use a lot of fuel. They are found on some fast modern jet aircraft.

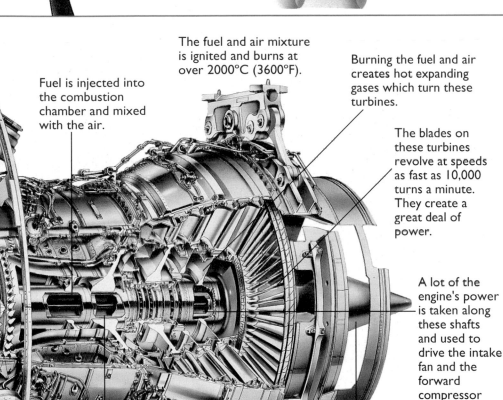

The fuel and air mixture is ignited and burns at over 2000°C (3600°F).

Burning the fuel and air creates hot expanding gases which turn these turbines.

Fuel is injected into the combustion chamber and mixed with the air.

The blades on these turbines revolve at speeds as fast as 10,000 turns a minute. They create a great deal of power.

A lot of the engine's power is taken along these shafts and used to drive the intake fan and the forward compressor blades.

The remaining power is pushed out of the back of the engine to create more thrust.

The compressed air enters this combustion chamber.

Concorde is powered by four Olympus 593 turbojet engines.

Turboprop engines have an extra turbine which uses much of the thrust created by the engine to drive a propeller. Turboprops burn less fuel and are much quieter than other turbine engines but cannot fly faster than about 800km/h (500mph).

Splitting the air

Air sucked in at the front of a turbofan engine is split. Some enters the core of the engine where it helps burn fuel to produce thrust. However, as much as ten times that amount of air bypasses the middle and flows through the engine's bypass duct. This air creates much more thrust and also helps cool the engine core.

Air drawn in by giant intake fan.

Most air flows through the bypass duct.

Some air speeds through engine core.

This Fokker F27 has two turboprops.

Aircraft construction

The very first planes were built from materials that were easily available and were quite light. Certain types of light wood were used as a skeleton which was then covered with cloth stretched tight.

Although these planes were light enough to be lifted into the air by the weak engines they had at the time, they were not very strong.

LVG CVI

This German LVG CVI two-seat bomber was built near the end of World War One. By that time, advances in aircraft design had helped to make planes less flimsy. For its time, the LVG CVI was a strong plane, but heavy and quite slow.

The engine produced almost as much power as three modern family car engines. Yet, because of its weight and shape, it's top speed was only 170km/h (105mph).

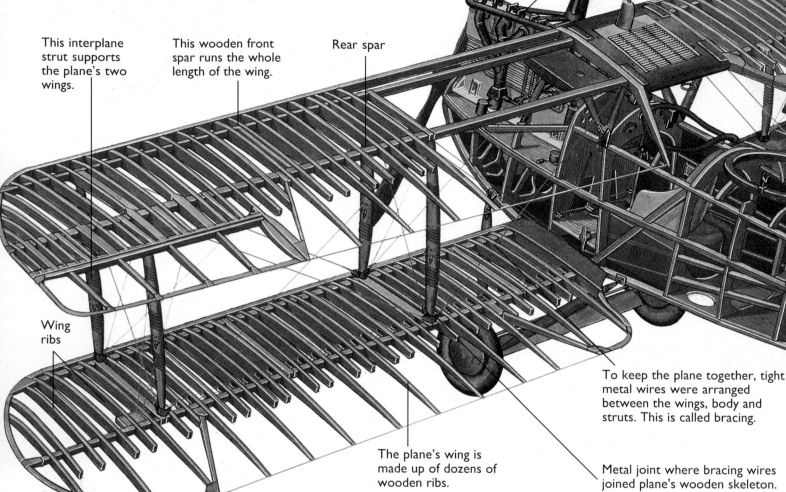

This interplane strut supports the plane's two wings.

This wooden front spar runs the whole length of the wing.

Rear spar

Wing ribs

To keep the plane together, tight metal wires were arranged between the wings, body and struts. This is called bracing.

The plane's wing is made up of dozens of wooden ribs.

Metal joint where bracing wires joined plane's wooden skeleton.

Advances in aircraft structure

After World War One, planes began to be built using more metal. Many plane makers used metal or thin sheets of wood instead of the outer covering of fabric. They also used tough metal steel tubing instead of wood for the inner skeleton.

The design of planes changed greatly as *duralumin**, a metal *alloy**, began to be made in sheets. Duralumin was used to make a stressed metal skin which was strong but lighter than large parts of the inner skeleton which it replaced.

Other metal alloys have since been invented which are stronger or lighter than duralumin, or are more heat resistant. Some of these contain a metal called titanium which is very strong and has an extremely high melting point.

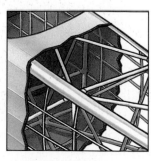

Here you can see part of the steel tube framework of an American, Curtiss Hawk plane.

This German BF109G has a stressed skin shell called a monocoque.

Many parts of this Sukhoi Su26 are made from advanced metal alloys.

This bright design, printed onto the cloth that covers the wing, is called a lozenge pattern.

The LVG CVI carried a pilot and a rear gunner who also aimed the plane's small bomb load.

Modern aircraft building

Like modern cars, planes are made from thousands of parts which are all made and tested separately, before being put together into bigger sections. The framework of the plane is built and then the moving parts and electronics are added.

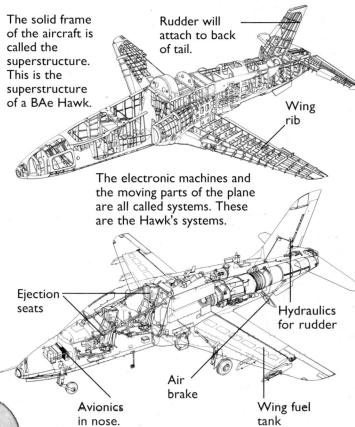

The plane's body and wings were covered with a light cloth. This was then varnished to make the cloth fit tightly over the wooden frame.

The solid frame of the aircraft is called the superstructure. This is the superstructure of a BAe Hawk.

Rudder will attach to back of tail.

Wing rib

The structure of the tailfin is quite simple.

The electronic machines and the moving parts of the plane are all called systems. These are the Hawk's systems.

These long struts run the length of the fuselage and are called longerons.

These fuselage body frames use a lot of wood.

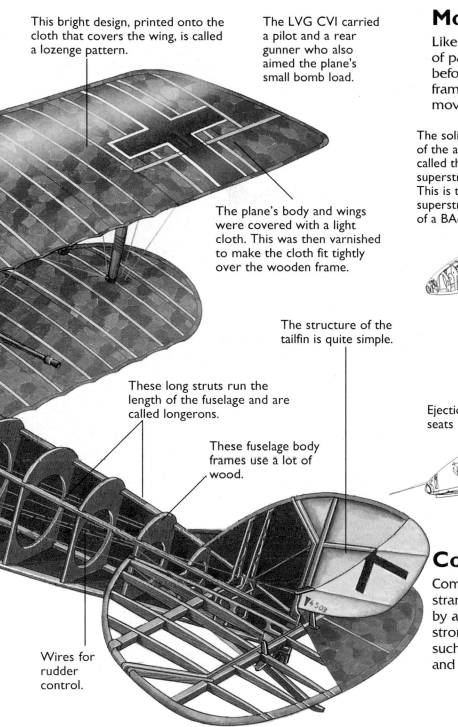

Ejection seats

Hydraulics for rudder

Air brake

Wires for rudder control.

Avionics in nose.

Wing fuel tank

Composites

Composites are materials made of millions of thin strands of man-made materials all bonded together by an incredibly strong adhesive. They are very strong and light. Advanced composites, such as Kevlar, are being used more and more in aircraft building.

This flap from a Slingsby Firefly has a covering of Kevlar sheet.

Computer Aided Design

This computer is helping design a Rolls Royce engine.

Computer Aided Design (C.A.D.) uses powerful computers that allow engineers to experiment with and accurately design aircraft parts on-screen. Once the design is decided upon, other computers simulate extreme conditions such as cold, heat, wear and stress, to test these parts thoroughly. C.A.D. is also used to design cars (see page 4).

This is a simulation of computer tests made on a military jet's structure.

Aerodynamics and fuel

Aerodynamics is the study of how a moving object travels through a liquid or a gas, such as air. It is vital to know how planes fly for lots of reasons. When a plane moves forward, the air flows over the wings which creates lift. When the air flows over the *control surfaces**, it allows the plane to change direction. When air flows over the whole plane, it creates drag. Drag slows a plane down and makes it use more fuel. Changing the shape and surface of a plane to reduce drag is called *streamlining**.

Box shape

Air flow

Air hits flat front of plane and cannot pass by easily. This creates lots of drag.

Air flows smoothly around a modern jet.

Concorde's delta wing shape was carefully designed to create the maximum amount of lift with as little drag as possible.

As many as 128 passenger seats can be squeezed close together.

Concorde

Concorde is the fastest airliner in the world with a top speed of 2300km/h (1430mph), more than twice the speed of other modern airliners. Concorde is so fast mainly because of its incredibly powerful engines and its advanced aerodynamic shape which is very streamlined.

This is the galley where food is prepared.

The pointed nose helps cut through the air.

The flight deck seats three people.

Twin nosewheels

The nose stays straight when flying but drops down to let the pilot see better for take-off and landing.

The fuselage is long and thin with a smooth, rounded shape. This makes it more streamlined.

Here you can see the complicated structure of the wing which is needed to make it strong while keeping it light.

Concorde has been carefully streamlined so that few parts stick out from its smooth shape.

Concorde's cruising speed means it flies 10km (6 miles) every 15 seconds.

Advances in streamlining

Early aircraft with lots of struts and wires made no real attempts at streamlining, but as planes got faster and exceeded 200km/h (125mph) streamlining became more important. Gradually, the number of struts and wires holding a plane together was reduced and the ones that were left were shaped to help the air flow more smoothly around them. Engines which had been left out in the open were later put inside smoothly-shaped engine covers which are called cowlings.

Engine cowling

Air flows smoothly past.

Monoplanes with one set of wings, which needed almost no struts or bracing, started to replace *biplanes** during the twenties and thirties. Fixed landing gears were replaced with retractable ones (see page 50). These could be lowered for take-off and landing and raised to create much less drag when flying.

The Supermarine Spitfire was among the first military planes to have a retractable landing gear.

With the arrival of jet engines, aircraft could travel much faster and this called for more changes in the shape of aircraft. Their surfaces were made as smooth as possible. The front of planes became sharper to cut through the air, and wings were swept back to make the aircraft even more streamlined.

The Hawker Hunter's swept back wings helped it reach a top speed of over 1100km/h (690mph).

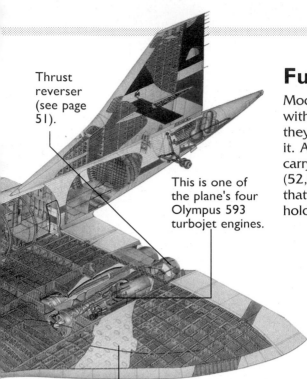

Thrust reverser (see page 51).

This is one of the plane's four Olympus 593 turbojet engines.

Concorde flies high where the air may be colder than -60°C (-76°F). These de-icing panels stop ice from forming on the wings which can reduce lift.

Fuel

Modern aircraft, especially those with jet engines, use fuel so quickly they have to carry huge amounts of it. A Boeing 747, for example, can carry as much as 197,000 litres (52,000 gallons) of fuel. Compare that to a typical family car which holds only 70 litres (15 gallons).

A plane must stay balanced as it flies. As fuel is used up, the balance of a plane changes. Many modern aircraft have *fuel management systems**. These measure how much fuel is in each tank and can switch which tank supplies fuel at any time, to even up their weight.

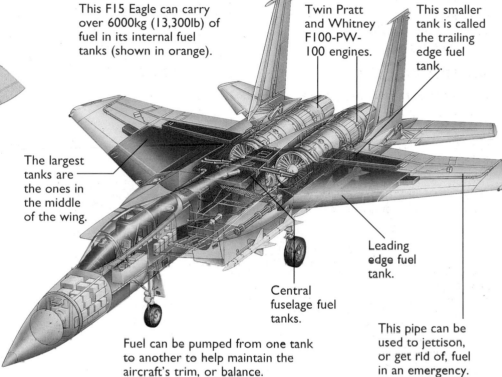

This F15 Eagle can carry over 6000kg (13,300lb) of fuel in its internal fuel tanks (shown in orange).

Twin Pratt and Whitney F100-PW-100 engines.

This smaller tank is called the trailing edge fuel tank.

The largest tanks are the ones in the middle of the wing.

Leading edge fuel tank.

Central fuselage fuel tanks.

This pipe can be used to jettison, or get rid of, fuel in an emergency.

Fuel can be pumped from one tank to another to help maintain the aircraft's trim, or balance.

Wind Tunnel

As scientists and engineers have learned more and more about aerodynamics, they have been able to build planes that fly faster, farther and more safely. Wind tunnels are used to study aerodynamics for both planes and cars (see page 17).

Even the very earliest planes were first tested as scale models inside simple wind tunnels. Wind tunnels today are much more complicated but the principles are still the same. Air is blown over a scale model of the aircraft, or part of it, and engineers see the effect this has. Computers are used to monitor results.

This airliner model is being tested in a high speed wind tunnel.

Adding fuel in-flight

The plane's fuel tank is usually filled on the ground where tanker trucks pump fuel into the tanks at incredibly fast speeds.

Some military planes, though, can take on extra fuel while flying. A large tanker aircraft, often a converted airliner or cargo plane, flies close to the plane in need of fuel. This requires great skill from both pilots.

This VC10 tanker can supply planes with up to 86,000kg (190,000lb) of fuel through its three fuel probes.

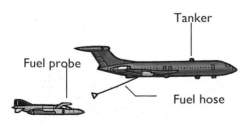

Tanker

Fuel probe

Fuel hose

The two aircraft fly extremely close to each other. The tanker extends its hose, the other plane extends its fuel probe.

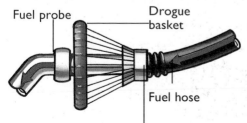

Fuel probe

Drogue basket

Fuel hose

When the two probes join, fuel is pumped quickly from the tanker to the plane that needs fuel.

Learning to fly

Becoming a pilot takes a long time and lots of hard work. This is because pilots have to know so much information about the aircraft they fly and about other important things, such as weather, maintainance, safety and navigation. Trainee pilots are tested on many lessons in the classroom as well as flying with an instructor in an aircraft called a trainer.

These trainees at a flying school are being taught about radio communications.

Aircrew, as well as pilots, need training. Here, aircrew learn what to do if there's a fire.

Trainers

Trainers often have two sets of controls so that the instructor can take over if the trainee pilot is having difficulty. There are trainers for all different types of aircraft.

This Cessna 150 is a light plane trainer. It is one of the most common planes in the world.

Pilot and trainee sit side by side.

This is a Northrop T38 Talon.

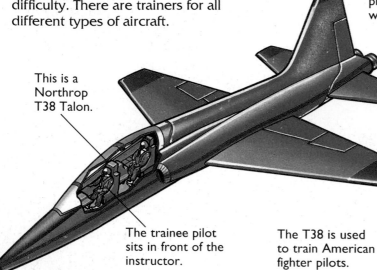

The trainee pilot sits in front of the instructor.

The T38 is used to train American fighter pilots.

Going solo

After many hours in the classroom and up in the air with an instructor, a trainee pilot must fly the aircraft alone, without the instructor's help. This is called going solo. Once trainees have flown solo for a certain time, have learned about flying cross-country and passed various tests, they will be given their first pilot's licence.

Gliding

Some people learn to fly in a type of plane without an engine called a glider or sailplane. Learning to glide is cheaper and easier than learning to fly a powered aircraft but it is still extremely exciting and demanding.

Gliders can be launched into the air in many ways. A few gliders have small engines just for take-off. Many gliders are launched using a powerful winch on the ground. The winch pulls the glider along fast enough for the air rushing over the wings to provide the lift needed for take-off.

Tow plane

Glider

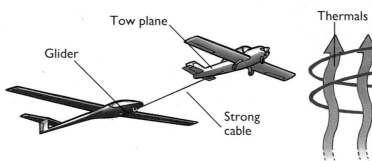

Strong cable

Thermals

Some gliders are towed into the air by a light aircraft known as a tug or tow plane. At an agreed height, the glider is released and the tow plane flies back to the airfield.

Once in the air, gliders circle around on pockets of warm air called thermals. An experienced pilot in good conditions can keep a glider flying for many hours.

T-shaped tail with the elevators on top of the tail fin.

Gliders are built from strong but very light materials to keep their weight down. These long wings provide lots of lift.

Single wheel landing gear

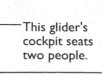

This glider's cockpit seats two people.

Aileron

Flight simulators

Flight simulators are complex machines which make you feel you are really flying. They do this by using a mixture of projector displays, realistic movement, and a complete copy of the real plane's cockpit. Flight simulators are not just flown by trainees. Experienced pilots also use them when learning to fly new aircraft or when working on how to cope with an emergency, which would be difficult or dangerous to do in a real aircraft.

This simulator is used by Japanese airline, JAL, to train their pilots.

Here is an example of the sort of realistic scene which can be generated by computers and viewed from inside an advanced simulator.

There are many different types of flight simulator. The most advanced, like this model at the National Aerospace Laboratory in Holland, are controlled by computers and *hydraulics**.

This part is called the dome. Computers and projectors display realistic pictures onto the inside surface of the dome.

Computers which control the simulator (see page 7).

Different cockpits can be put inside the dome. This cockpit is from an American F16 jet fighter.

The legs are powered by these strong hydraulic systems which react quickly to the pilot's controls.

This is one of the legs which tilt the simulator in all directions. They give the impression of turning, climbing and descending.

Details about how the pilot flies can be recorded and looked at later.

Platform

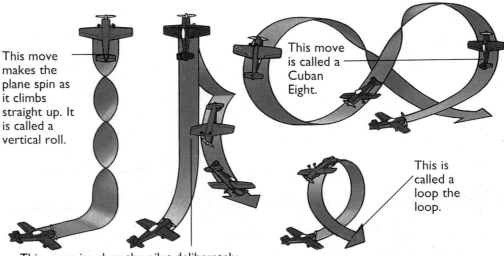

Aerobatics

Tricks and special moves performed by a pilot in a plane are called aerobatics. It takes a long time for even experienced pilots to learn how to do them.

This Pitts Special is a very rugged biplane often used for aerobatics.

This move makes the plane spin as it climbs straight up. It is called a vertical roll.

This move is called a Cuban Eight.

This is called a loop the loop.

This move involves the pilot deliberately *stalling** the plane so that it drops out of the sky. It is called a stall turn.

Take-off and landing

Nearly all planes need a long stretch of flat ground or calm water for take-off and landing. Take-off and landing are a pilot's busiest times.

How a plane takes off

Taking off needs more power than any other part of a flight. A plane at take-off is at its heaviest because it hasn't used much of its fuel. The engines must move the plane fast enough for the wings to overcome the plane's weight and lift the plane into the sky. Below is a diagram of how a plane takes off and lands.

Floats and skids

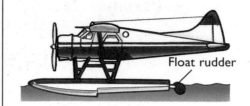

Float rudder

This Canadian DHC-2 Beaver can be fitted with floats or skids.

Some aircraft don't need a runway for take-off and landing. Their landing gear wheels (see below) may be replaced with skids for landing on ground; or replaced with floats, underneath their fuselage or wing, for landing on water. These floats usually have small rudders on the back to allow the pilot to steer the plane once it is on the water.

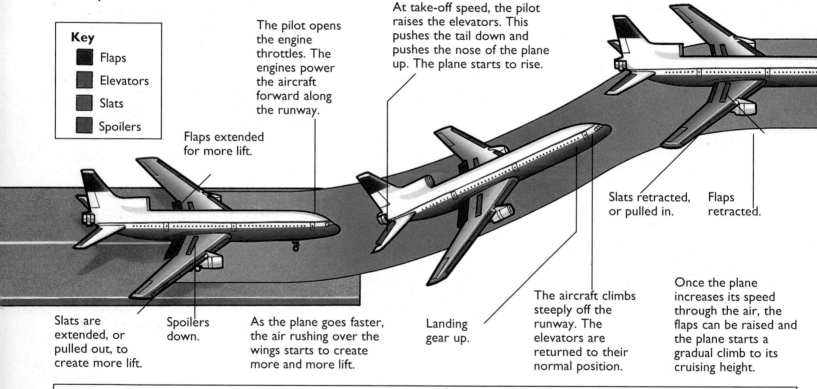

Key
- ■ Flaps
- ■ Elevators
- ■ Slats
- ■ Spoilers

The pilot opens the engine throttles. The engines power the aircraft forward along the runway.

Flaps extended for more lift.

At take-off speed, the pilot raises the elevators. This pushes the tail down and pushes the nose of the plane up. The plane starts to rise.

Slats retracted, or pulled in.

Flaps retracted.

Slats are extended, or pulled out, to create more lift.

Spoilers down.

As the plane goes faster, the air rushing over the wings starts to create more and more lift.

Landing gear up.

The aircraft climbs steeply off the runway. The elevators are returned to their normal position.

Once the plane increases its speed through the air, the flaps can be raised and the plane starts a gradual climb to its cruising height.

The landing gear

The parts of the plane that touch the ground at take-off and landing, and the parts that support them, are called the landing gear. As a plane lands, the landing gear is put under great strain. Modern landing gears are very strong. For example, the entire Boeing 747 landing gear is tested to support almost double the plane's actual weight, which is an incredible 360,000kg (800,000lb).

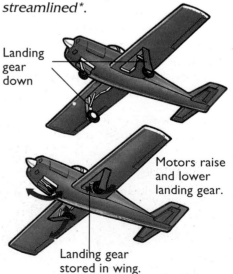

This is part of the landing gear of a Falcon 900 business jet.

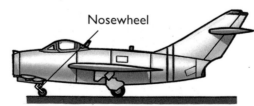

Nosewheel

The most common form of landing gear has three sets of wheels and is called a tricycle landing gear. Both these planes have this sort of landing gear.

Tailwheel

Two sets, the main gear, are placed under the body or wings of the plane.

The third set is either under the nose or tail to keep the plane level.

Retractable landing gear first became common in the 1930s. It helps make the plane much more *streamlined**.

Landing gear down

Motors raise and lower landing gear.

Landing gear stored in wing.

How a plane lands

The pilot carefully sets a course to fly down to the runway. As the plane starts to descend, the pilot makes small changes to the position of the elevators and the power of the engines. When the plane is within 5 or 6m (16-20ft) of the ground, the pilot reduces engine power and raises the elevators a little more. The plane gently hits the runway.

Slats and flaps out for extra lift.

Take-off and landing at sea

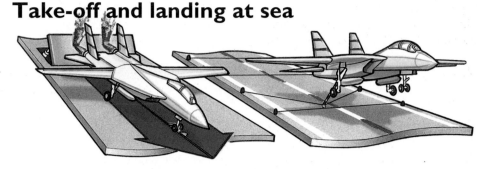

On many aircraft carriers, a strong catapult driven by steam from the ship's boilers can pull an aircraft from a standstill to 240km/h (150mph) in under two seconds.

An arrester hook is fitted to many aircraft on ships. As the plane lands, the hook trails along the deck and catches on a strong set of cables which act as an anchor.

Ideally, a plane lands into the wind. This cuts down the landing speed.

Once the plane is safely onto the runway, the pilot operates the wheel brakes to slow the aircraft down.

A modern airliner touches the runway at a speed of about 300km/h (180mph).

Landing gear down

The plane descends at a small angle. The pilot adjusts the throttles to keep the plane at a steady speed.

As the plane's wheels touch the runway, the pilot closes the throttle to cut the speed of the engines right down.

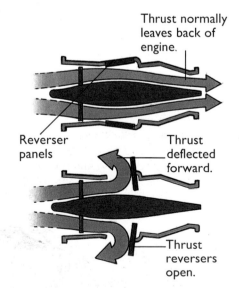

Spoilers raised which cuts down lift.

Stopping after landing

Modern aircraft land at high speeds. They have other methods, apart from the wheel brakes, to help them stop quickly.

Air brakes or spoilers can be on a planes's body or its wings (see page 37). They are flaps that open out to disrupt the flow of air. This creates plenty of drag which slows the aircraft down.

Thrust normally leaves back of engine.

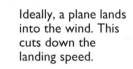

Reverser panels

Thrust deflected forward.

Thrust reversers open.

Thrust reversers simply change the direction the engine's power is pushing. Instead of the power pushing the plane forward, it pushes against the way the plane is moving, so the plane slows down.

Air brakes open.

Lots of drag created.

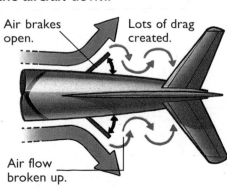

Air flow broken up.

Some planes are fitted with brake parachutes. These open up from the back of the aircraft and create a lot of drag which helps slow the plane down. A brake parachute on a military jet fighter may take only two seconds to inflate fully but can cut 25% off the braking distance in dry conditions and as much as 50% in the wet.

This F117A stealth fighter has used its brake parachute on landing.

VSTOL planes

VSTOL stands for Vertical or Short Take-Off and Landing. A VSTOL plane can either use a short stretch of runway or can take off and land straight up and down from a small space such as a clearing in a forest or jungle. Much of the time, VSTOL planes use a runway for a short take-off but land vertically. This saves a lot of fuel.

This machine, called the Flying Bedstead, was built by Rolls Royce to test engines for VSTOL. It was first used in 1953.

BAe Sea Harrier MkI

The Harrier is the best known VSTOL plane. It was first built by British company Hawker Siddeley (later British Aerospace) and Harriers have served in the British, Indian, Italian, Spanish and United States military services. The Sea Harrier is a version of the Harrier used by navies. It can take off and land from the decks of aircraft carriers and has a top speed of 1,120km/h (720mph).

This Sea Harrier is landing vertically onto the deck of an aircraft carrier.

The wing joins the very top of the fuselage. This is called a shoulder type wing.

This is the engine's front or intake fan.

Front exhaust nozzle (see below).

Advanced Blue Fox radar is stored in the nose.

This measures how much the plane yaws (see page 36). It is called a yaw vane.

The single pilot sits on a Martin Baker Type 10 ejection seat. He can eject safely even from the ship's deck.

Wedges called chocks stop the plane from moving when parked on the ground.

This external fuel tank holds more fuel than the tanks of 12 family cars.

Pegasus engine

The Harrier is powered by a single turbofan engine called the Rolls Royce Pegasus. The main difference between the Pegasus and other turbofans is that the direction the gases leave the engine can be controlled. This is called vectored thrust (see opposite page). The engine has four linked exhaust nozzles through which the hot gases and cold air are forced out. These nozzles can be turned around by the pilot from the cockpit.

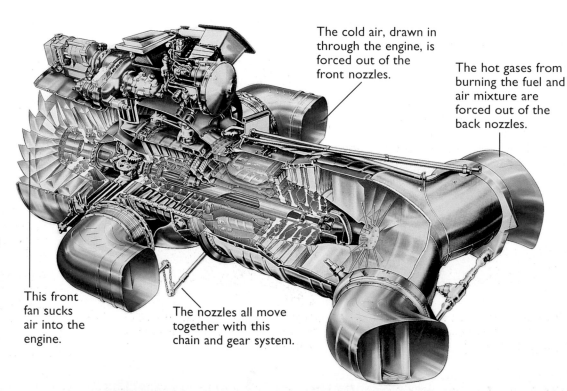

The cold air, drawn in through the engine, is forced out of the front nozzles.

The hot gases from burning the fuel and air mixture are forced out of the back nozzles.

This front fan sucks air into the engine.

The nozzles all move together with this chain and gear system.

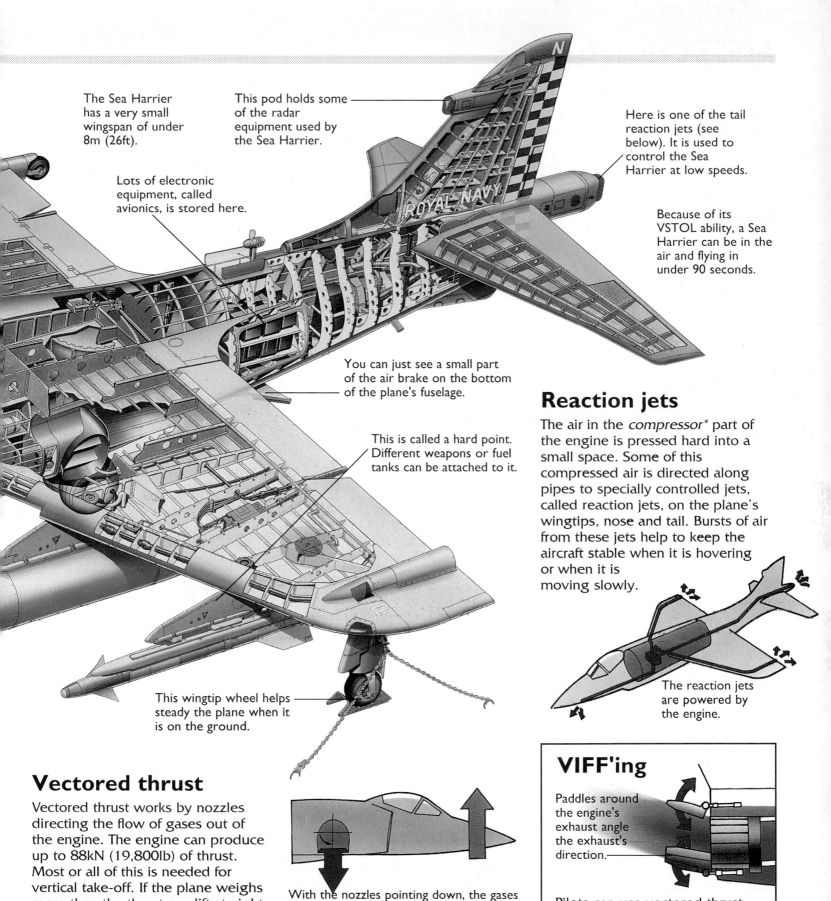

The Sea Harrier has a very small wingspan of under 8m (26ft).

This pod holds some of the radar equipment used by the Sea Harrier.

Here is one of the tail reaction jets (see below). It is used to control the Sea Harrier at low speeds.

Lots of electronic equipment, called avionics, is stored here.

Because of its VSTOL ability, a Sea Harrier can be in the air and flying in under 90 seconds.

ROYAL NAVY

You can just see a small part of the air brake on the bottom of the plane's fuselage.

Reaction jets

The air in the *compressor** part of the engine is pressed hard into a small space. Some of this compressed air is directed along pipes to specially controlled jets, called reaction jets, on the plane's wingtips, nose and tail. Bursts of air from these jets help to keep the aircraft stable when it is hovering or when it is moving slowly.

This is called a hard point. Different weapons or fuel tanks can be attached to it.

The reaction jets are powered by the engine.

This wingtip wheel helps steady the plane when it is on the ground.

Vectored thrust

Vectored thrust works by nozzles directing the flow of gases out of the engine. The engine can produce up to 88kN (19,800lb) of thrust. Most or all of this is needed for vertical take-off. If the plane weighs more than the thrust can lift straight up, it cannot take off vertically and must use a ramp or runway instead.

With the nozzles pointing down, the gases are forced down which provides up-thrust, lifting the plane off the ground.

When the nozzles are set pointing back, the gases are forced back which powers the aircraft forward.

Angling the nozzles diagonally down moves the aircraft both up and forward at the same time.

VIFF'ing

Paddles around the engine's exhaust angle the exhaust's direction.

Pilots can use vectored thrust while flying. By altering the direction of the exhaust, a plane can make tighter turns and climb faster than normal. This is called VIFF'ing (Vectoring In Forward Flight). Some military fighters which are not VSTOL aircraft are now being fitted with equipment which allows them to VIFF. This will make them faster and easier to move around in combat.

Safety

Early planes were often dangerous to fly. They were difficult to control and had few safety features or instruments to help the pilot. Modern aircraft are not only easier to control but also contain many instruments designed to avoid accidents. For example, radar warns of aircraft or other problems ahead.

The flight data recorder, often called the black box, records all the details of a flight.

The black box is examined by experts if there's a crash or other problem.

Passenger safety

Modern airliners are designed carefully to avoid accidents and can still fly even if one engine stops working. They all have many features built in to help passengers survive and escape from the plane if it crashes.

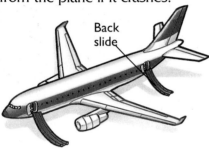

Back slide

These slides are a quick and safe way to leave the aircraft. They are filled with air and are worked by the airliner's aircrew.

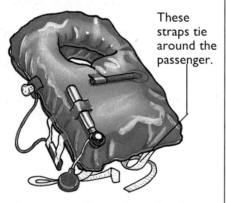

These straps tie around the passenger.

All passengers have a life jacket by or under their seats. They inflate automatically when you pull a tab.

Life rafts provide safety and shelter for survivors if a plane crashes in water. This raft, made by RFD Equipment, holds up to 9 people.

Ejection seats

Jet aircraft fly too fast for pilots and crew members to jump out of the plane and use a parachute. So an ejection seat is used to fire crew members safely out of the plane and away from danger.

Since they were introduced in the 1940s, ejection seats have saved over 10,000 lives. Ejection seats made by one British company alone, called Martin-Baker, have saved over 7000 people.

This Mk16 ejection seat was built by Martin Baker. It is used in both the Eurofighter and the Dassault Rafale military jets. Although it weighs less than a man, the ejection seat can safely eject the pilot from any altitude including ground level. The whole ejection process is incredibly fast. In 0.25 seconds the pilot is out of the aircraft and in under 3 seconds, the main parachute is fully opened.

Parachute container

The straps in the harness are tightened automatically.

Firing handle

Guide rails

Oxygen supply

Leg straps tighten to help secure pilot firmly in seat.

Rocket pack

How ejection seats work

The pilot pulls the firing handle. This sets off a computer-controlled sequence. The seat straps tighten automatically, and all or part of the plane's canopy is fired away.

The pilot's radio and oxygen are disconnected and replaced by emergency ones built into the seat. The ejection gun fires the seat up the guide rails and free of the plane.

Pilot safety

Pilots and aircrew flying military jets need to be well-protected. They are often flying at very high altitudes and need oxygen to breathe. They usually sit on a pack of equipment that contains tools, a life raft, and even food to help them survive if they crash in an isolated place.

When a fast jet makes a tight turn or pulls out of a steep dive, the force of *gravity** presses hard on the pilot. An anti-G suit stops the force from hurting him. It is filled with air and is worn over the flying suit.

The knee parts of the G-suit are cut out to allow the pilot to bend his knees more easily.

This is the oxygen face mask. The ejection seat has 15-20 minutes supply of oxygen on board.

The tinted sun visor protects the pilot from strong glare.

Oxygen supply pipe

These leather gloves are fire-resistant.

The pilot's flying suit and underwear are made from material that is hard to set fire to.

Parachutes

Parachutes slow down a person falling through the air. This means that he or she can land safely when bailing (jumping) out of a plane. A parachute is a large canopy made of flame-resistant material. When open, it creates lots of drag as air pushes against its underside. This slows its fall.

Air enters parachute.

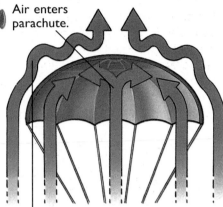

Drag created by catching the air.

Parachutes are tightly fitted into packs either worn by the aircrew or stored on the ejection seat. Sometimes, a second, smaller reserve pack is attached just in case the main one doesn't work.

Parachutes are used for other jobs too. They can slow fast planes down when they land (see page 51). Parachutes are also put on supplies and food so they can be dropped to places without runways or roads.

When just clear of the aircraft, a rocket pack under the seat fires for about a fifth of a second. This pushes the seat about 100m (330ft) away from the plane.

An explosive charge opens a small parachute called a drogue. The drogue parachute helps slow the seat down and, on some ejection seats, pulls out the main parachute.

Once the main parachute is deployed, or fully opened, the seat falls away from the pilot who is then left to make an ordinary safe parachute landing.

Modern military planes

This C17 Globemaster transports troops and tanks.

Modern military planes come in all shapes and sizes and perform lots of different jobs. Many of them are designed either to defend an area against an enemy attack or strike at a target with weapons. Not all military aircraft are used just for combat though. Some are used for training, rescue work and transport. Others are used to gather information about an area. This is called reconnaissance. Military reconnaissance planes photograph and check on enemy sites and troop movements.

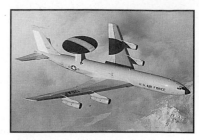

This Boeing AWACS is used for reconnaissance.

Panavia Tornado GR.1

This military jet was built by a group of companies from Germany, Italy and Great Britain. It is used for a number of different tasks and is called a Multi-Role Combat Aircraft (MRCA). This GR.1 version is used mainly as a strike aircraft but also sometimes for reconnaissance.

Here is a GR.1 used by the Royal Air Force in Britain.

This probe collects information about the air and sends it to one of the plane's computers.

This radar antenna maps the ground as the Tornado flies along.

The nosecone unhinges to allow engineers to reach the radar equipment stored there.

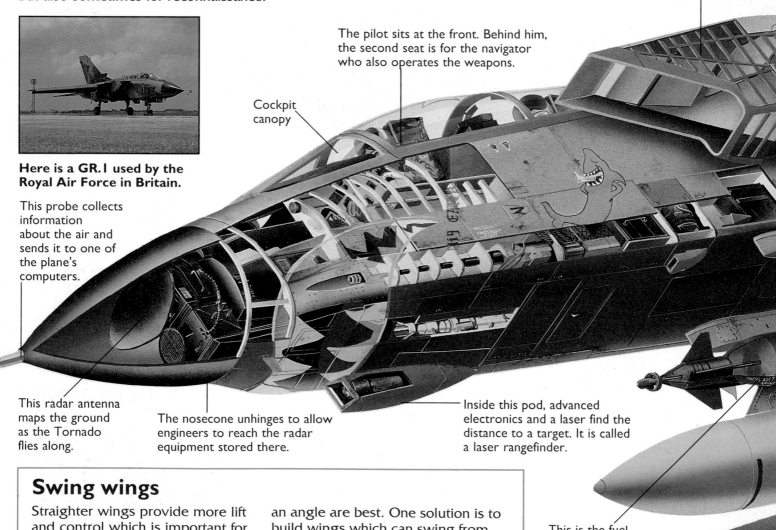

This is an air intake. You can see how it is made up of a frame of metal strips all joined together.

The pilot sits at the front. Behind him, the second seat is for the navigator who also operates the weapons.

Cockpit canopy

Inside this pod, advanced electronics and a laser find the distance to a target. It is called a laser rangefinder.

This is the fuel tank of one of the Tornado's missiles.

The Tornado is a small plane but it weighs more than many bigger aircraft. This is partly because of the heavy load it carries. Almost half of the Tornado's weight is fuel and weapons.

Swing wings

Straighter wings provide more lift and control which is important for take-off and landing. However, for fast speeds, wings swept back at an angle are best. One solution is to build wings which can swing from one position to another. These are called swing wings.

The Tornado's wings can be moved into one of four different positions, 67°, 58°, 45° and 25°.

67° 58° 45° 25°

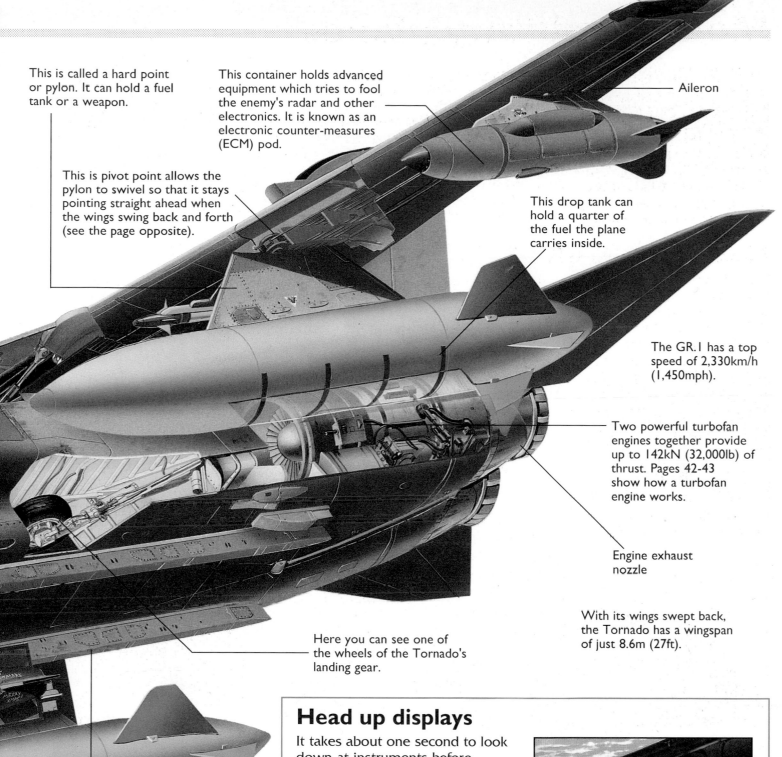

This is called a hard point or pylon. It can hold a fuel tank or a weapon.

This container holds advanced equipment which tries to fool the enemy's radar and other electronics. It is known as an electronic counter-measures (ECM) pod.

Aileron

This is pivot point allows the pylon to swivel so that it stays pointing straight ahead when the wings swing back and forth (see the page opposite).

This drop tank can hold a quarter of the fuel the plane carries inside.

The GR.1 has a top speed of 2,330km/h (1,450mph).

Two powerful turbofan engines together provide up to 142kN (32,000lb) of thrust. Pages 42-43 show how a turbofan engine works.

Engine exhaust nozzle

With its wings swept back, the Tornado has a wingspan of just 8.6m (27ft).

Here you can see one of the wheels of the Tornado's landing gear.

Missiles can be launched from these hard points attached to the bottom of the fuselage.

From take-off, the Tornado takes under two minutes to climb to over 9,000m (30,000ft).

Head up displays

It takes about one second to look down at instruments before bringing your head up again to look ahead. This may be fine in a slow vehicle but in a jet flying at 2,000km/h (1,250mph) it could be extremely dangerous. In that time, the plane could have flown over 500m (530 yards).

Head Up Displays, or HUDs for short, are found in many of today's modern military fast jets. They allow information to be displayed straight in front of the pilot either on a clear screen in the cockpit or directly onto the pilot's visor. The screen is see-through so that the pilot can look past the details at the view outside without moving his head.

The projector in this helmet displays important information onto the pilot's helmet visor.

57

Navigation

The pilots of early planes had little more than maps and a compass to find their way with. They had to plan their course by watching the ground for landmarks. This is called dead reckoning. Today, pilots occasionally use dead reckoning but they usually rely on radio and radar navigation, map computers, and instruments which show the plane's height, speed and heading.

This is a Magellan EG-10 portable electronic map. It can be used in small civil aircraft which don't have expensive map computers built into their cockpit.

Gyroscopes

There are two main devices which help detect a change in the direction of the plane's movement. These are gyroscopes and accelerometers.

A gyroscope used on an aircraft is a fast-spinning wheel joined to a frame. The wheel always stays in exactly the same position, while the frame moves with the plane. The direction and distance that the frame moves is turned into a reading, telling the pilot the change in the aircraft's movement.

Gyroscopes are used in important navigational instruments like the artificial horizon and the directional gyro, which is a type of non-magnetic compass.

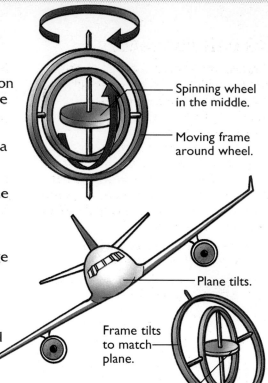

Spinning wheel in the middle.

Moving frame around wheel.

Plane tilts.

Frame tilts to match plane.

Wheel stays level.

Radar

Radar helps aircraft fly safely through the crowded skies. A radar transmitter sends out short bursts of radio waves which bounce off any object they hit and return to the transmitter. The exact time it takes these signals to return can be changed into a reading that tells the pilot how far he is from an object.

Radar signals can be sent 150km (90 miles) and bounce back in only 1/1000th of a second.

Modern planes carry several different sets of radar, each of which does a different job.

Weather radar sends signals out in front of the plane. These signals bounce back off any water droplets ahead. The signals give an idea of what the weather will be like along the plane's route.

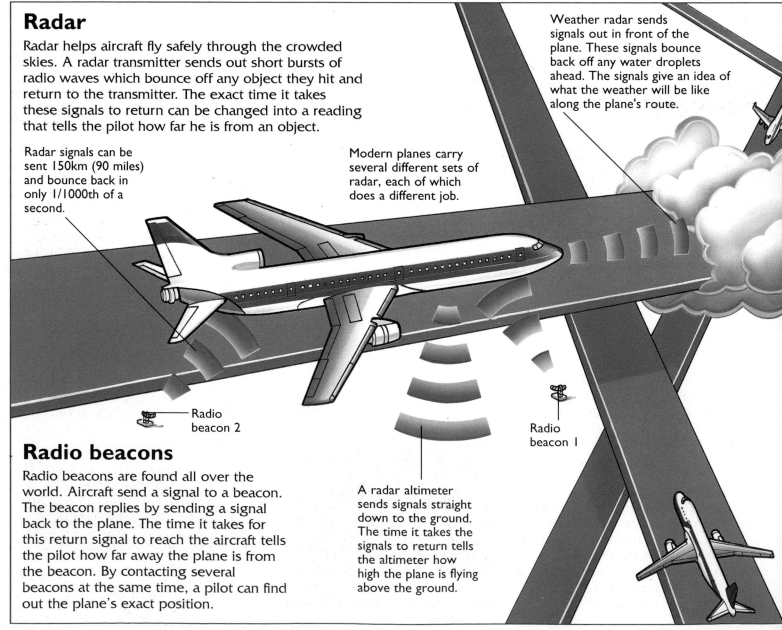

Radio beacon 2

Radio beacon 1

Radio beacons

Radio beacons are found all over the world. Aircraft send a signal to a beacon. The beacon replies by sending a signal back to the plane. The time it takes for this return signal to reach the aircraft tells the pilot how far away the plane is from the beacon. By contacting several beacons at the same time, a pilot can find out the plane's exact position.

A radar altimeter sends signals straight down to the ground. The time it takes the signals to return tells the altimeter how high the plane is flying above the ground.

Accelerometers

An accelerometer is an electronic device which does a similar job to a gyroscope. One part of an accelerometer is in a fixed position and another part can move with the plane. Electricity produces a *magnetic field** between the two parts and any change in movement disturbs the field. This change is fed into a computer which calculates the amount of movement.

Magnetic fields created between the two parts of an accelerometer.

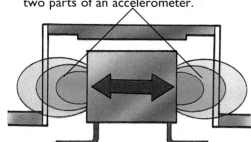

Autopilot

Most planes today have a system called an autopilot. It allows a plane to stay on a set course without the pilot having to hold the controls all of the time. An autopilot uses accelerometers and gyroscopes to detect movement. If the plane is moving off course, the autopilot's computer triggers electric or hydraulic motors, called servos.

These move the flight controls to bring the plane back on course. If the plane moves a large distance off course, the autopilot also warns the pilot. Autopilots are incredibly accurate, but there are some situations where the pilot's skill and experience are needed and autopilots cannot be used, such as flying through very bad weather.

The gyroscopes detect movement in all directions.

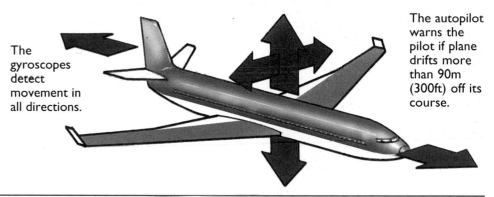

The autopilot warns the pilot if plane drifts more than 90m (300ft) off its course.

Air corridors

With so many planes flying, important rules have been made to prevent collisions. Systems of aerial highways, called air corridors, have been created. Each plane flies along one specific corridor a safe distance away from any other planes.

Each corridor is about 15km (9 miles) wide and runs at a certain height above the ground.

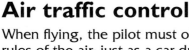

There is usually a height difference of 500m (1600ft) between air corridors.

The descent towards the airport runway is called the approach.

Air traffic control

When flying, the pilot must obey the rules of the air, just as a car driver follows road traffic laws. Air traffic controllers manage aircraft in the skies and advise them on route changes or emergencies. Air traffic controllers use radios to speak to pilots but they also use two systems of radar. The first finds all the planes in the area a controller is scanning. The second receives an automatic signal from each aircraft which gives the controller the plane's identity, height and planned route. As a plane travels out of one area, it is handed from one controller to another.

This is part of air traffic control near London's Heathrow Airport.

Stacking and landing

When a plane gets close to a busy airport, it often has to join what is called a stack. This is like an aerial ladder made up of lots of different levels or rungs. When a plane arrives, it usually joins the stack at the highest point. The plane then travels around an oval-shaped route. Gradually, as aircraft below it land, the plane is ordered down the rungs of the ladder by the air traffic controllers. Eventually, it will reach the bottom level and then begin its approach to land.

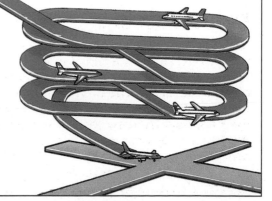

Stealth planes

This is a F117A on a test flight over the United States.

Radar is very successful at spotting aircraft. Recently, engineers have found ways to make it harder for radar to see planes. Aircraft which are built with these anti-radar features are called stealth planes. Stealth confuses an enemy's electronics and radar equipment so the plane can fly by unnoticed. The United States has two stealth planes, the Northrop B2 bomber and the Lockheed F117A strike aircraft.

Here you can see the Northrop B2's shape which is called a flying wing.

Lockheed F117A

This was the first stealth plane to be built and it first flew in 1981. It can travel secretly past heavily-defended enemy sites at night. The F117A is believed not to carry guns or air-to-air missiles. Instead, it relies on its stealth to escape harm.

The cockpit canopy is fitted with treated windows which do not reflect radar signals.

The weapons bay can hold two large laser-guided bombs.

These spikes are called pitot tubes (see page 39).

Air data computers use the information from the pitot tubes.

Infrared light beams can show you things in the dark. This forward-looking infrared machine (known as FLIR) gives the pilot a clear picture at night.

This intake allows air into the engine. It can also be heated to prevent ice from forming in cold weather.

LT COL JERRY CARPENTER

RESCUE

Facets and radar absorbant material (RAM)

What a plane looks like on a radar screen is called its radar cross-section, or RCS for short.

Radar bounces off large curved shapes best. So, instead, stealth planes are built with lots of differently-angled faces or facets. The facets are coated with a mixture of materials (called RAM) which absorb the radar signals rather than letting them bounce off. Together, facets and RAM make a stealth plane look more like birds than an aircraft on a radar screen.

Radar signals bounce smoothly off.

The facets confuse the radar signals which bounce off in all directions.

The R.A.M. coating absorbs many of the radar signals.

On a normal aircraft, radar waves bounce off the large metal surfaces and back to the radar system.

On a stealth aircraft with facets, the signals bounce off at all angles and send back a confusing message to the radar station.

Avoiding the enemy

There are other ways to avoid being seen by the enemy apart from using stealth. Many warplanes since earliest times have been painted in shades and patterns to match the sky or ground, called camouflage. Some very fast jet planes use sheer speed to avoid being seen. Other planes, like the SR71 Blackbird, fly at extremely high altitudes.

The SR71 Blackbird is the fastest jet aircraft ever. Its top speed is over 3500km/h (2180mph).

This Sukhoi Su35 Russian jet fighter is camouflaged to match the winter landscape in Europe.

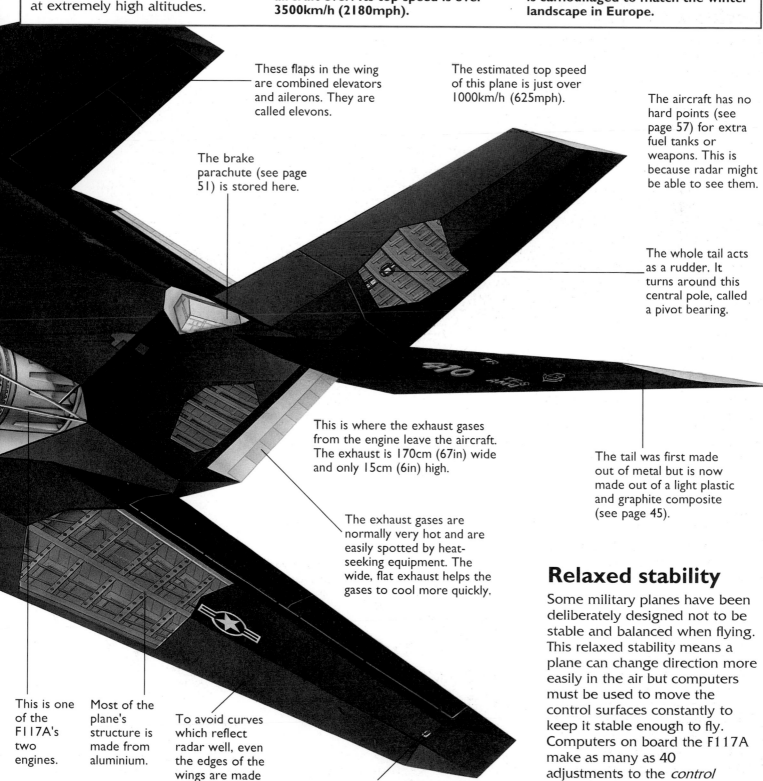

These flaps in the wing are combined elevators and ailerons. They are called elevons.

The estimated top speed of this plane is just over 1000km/h (625mph).

The aircraft has no hard points (see page 57) for extra fuel tanks or weapons. This is because radar might be able to see them.

The brake parachute (see page 51) is stored here.

The whole tail acts as a rudder. It turns around this central pole, called a pivot bearing.

This is where the exhaust gases from the engine leave the aircraft. The exhaust is 170cm (67in) wide and only 15cm (6in) high.

The tail was first made out of metal but is now made out of a light plastic and graphite composite (see page 45).

The exhaust gases are normally very hot and are easily spotted by heat-seeking equipment. The wide, flat exhaust helps the gases to cool more quickly.

This is one of the F117A's two engines.

Most of the plane's structure is made from aluminium.

To avoid curves which reflect radar well, even the edges of the wings are made up of facets.

Navigation light

Relaxed stability

Some military planes have been deliberately designed not to be stable and balanced when flying. This relaxed stability means a plane can change direction more easily in the air but computers must be used to move the control surfaces constantly to keep it stable enough to fly. Computers on board the F117A make as many as 40 adjustments to the *control surfaces** every second.

The future

In less than a century, aircraft have gone from being a dream to having a big impact on our lives. Nobody knows what will happen in another hundred years but it is possible to suggest what may happen in the near future.

Giant airliners

Aircraft makers will continue to look at ways of building airliners which are quieter, use less fuel and which can transport passengers at less cost.

This fuselage has two floors of seats.

This shape is called a clover-leaf body.

This design has two airliner fuselages joined together. It is called a horizontal double bubble.

More and more people want to travel by air and major airports cannot easily handle lots more flights. One solution is to build bigger airliners. Here are some possible airliner fuselage designs for the future.

Airbus A3XX

The Airbus A3XX is a giant airliner planned by Airbus Industries to hold as many as 830 passengers. It would not be much longer than a Boeing 747 but would have a much larger fuselage. There would be two floors for passengers and a bottom deck for cargo. As it will be made using some of the same parts as the Airbus airliners already in service, the A3XX could be flying by the year 2003.

A computer-generated picture of what the A3XX may look like.

Rocket engines

Rocket engines are used for space vehicles but a small number of aircraft such as the fastest ever plane, the Bell X-15, have been powered by rocket engines. Rocket engines are similar to gas turbine or jet engines (see pages 42-43) except that they don't have *turbines** and carry their own supply of oxygen on board.

The Bell X-15's top speed of 7300km/h (4530mph) makes it the fastest ever.

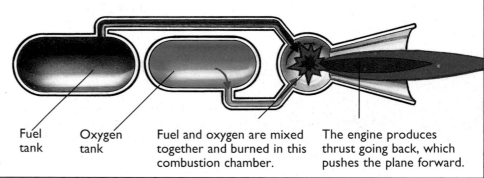

Fuel tank

Oxygen tank

Fuel and oxygen are mixed together and burned in this combustion chamber.

The engine produces thrust going back, which pushes the plane forward.

Space airliner

In the future, you may see airliners powered by a mixture of rocket and jet engines. They would be extremely fast and designed to fly partly in space and partly in the Earth's atmosphere. They would cut down the journey time from one side of the planet to the other to perhaps as little as two or three hours.

This is an artist's impression of a Japanese rocket airliner flying in the 21st century.

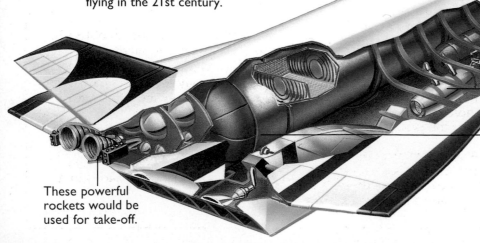

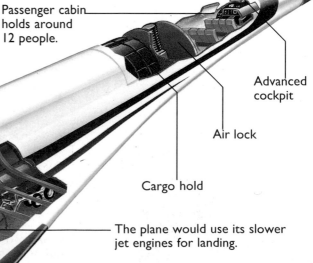

Passenger cabin holds around 12 people.

Advanced cockpit

Air lock

Cargo hold

The plane would use its slower jet engines for landing.

Enormous hydrogen fuel tanks fill most of the plane.

These powerful rockets would be used for take-off.

Cruising through space, the high-powered engines could push the plane to speeds as high as 10,000km/h (6200mph).

Pilotless planes

Electronics and computers will become more advanced and control more and more parts of an aircraft. In the future, pilotless planes could shuttle cargo and passengers from one place to another, guided by navigation systems from the ground.

An artist's idea of what a pilotless plane might look like.

Space cargo carriers

Many companies are working on designs for reusable space vehicles to help or replace the Space Shuttle. The design below, from an American company, Lockheed, has no wings. Instead, it relies on its body to create lift. It would take off like a rocket but land like a normal plane on a runway.

Just over 33m (110ft) long, this craft would carry as much as 500 metric tonnes (550 US tons) of fuel.

Advanced take-off

Many aircraft makers are working on military aircraft with advanced take-off and landing systems. Some are even planning designs for small airliners which could operate from very short runways.

Lockheed's design for a lightweight fighter jet includes a lift fan for very short take-offs and vertical landings.

Glossary

Aerodynamics. The science of how gases, such as air, move over an object. Aerodynamics greatly affect the way planes are designed, built and flown.

Aerofoil. An object shaped to produce lift when air flows over or under it. This shape is most often seen in aircraft wings.

Air pressure. The force with which air pushes against an object. Air pressure is increased by pushing air into a small space. This is called compressing.

Alloys. A metal which is mixed with other metals or substances. For example, steel is an alloy made by mixing iron with carbon. Alloys, particularly of aluminium, are very important in the aircraft industry.

Biplane. An aircraft which has two sets of wings.

Combustion chamber. The part of a gas turbine engine where the air and fuel mixture is set alight.

Compressor. The part of a gas turbine engine where air is squashed together just before it is mixed with fuel and burnt.

Control surfaces. The hinged parts of a plane's wing and tail that help the plane change direction.

Duralumin. A metal alloy (see above) made by adding a small amount of copper to aluminium.

Four forces of flight. The four forces acting on a plane when it flies. The forces are drag, thrust, lift and gravity (see below).

Friction. The resistance made when one surface moves and rubs against another surface and when air moves over a plane.

Fuel management system. A system which adjusts the amount of fuel in each tank and how the tanks supply fuel to the engine or engines.

Galley. The mini kitchen on an airliner where food and drink are prepared for the passengers.

Gravity. A force which pulls objects towards the ground. Gravity has to be overcome by lift from the plane's wings for a plane to rise into the air.

HOTAS. Stands for hands on throttle and stick. Some modern military jets are fitted with an advanced throttle and control column or stick which contains all the controls needed for air combat.

Hydraulics. A system which uses liquid to transmit power from one place to another.

Ignite. To set fire to something.

Inertial Navigation System (INS). An advanced navigation system which measures any changes in the aircraft's speed and direction of movement. The changes are fed into a computer which constantly plots a plane's position. INS is very accurate over long distances.

Mach 1. Mach is a measure of speed. Mach 1 is the speed at which sound travels.

Magnetic field. The area around a magnet that responds to the magnet's power to attract or repel.

Monoplane. An aircraft which has one set of wings.

Pressurization. Keeping the inside of a plane filled with air at a greater air pressure (see above) than the air outside of the plane. This is so that the aircrew and passengers can breathe normally.

Range. The distance an aircraft can travel without running out of fuel.

Stalling. The break up of airflow over the wings caused by not flying fast enough or angling the nose upwards too steeply. Unless corrected, stalling will cause the aircraft to dive dangerously.

Streamlining. To shape an object in a way that makes it move as smoothly as possible through the air. The more easily an aircraft can move, the less power it has to use.

Triplane. An aircraft with three sets of wings.

Turbines. The spinning blades in a gas turbine engine.

Planes: Facts

1783 Invention of the **hot-air balloon** by Joseph and Étienne Montgolfier, two French brothers. The **first hydrogen balloon** was released two months later by another Frenchman, J. Charles.

1804 The English scientist Sir George Cayley built a model glider which is regarded as the **first real plane**.

1852 Henri Giffard from France made the **first controlled, powered flight in an airship** over Paris.

1853 Sir George Cayley built a **glider**, the first heavier-than-air machine to carry a person.

1890 Clément Ader, a French designer, was the **first man to fly in a machine powered by its own engine**.

1890s **Otto Lilienthal**, a German known as "The Flying Man", made **more than two thousand glider flights**.

1900 Ferdinand von Zeppelin from Germany built the **first successful dirigible airship**. A dirigible is an airship which can be propelled and steered.

1903 Orville and Wilbur Wright made the **first flight in a powered and controlled aircraft** called the *Flyer*. Aviation as we know it began with the Wright Brothers' first powered flights near Kitty Hawk in North Carolina, USA (see page 34).

1905 The Wright Brothers first flew their *Flyer III*. They managed to travel 39km (24 miles). This was the **first efficient plane**. It was able to turn and circle with ease and could fly for over half an hour.

1909 The **first flight across the English Channel** was achieved by a Frenchman, Louis Blériot. He designed and built the plane himself. Blériot was one of the **first to build a successful monoplane** (an aircraft with only one pair of wings).

1910 Henri Fabre, a Frenchman, built a **sea plane**, the *Hydravion*, the **first aircraft to take off from water**.

1913 Igor Sikorsky, a Russian engineer, **built and flew the first four-engined aircraft**.

1913 New, faster airplanes were designed with the advent of air-races during this decade. Adolphe Pégoud was the **first man to loop the loop** and invented what we now call aerobatics (see page 49).

1919 The **first transatlantic crossing**. Lieutenant Commander Read of the United States Navy piloted a flying boat, *N-C-4*, from New York to Plymouth, U.K.

1919 John Alcock and Arthur Brown made the **first nonstop transatlantic flight** in a twin-engined Vickers Vimy biplane (a plane that has two sets of wings, one above the other). They flew 1,936 miles from Newfoundland to Ireland.

1919 G. Scott commanded the **first two-way transatlantic flight** from Scotland to New York in the British airship R-34.

1919 **Aircraft and Travel Ltd.** started the **first regular international airline service** between London and Paris, using converted biplane bombers.

1923 The *Autogyro* by Juan de la Cierva made its first flight in Madrid. This was the **first practical aircraft with a rotary wing**, foreshadowing the helicopter.

1926 The **first successful flight over the North Pole** was in a Fokker monoplane by Richard Byrd of the US Navy and Floyd Bennet.

1927 The **first solo, nonstop transatlantic flight** was by Charles Lindbergh in his monoplane, *Spirit of St. Louis*. The journey from Roosevelt field, near New York, to an airport near Paris took 33 hrs 30 mins.

1928 The Australian pilot Sir Charles Kingsford Smith and his crew made the **first trans-Pacific flight** in a Fokker monoplane called the *Southern Cross*.

1930 Frank Whittle, a British engineer, patented a **design for a jet aircraft engine**. Amy Johnson became the **first woman in the world to fly solo** from England to Australia in a second-hand Gypsy Moth.

1932 Amelia Earhart made the **first solo transatlantic flight by a woman** in a Lockheed Vega monoplane.

1933 Wiley Post, an American, was the **first person to fly around the world**.

1933 The **Boeing 247** was built. It was a *streamlined**, all-metal construction. This airplane was the first of the new generation of US domestic air transportation.

1936 The Focke-Achgelis (called the FA 61) flew. This was the **first practical helicopter**.

1939 The **first jet-propelled airplane**, the Heinkel *He 178,* was designed by a German, Ernst Heinkel.

1939 The **first successful flight in a single-rotor helicopter** by Igor Sikorsky. He also built several **flying boats**.

1944 The world's **first production jet aircraft**, *Me 262*, entered service with a maximum speed of just over 800 kph/ 500 mph.

1944 The Germans began to attack London with *V-1* **flying bombs**. The *V-1s* were powered by a type of jet engine known as the pulse jet and could fly without a pilot.

1947 The **first supersonic** (faster than sound) **flight** was successfully completed by an American, Charles Yeager, in a rocket-powered aircraft called the *Bell X-1*.

1947 The **largest plane ever made**, the *Spruce Goose*, made its only flight and traveled one mile (1.6km). It had eight engines and a wingspan the length of a soccer field.

1949 The **first jet airliner**, the De Havilland Comet, flew.

1953 The **first flight in a VTOL (Vertical Take Off and Landing) plane** (see page 52).

1958 The **first transatlantic jet airline service** was introduced.

1965 The **first flight of a spy plane**, the *SR-71 Blackbird*, built in the United States. It could fly very high and at great speed but has not been used since 1990.

1968 The **first flight of the Russian Tu 144 supersonic airliner**. It was designed to carry 120 passengers at about 1, 550 mph.

1969 The **first flight of the Boeing 747 "Jumbo Jet"**. This aircraft is 195ft long and has over 400 seats (see pages 47 and 50). The **first flight of the airliner Concorde 001**.

1970 The **Boeing 747 "Jumbo Jet"** began **regular passenger service**.

1976 **Concorde entered full-time service** and is the only supersonic plane (see pages 46-47).

1989 The **first flight of stealth plane Northrop B-2 Spirit**. It can fly 8,000km (5,000 miles) in one trip (see page 60).

1991 The **Airbus A340 made its first flight** (see pages 39 and 40). This was built by a group of European companies and can travel from London to Chicago and back before it needs more fuel.

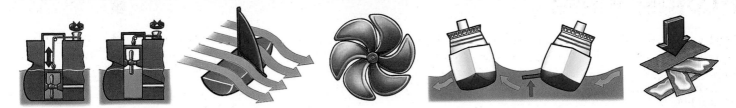

THE USBORNE BOOK OF
CUTAWAY
BOATS

Christopher Maynard

Designed by
Isaac Quaye & Steve Page

Illustrated by: Mick Gillah, Sean Wilkinson, Ian Cleaver, Gary Bines,
Justine Peek and artists from the School of Illustration,
Bournemouth and Poole College of Art and Design.

Consultants: Guy Robbins & David Topliss,
National Maritime Museum, London

Edited by Jane Chisholm

Additional designs by Robert Walster

Usborne Publishing wish to thank the following for their help with this book:

Joan Barrett, Atlantic Container Line · Alan L. Bates · Historic Royal Dockyard, Chatham ·
Michael Leek, Cordwainer's College · Flarecraft Inc. · Howard Smith (London) Ltd · Incat Designs Ltd.,
Japan Ship Centre · National Motorboat Museum · O.Y. Nautor Ab. · P & O · P & O European Ferries ·
Princess Cruises · Royal National Lifeboat Institution · Eamon Holland, Strategic Advertising ·
Vasa Museum, Stockholm · Yamaha Motor (UK) Ltd. · Yanmar Diesel Engine Co., Ltd.

Contents

Introduction.........................66

Triremes 68

The Age of Sail 70

Steamships 72

Riverboats 74

Yachts 76

Ferries 78

Engines 80

Lifeboats 82

Racing boats 84

Container ships 86

Tugs 88

Cruise ships 90

Submersibles 92

The future 94

Glossary 95

Index 96

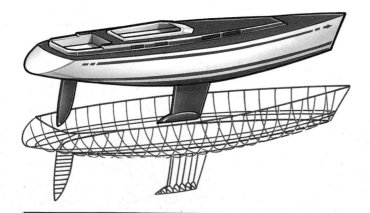

Words in *italic* type

Words in this section which appear in *italic* type and are followed by a small star (for example, *knots**) can be found in the glossary on page 95.

Introduction

Boats have been around since Stone Age times. The earliest boats - dugout canoes, log rafts and frames of sticks covered in animal skins - were all paddled or rowed.

The Ancient Egyptians, in around 3000BC, were the first to use sails to harness the wind. By doing so, they discovered a much easier way to travel, and created enough power to drive much bigger boats.

But really large ships need engines to power them, and it's only in the past 200 years that these have come into use. Some run on diesel, but the fastest and biggest ships use gas or steam turbines.

A tug boat

This is an old tug that was used about 70 years ago to tow ocean-going ships in and out of port. Its power came from a large steam engine that ran on coal.

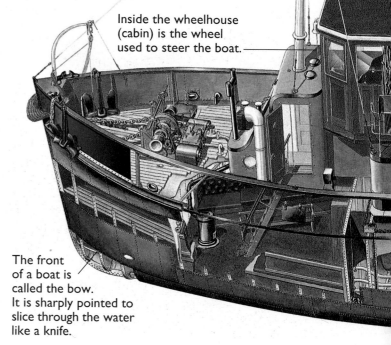

Inside the wheelhouse (cabin) is the wheel used to steer the boat.

The front of a boat is called the bow. It is sharply pointed to slice through the water like a knife.

How boats float.

When a boat is placed in water, it pushes water aside, or displaces it. The water pushes back with a force called upthrust. The size of the upthrust depends on the weight of water displaced. In order to float, an object must displace enough water so that the upthrust is as great as the weight of that object.

The amount of water an object displaces depends on its shape. For example, a ball of clay will sink, but if you hollow it out into a bowl shape it will float. By changing the clay's shape, you have increased the amount of water it displaces. This is what boat builders do. A solid lump of steel would sink, but a ship made of hollowed out steel will float.

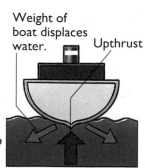

Weight of boat displaces water.

Upthrust

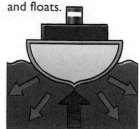

Upthrust equals weight of boat. Boat settles and floats.

How boats steer

A boat is steered by a rudder or a steering oar, which is a big blade-shaped object at the stern (the back of the boat). This cuts into the flow of water and can swivel to deflect the water to either side. As the water pushes hard against the blade, it causes the stern to swing around, pointing the bow of the boat in a new direction.

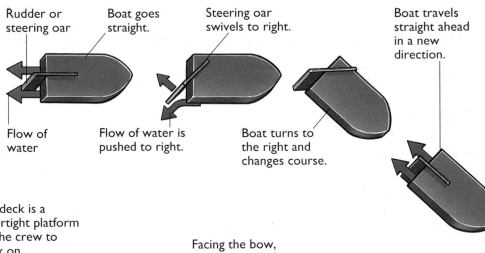

Rudder or steering oar

Boat goes straight.

Steering oar swivels to right.

Boat travels straight ahead in a new direction.

Flow of water

Flow of water is pushed to right.

Boat turns to the right and changes course.

The funnel lets out smoke from the burning coal.

The deck is a watertight platform for the crew to work on.

The body of a boat is called the hull. This one is made of tough, watertight steel.

Facing the bow, the left is called the port side, the right is the starboard side.

The back of a ship is called the stern. It is rounded to let the boat slip easily through the water.

This is the hold, where freight is stored and the engine and fuel are kept.

Coal fires heat water in the boilers, making steam. This drives the engine, providing the power to turn the propeller.

This is the propeller. As it spins, it drives the ship forward.

This is the rudder, which steers the boat.

How boats sail

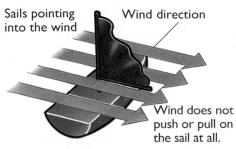

Sails pointing into the wind

Wind direction

Wind does not push or pull on the sail at all.

Sails sideways to the wind

Wind creates lift at the front of the sail and pulls the boat forward.

Wind pushes on back of sail and shoves boat along.

Sails too far into the wind

No pull on front of sail

Wind still pushes against sail.

A boat moves by trapping the wind in its sails. But if the sails point directly into the wind, they only flap noisily, producing no power.

Sideways to the wind, the sail fills and creates two forces: lift, which pulls the boat forward, and push, which shoves the boat along.

But if a sail is hauled too far into the wind, the airflow behind it breaks up and stops pulling. The sail loses lift and produces much less power.

Triremes

About 2,500 years ago, in Ancient Greece, the most powerful and famous warship in the world was the trireme. It was big, fast and deadly, even though it was always rowed into battle.

As Greek cities grew rich and powerful, fleets of triremes were built to patrol the waters of the eastern Mediterranean. These ships cost a great deal to run, so only the richest cities, such as Athens or Corinth, could afford very many of them.

Olympias

In 1985, a group of ship lovers and historians from all over the world launched a full-size replica trireme. It was called *Olympias* and, fittingly, it was built in Greece.

The main mast and the foremast each had one sail. The sails were only used on longer journeys when the wind was in the right direction.

A fast-moving ship might pack a punch of 60 tonnes (58.8 tons) or more as it hit another boat.

A flat deck ran from end to end. It served as a platform for handling the sails and for fighting other ships at close quarters.

Triremes were so long and narrow that cables of rope from bow to stern were needed to stiffen them. Otherwise they would have drooped at either end.

The bow ended in a 2m (6.5ft) wooden ram fitted with a heavy jacket of bronze. Rams were used to punch holes in the hulls of enemy ships.

The bow was decorated with a painted eye to scare the enemy.

A sunken gangway down the middle of the deck let rowers climb in and out of their seats.

The engine room

Three banks of rowers were the engine that drove a trireme. They all used incredibly long oars, and could drive a ship at an amazing speed of over eight *knots** (almost 15 km or 9 miles an hour) all day long. This was much faster than it could travel by sail. When going a long distance in a hurry, triremes were almost always rowed. A long day's voyage from dawn to dusk might cover as much as 220km (136 miles).

The upper rowers were called thranites. They sat in two lines of 31.

Middle rowers were called zygites. They sat in two rows of 27.

On the bottom tier were the thalamites. They sat in rows of 27, too.

Triremes floated at a depth of 1m (just over 3ft). Being so shallow meant they could sail very close to shore and haul up onto a beach.

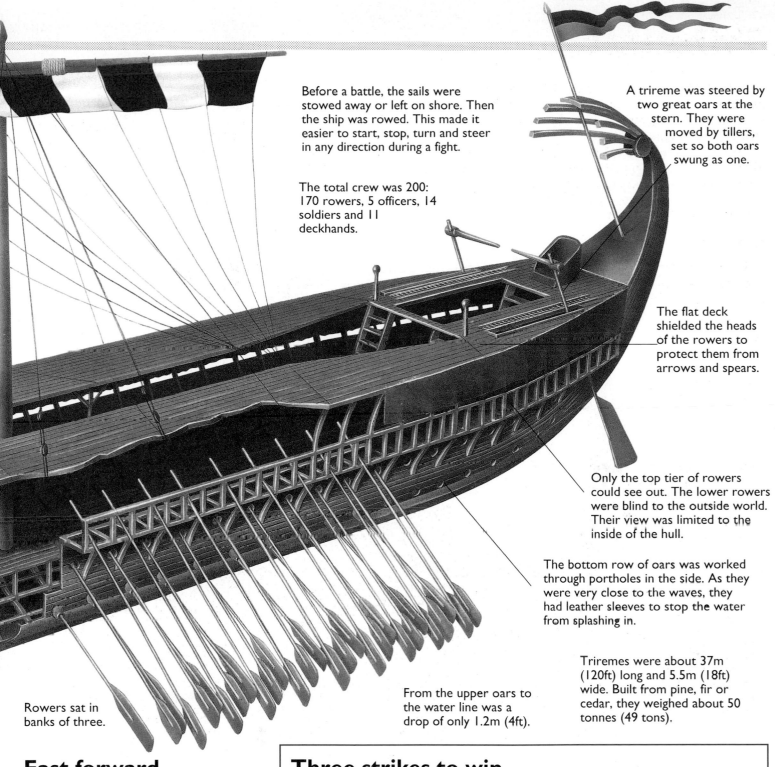

Before a battle, the sails were stowed away or left on shore. Then the ship was rowed. This made it easier to start, stop, turn and steer in any direction during a fight.

The total crew was 200: 170 rowers, 5 officers, 14 soldiers and 11 deckhands.

A trireme was steered by two great oars at the stern. They were moved by tillers, set so both oars swung as one.

The flat deck shielded the heads of the rowers to protect them from arrows and spears.

Only the top tier of rowers could see out. The lower rowers were blind to the outside world. Their view was limited to the inside of the hull.

The bottom row of oars was worked through portholes in the side. As they were very close to the waves, they had leather sleeves to stop the water from splashing in.

Triremes were about 37m (120ft) long and 5.5m (18ft) wide. Built from pine, fir or cedar, they weighed about 50 tonnes (49 tons).

From the upper oars to the water line was a drop of only 1.2m (4ft).

Rowers sat in banks of three.

Fast forward

Trireme oars were long - 4.3m (14ft) from tip to handle. That's far higher than the ceiling of most modern rooms. The Ancient Greeks knew that the blade of a long oar swept much farther - and more powerfully - through the water than a short oar.

A Greek rower making a single stroke of his oar.

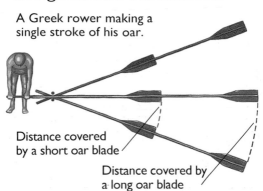

Distance covered by a short oar blade

Distance covered by a long oar blade

Three strikes to win

At the start of battle, triremes often faced off in two long lines. Each ship would pick out a target, then dart forward to try to ram an opponent and sink him. The best places to aim for were the stern and sides of another ship.

A trick often used was to sweep around the far end of the opposing line of ships and strike from the rear.

A daring move was to break through a gap in the line, wheel and strike from behind.

Sometimes a ship made for a gap in the line, then veered at the last moment to smash into the side of an enemy with its ram and shear off its oars.

The Age of Sail

Rowing is fine for lightweight boats, but it takes a lot more power to drive a really big ship through the water. For thousands of years, people relied on the wind. Using masts and sails, they were able to harness its energy to propel big ships all over the world.

The Vasa

The *Vasa*, launched in 1628, was the pride of the Swedish navy. But, because of a faulty design, she sailed a very short distance before sinking. Raised from the sea in 1961, she is the only complete 17th century warship in the world.

The Vasa	
Length:	69m (226ft)
Width:	12m (39ft)
Height:	53m (174ft)
Weight:	1,300 tonnes (1,274tons)
Guns:	64 guns
Crew:	135 sailors
	300 soldiers

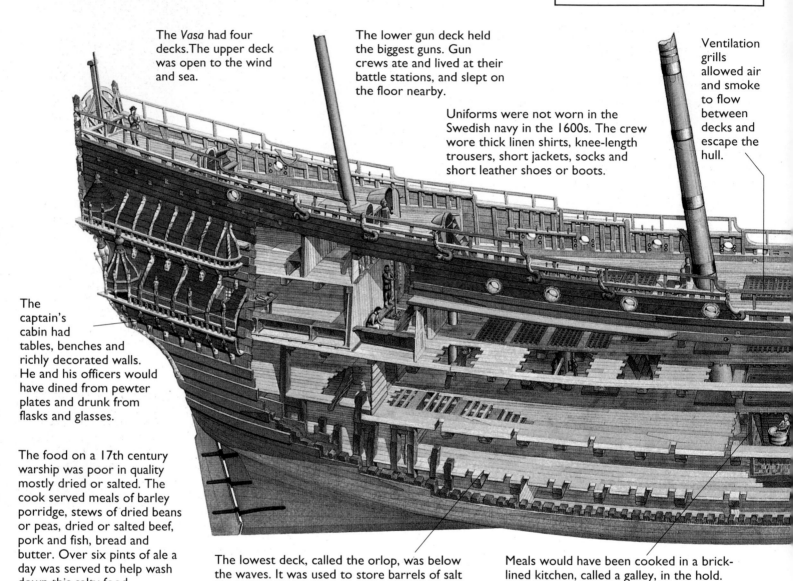

The *Vasa* had four decks. The upper deck was open to the wind and sea.

The lower gun deck held the biggest guns. Gun crews ate and lived at their battle stations, and slept on the floor nearby.

Ventilation grills allowed air and smoke to flow between decks and escape the hull.

Uniforms were not worn in the Swedish navy in the 1600s. The crew wore thick linen shirts, knee-length trousers, short jackets, socks and short leather shoes or boots.

The captain's cabin had tables, benches and richly decorated walls. He and his officers would have dined from pewter plates and drunk from flasks and glasses.

The food on a 17th century warship was poor in quality mostly dried or salted. The cook served meals of barley porridge, stews of dried beans or peas, dried or salted beef, pork and fish, bread and butter. Over six pints of ale a day was served to help wash down this salty food.

The lowest deck, called the orlop, was below the waves. It was used to store barrels of salt beef and pork and other dried food. Sails, ropes and spare equipment was kept here too.

Meals would have been cooked in a brick-lined kitchen, called a galley, in the hold. A cauldron hung over an open fire. Smoke flowed freely up to the decks above.

Packing a big punch

Vasa was one of the most powerful ships of the Swedish Navy. It carried 64 guns, including 48 big ones able to fire 11kg (24 lb) cannonballs. Together they weighed over 72 tonnes (71 tons).

The *Vasa*'s guns were the most high-tech weapons of their time. But they were slow. Ten rounds an hour was considered outstanding. Between each firing, the gun had to be cleaned and left to cool.

Gunport

Cannon is loaded with a charge and cannonball.

Cannon is pulled through gunport and aimed.

Firing hole is cleaned and small hole made in main charge.

Gunpowder is poured into firing hole.

Gunpowder is lit with an explosive fuse.

Rigged for sailing

The *Vasa* was a three-masted ship. She could put up ten sails in all, and a flutter of pennants and flags. At the time of sinking she was flying four sails. The other six were still in lockers. Today they are preserved intact in the Vasa Museum in Stockholm.

Royal warship

The *Vasa* was a fighting ship, but she was also built to show off the wealth and power of the King of Sweden, Gustavus Adolphus. From top to bottom, the entire stern was richly carved with hundreds of gilded figures and ornaments, including a huge royal coat of arms flanked by two crowned lions. Even the hatch covers of the gunports had faces of roaring lions carved onto them.

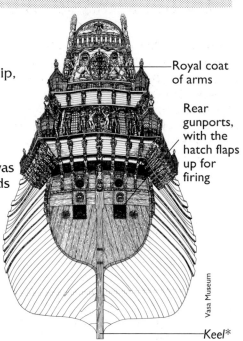

Royal coat of arms

Rear gunports, with the hatch flaps up for firing

Keel*

Over 1,000 oak trees were cut down to build the ship.

Grinning lion heads were carved onto the insides of the gun hatches. They would have been revealed to the enemy only when the hatches flipped up and the guns became visible.

The cannons poked out through holes in the hull called gunports. These were covered by wooden hatches, hung outside, that were lifted by ropes when the guns were ready to fire.

120 tonnes (118 tons) of stone *ballast** were packed in the hold to balance the weight of the masts and sails.

Gunpowder was stored in the hold, well below the water line.

The gun decks were dark, damp and crowded. The ship had no heating to keep out the chill.

Why did the *Vasa* sink ?

The *Vasa* sank because she was top-heavy. She was built too big and strong, and had too many heavy guns on the deck for the size of *hull**. She was also far too narrow to carry all that weight above the water line and still keep her balance. Just a mild gust of wind was enough to overturn her.

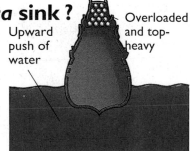

Upward push of water

Overloaded and top-heavy

Although the *Vasa* was heavy, she could still float, because the upward push of water was equal to her weight. But being top-heavy made her unstable.

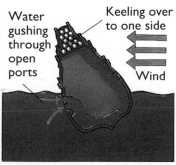

Water gushing through open ports

Keeling over to one side

Wind

The ship began to roll heavily in the breeze and a sudden gust of wind made her lean sharply to one side. Then water began to flood in through open gunports.

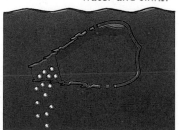

Ship fills with water and sinks.

The water flooding in added extra weight to the ship, overcoming the upward push of the water below. The ship sank like a stone.

Steamships

In the 1800s, steam engines began to be installed in ships powered by sail, like *H.M.S.Gannet* shown here. This new source of power enabled a ship to travel without being dependent on winds or tides. With an engine to drive a propeller, it could make headway even in complete calm.

H.M.S. Gannet was a three-masted ship built by the British Navy to protect the sea routes of the empire.

The ship had a crew of 140 men and boys.

Foredeck

H.M.S Gannet was fitted with six medium guns that fired shells of solid steel, and six to eight machine guns.

Switching to sail

When the *Gannet* wanted to sail, the engine was shut down. The funnel - which lowered like a telescope - was dropped and the sails were hoisted.

As the propeller (also known as the screw) now slowed the ship down, it was unhooked and lifted out of the water. The crew used a big deck winch and chain to raise it.

At full speed, the engine could drive the ship at 11.5 knots. Yet under sail the ship went even faster - sometimes as much as 15 knots.

Every corner of the hold was stuffed with equipment intended to last for two or three years. Spare parts for the ship were almost impossible to find in the regions to which she sailed.

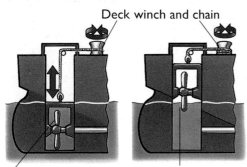

Deck winch and chain

Propeller unhooked   Propeller lifted up

The *Gannet* carried over 142 tonnes (140 tons) of coal in her bunkers, enough to travel more than 1,600km (994 miles).

Ten iron bulkheads (walls with-watertight doors) divided up the hull. They prevented the whole hull from flooding if any part of it was holed.

The hull was built as an iron frame. A double layer of thick teak planks was bolted onto it.

Steam engines

Steam ships are powered by engines which have boilers and furnaces to produce steam. Once the steam is at high pressure, it is piped to a small cylinder. It then flows on to a large cylinder at lower pressure. These two cylinders drive the pistons that turn the propeller that drives the ship forward.

Boiler containing water

Coal-burning furnace

Water boils and turns into steam.

Steam rushes into small high-pressure cylinder.

Small high-pressure cylinder

Steam forces piston back and forth.

Steam cools and loses some pressure.

Steam enters the larger cylinder and sets the second piston moving.

Propeller

The pistons turn the shaft that drives the propeller.

Large low-pressure cylinder

Historic Dockyard, Chatham

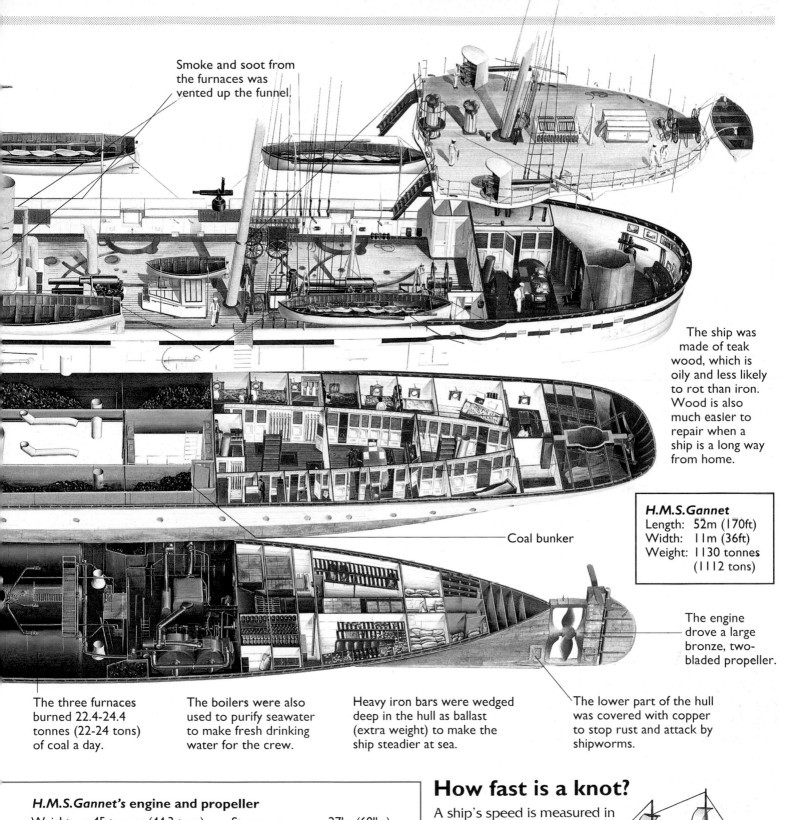

Smoke and soot from
the furnaces was
vented up the funnel.

The ship was
made of teak
wood, which is
oily and less likely
to rot than iron.
Wood is also
much easier to
repair when a
ship is a long way
from home.

H.M.S.Gannet
Length: 52m (170ft)
Width: 11m (36ft)
Weight: 1130 tonnes
(1112 tons)

Coal bunker

The engine
drove a large
bronze, two-
bladed propeller.

The three furnaces
burned 22.4-24.4
tonnes (22-24 tons)
of coal a day.

The boilers were also
used to purify seawater
to make fresh drinking
water for the crew.

Heavy iron bars were wedged
deep in the hull as ballast
(extra weight) to make the
ship steadier at sea.

The lower part of the hull
was covered with copper
to stop rust and attack by
shipworms.

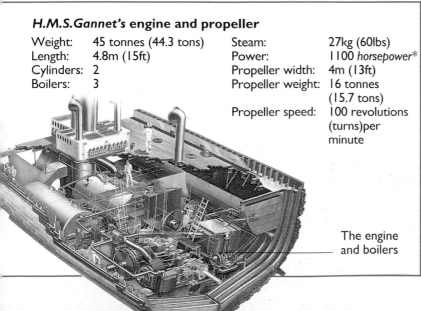

H.M.S.Gannet's engine and propeller

Weight:	45 tonnes (44.3 tons)	Steam:	27kg (60lbs)
Length:	4.8m (15ft)	Power:	1100 *horsepower**
Cylinders:	2	Propeller width:	4m (13ft)
Boilers:	3	Propeller weight:	16 tonnes (15.7 tons)
		Propeller speed:	100 revolutions (turns)per minute

The engine
and boilers

How fast is a knot?

A ship's speed is measured in
knots. One knot is the same
as 1.8km/h (just over a
mile an hour). The
word comes from
the old custom of
throwing a knotted
rope, tied to a
small plank, over
the bow. As the wood
floated toward the
stern, knots in
the rope were
counted out
to calculate the
ship's speed.

Riverboats

The riverboat fleet that plied the Mississippi River basin in the 1800s was everything that trucks, trains and planes are today. For years it was the main form of transportation in the region. In 1860, a total of 10 million tons of cargo was shipped this way.

Riverboats that carried passengers and freight were called packets. The biggest were stately palaces that ran long distance express services. They were lightly built, flimsy even, compared to ocean-going ships. They had flat, shallow hulls, since anything deeper than 1.5m (5ft) really limited the places they could get to. But they all had huge steam engines to battle upstream against fast-flowing currents.

The Rob't. E. Lee

The *Rob't. E. Lee*, named after the Confederate commander-in-chief of the southern troops in the American Civil War, was the most celebrated riverboat of all. Built in Indiana in 1866, for the next ten years she worked the Mississippi up and down from New Orleans.

The Rob't. E. Lee	
Length:	87m (285ft)
Width:	14m (46ft)
Engines:	2 steam engines
Boilers:	8 boilers producing 55kg (120lbs) of steam each
Weight:	1,432 tonnes (1,456 tons)
Fuel:	Coal and wood burning

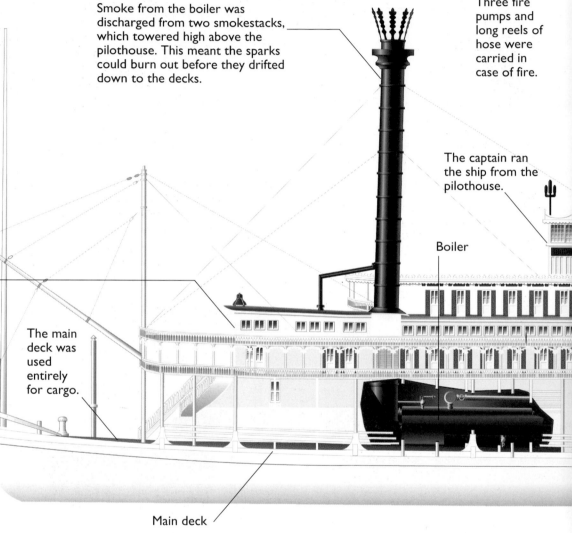

Smoke from the boiler was discharged from two smokestacks, which towered high above the pilothouse. This meant the sparks could burn out before they drifted down to the decks.

Three fire pumps and long reels of hose were carried in case of fire.

The captain ran the ship from the pilothouse.

Boiler

The main cabin was furnished with everything from a velvet carpet to rosewood chairs and sofas.

The entire ship was built of wood, nails, bolts and iron fastenings.

The main deck was used entirely for cargo.

Two steam engines generated 2,700hp* of power, enough to drive her along at over 32 kmph (20mph) in calm waters.

Main deck

Deck cargo

Riverboats took passengers and baggage, but their main business was freight, especially cotton. They carried it from all over the southern states of the USA down to New Orleans to be shipped overseas.

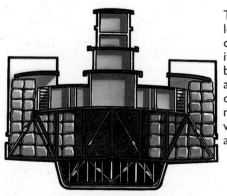

The *Rob't. E. Lee* once loaded 5,741 bales of cotton along the sides of its main deck. They could be stacked one on top of another, past all three decks. Passengers might make a whole trip without ever glimpsing any scenery.

Paddlewheels

Riverboats were powered by huge paddlewheels, mounted on each side, or at the stern. The big advantage over propellers was that they didn't dip below the hull, so the boats could keep going in very shallow waters.

At the end of the arms, wide planks of wood were bolted on to make the paddles.

The arms were braced to stop them flexing as the wheel turned.

The wheel was turned by a heavy central shaft linked to the engine.

Side-wheelers and stern-wheelers

All riverboats had flat, shallow hulls, no keel and did not float very deep in the water. Side-wheelers had one paddlewheel on each side, and an overhanging main deck which stuck out far beyond the hull. Stern-wheelers had only one wheel at the back, and their main deck was a lot narrower.

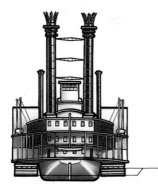

Paddlewheels did not dip below the bottom of the hull. This protected them from rocks, logs and other clutter lying on the bed of the river.

Paddlewheels

Side-wheeler seen from the bow (front)

Paddlewheel

Stern-wheeler seen from the stern (back)

The middle and top decks were for passenger cabins.

The top deck, known as the Texas deck, had 24 cabins for passengers.

The two main engines had cylinders wide enough for two men to crawl inside.

The main deck had 61 staterooms.

Steam engines

Paddlewheel

Rudder

Braces and chains

The hulls of riverboats were so long and thin that they became rather floppy. The bow and stern tended to sag into the water, a habit known as hogging. To correct this, sets of posts and chains were rigged up on deck to stiffen the frame of the hull.

Hog chains

Wooden posts

From bow to stern, sets of hog chains were rigged above the deck to stiffen the hull. They were made of lengths of iron rod, screwed together and braced by wooden posts.

Cross-section of hull showing chains from side to side

Bracing poles

Knuckle chains

Cross chains

The Great Race

In 1870, the *Rob't. E. Lee* gained lasting fame for itself in a great river race against the *Natchez*.

Both boats were due to leave New Orleans at 5pm on June 30th, bound for St. Louis, and the event grew into a feverishly-awaited race. Hundreds of thousands of dollars were laid as bets, and a huge, excited crowd lined the riverbanks to see the start.

The *Rob't. E. Lee* pulled away a couple of minutes before 5pm, her rival four minutes later. Throughout the lengthy race she was never really challenged again, although a leak in one of her boilers almost put out the fires below before it was finally plugged. The loss of speed let the *Natchez* get within 400 yards for a short while. On the last stage, by chance, night fog let the *Robt. E. Lee* gain several hours lead . She finally arrived in St. Louis on July 4th, a record 3 days, 18 hours and 14 minutes after setting out (and more than 6.5 hours ahead of the *Natchez*). To this day, no steamboat has ever beaten her time.

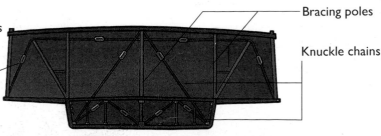

St. Louis (Finish line)

Cairo

Memphis

Vicksburg

Mississippi River

Natchez

New Orleans

(Start of race)

Yachts

Using sail power today may seem old-fashioned, but modern yachts are very different from their forerunners. Their hulls are made from synthetic materials and super-strong glue, which is far tougher and longer-lasting than wood. The masts are shaped from lightweight metal, which is lighter than wood and doesn't rot in salt water. Many yachts are equipped with quiet diesel engines, as well as the latest satellite navigation gear, two-way radios and depth finders.

Modern sails are made of terylene, a strong material which holds its shape well.

The *Swan 55*

The *Swan 55* is a single-masted yacht, known as a sloop. This yacht is built beside the Baltic Sea, in northern Finland, and is designed to be sailed across oceans. It has a deep, rounded hull and high sides. These features are common to all cruising yachts, making them stable and dry at sea.

Navigation area

The helmsman steers the yacht from the cockpit.

Small sundeck

The rear deck locker stores gas bottles for the stove, a life raft and ropes.

The rudder steers the yacht. It is moved by wires linked to a wheel in the cockpit. The rudder's long blade digs deep into the water to keep the boat dead on course.

Fully-equipped galley (kitchen)

Locker space between the inside walls and the hull

There is a sound-proofed walk-in engine room.

The three-blade propeller is driven by a six-cylinder, 116*hp** diesel engine. In calm waters it can do 10 *knots**.

The *Swan 55*	
Length:	16.7m (55ft)
Width:	4.8m (16ft)
Weight:	23 tonnes (22.5 tons)
Draught:	2.6m (8ft)
Sail area:	125m^2 (1345ft^2)

Different yacht types

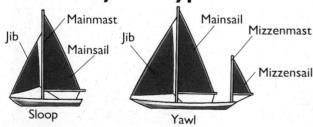

Jib, Mainmast, Mainsail — Sloop

Jib, Mainsail, Mizzenmast, Mizzensail — Yawl

Jib, Mainsail, Mizzenmast, Mizzensail — Ketch

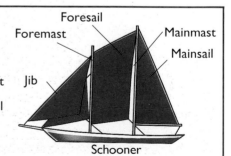

Foresail, Foremast, Mainmast, Mainsail, Jib — Schooner

Sailing yachts get their names from the way their masts and sails are rigged. A boat rigged with one mast is known as a sloop.

Yawls and ketches have two masts and can fly three or more sails. A mainsail, mizzensail and jib are the most common.

Schooners have a foremast ahead of the mainmast. They are bigger and can carry more sails than most other kinds of yachts.

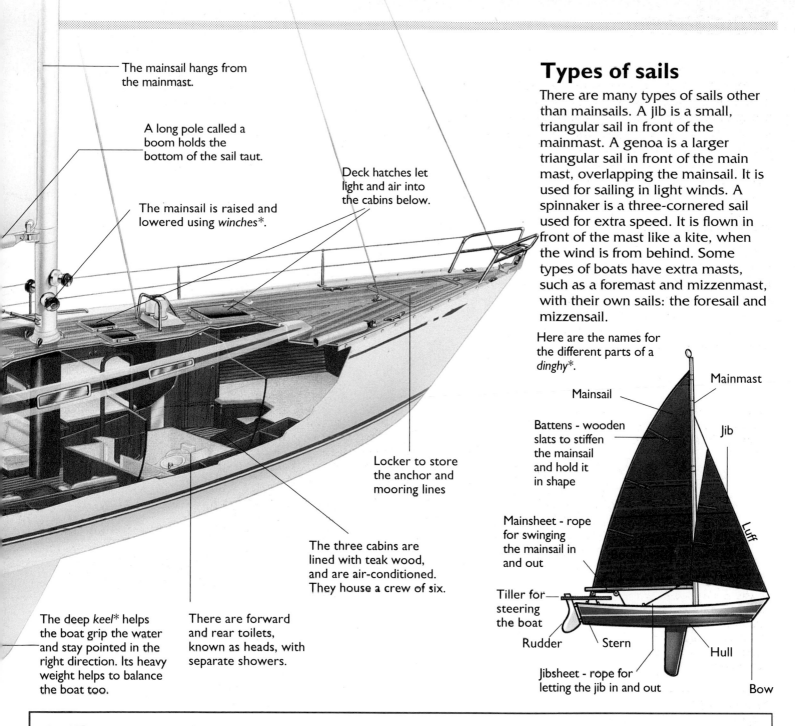

The mainsail hangs from the mainmast.

A long pole called a boom holds the bottom of the sail taut.

The mainsail is raised and lowered using *winches**.

Deck hatches let light and air into the cabins below.

Locker to store the anchor and mooring lines

The three cabins are lined with teak wood, and are air-conditioned. They house a crew of six.

The deep *keel** helps the boat grip the water and stay pointed in the right direction. Its heavy weight helps to balance the boat too.

There are forward and rear toilets, known as heads, with separate showers.

Types of sails

There are many types of sails other than mainsails. A jib is a small, triangular sail in front of the mainmast. A genoa is a larger triangular sail in front of the main mast, overlapping the mainsail. It is used for sailing in light winds. A spinnaker is a three-cornered sail used for extra speed. It is flown in front of the mast like a kite, when the wind is from behind. Some types of boats have extra masts, such as a foremast and mizzenmast, with their own sails: the foresail and mizzensail.

Here are the names for the different parts of a *dinghy**.

Mainmast

Mainsail

Jib

Battens - wooden slats to stiffen the mainsail and hold it in shape

Luff

Mainsheet - rope for swinging the mainsail in and out

Tiller for steering the boat

Rudder   Stern

Hull

Jibsheet - rope for letting the jib in and out

Bow

Sailing and wind direction

Boats can sail in any direction, except straight into the wind, or up to 45° either side of it. Within this area (called the "No Go Zone"), sails flap and lose the power to drive a boat forward. So, to sail into the wind, a boat has to zigzag its way forward. This is known as tacking. Here are three ways of using the wind to sail a boat.

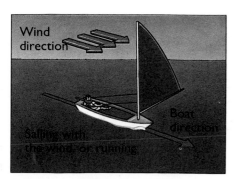

Here, the boat heads in more or less the same direction as the wind, with the sail set at right angles to it. This is a slow way to sail.

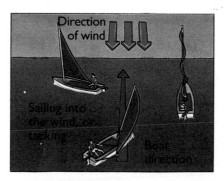

The boat zigzags its way forward at an angle to the wind. It keeps switching the side of the sail that faces the wind to stay on course.

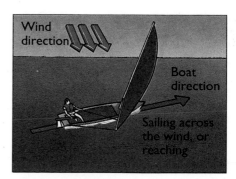

Both the sails and the boat lie sideways to the wind. This is a course that traps the wind best and makes for the most speed.

Ferries

Some of the busiest ferry routes in the world cross the English Channel. At the height of summer, over 130 trips a day are made between Calais in France and Dover in England, with ships leaving port every 30 minutes.

From inside, the ferries on this short sea journey look like multilevel car parks. Beneath their comfortable passenger areas, they stow hundreds of cars and trucks.

Pride of Calais

On a single trip from Dover to Calais, the *Pride of Calais* superferry can carry up to 2,300 passengers and 650 cars or 100 trucks. The ship works day and night, all year long. It makes the 42km (26 mile) crossing in about 75 minutes, and usually stays in port for less than an hour before its next trip.

P&O European Ferries

One of the busiest lines in the English Channel is P&O European Ferries. It runs five ships from Dover to Calais, including the *Pride of Calais*.

Pride of Calais
Weight:	26,500 tonnes (25,970 tons)
Length:	170m (558ft) (as long as 1½ soccer fields)
Width:	28m (92ft)
Speed:	22 knots
Crew:	110-120 per shift

The *Pride of Calais* and its sister ship the *Pride of Dover* between them carried 5 million passengers in 1995.

Over two million meals a year are served in four different types of restaurants.

Cars and trucks can drive on at one end, park, and then drive straight off at the far end, without ever having to turn or back up.

People in the Club Class lounge have access to phones, faxes, writing desks and photocopiers, so they can work as they travel.

The main diesel engine sits below the car deck.

Electronic eyes

In crowded waters, fishing boats and yachts sail by every day. The heavy traffic keeps a captain alert even in fine weather. But at night, or in fog or storms, the only way to see what's out there is by radar. The long whirling bars at the top of ferry masts are radar antennae. They can see ships, islands, marker buoys and even landmarks on the coast.

1. Radar signals are broadcast from the ferry, some 500 times a second. They travel at the speed of light.

2. If they hit another ship 30 km (18.6 miles) away, a faint echo bounces back.

3. The signals are reflected back to the ferry 1/500th second later.

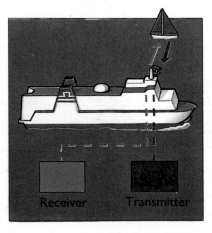

Receiver   Transmitter

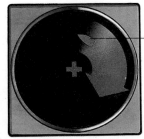

Ship on screen

The receiver turns the echo into a bright light on the radar screen. The navigator uses this to track the direction, speed and distance of the ship and steers a course to avoid it.

Roll-on, roll-off

The vehicle decks have wide bow and stern doors, and huge open parking spaces. This means that hundreds of vehicles can drive in and out swiftly with ease, so loading never takes long. This arrangement is known as roll-on, roll-off, or ro-ro.

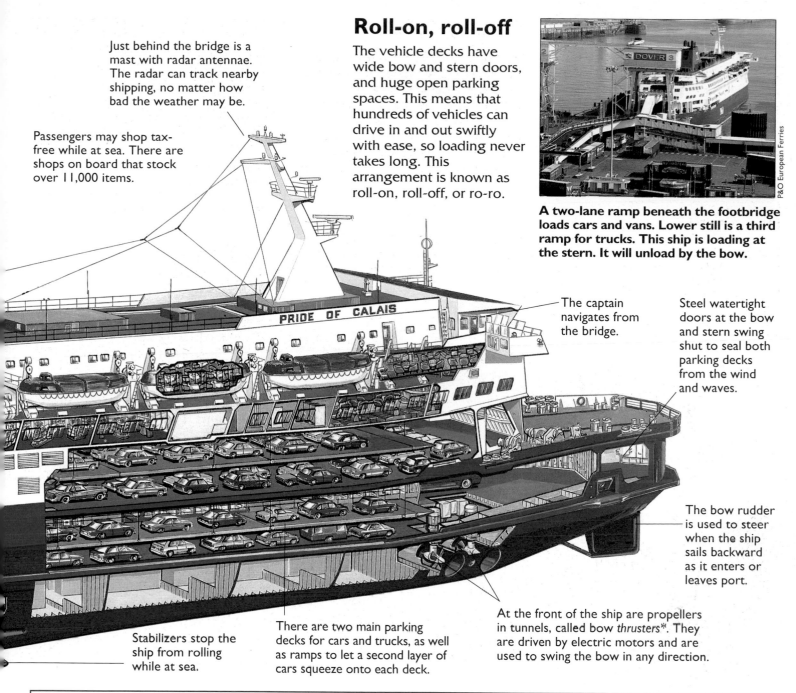

Just behind the bridge is a mast with radar antennae. The radar can track nearby shipping, no matter how bad the weather may be.

Passengers may shop tax-free while at sea. There are shops on board that stock over 11,000 items.

P&O European Ferries

A two-lane ramp beneath the footbridge loads cars and vans. Lower still is a third ramp for trucks. This ship is loading at the stern. It will unload by the bow.

The captain navigates from the bridge.

Steel watertight doors at the bow and stern swing shut to seal both parking decks from the wind and waves.

PRIDE OF CALAIS

The bow rudder is used to steer when the ship sails backward as it enters or leaves port.

Stabilizers stop the ship from rolling while at sea.

There are two main parking decks for cars and trucks, as well as ramps to let a second layer of cars squeeze onto each deck.

At the front of the ship are propellers in tunnels, called bow *thrusters*٭. They are driven by electric motors and are used to swing the bow in any direction.

Air-cushioned vehicles

Ferries that use a powerful cushion of air to lift themselves off the ground are called air-cushioned vehicles, or ACVs. ACVs can hover in one place, or move forward, backward and sideways. They can cross water, mud, sand and level ground, which means that they are able to fly from shore to shore without having to use special ports. On a single trip, a big air-cushioned vehicle can take up to 400 passengers and 60 cars.

This ACV is a BHC AP. 1-88. It can carry 101 passengers with a top speed of 92 km/h (56mph).

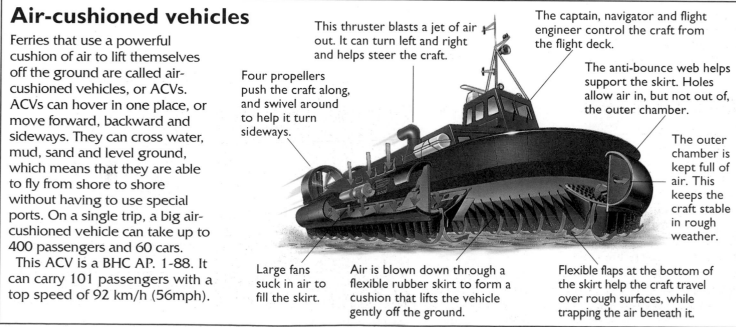

This thruster blasts a jet of air out. It can turn left and right and helps steer the craft.

Four propellers push the craft along, and swivel around to help it turn sideways.

The captain, navigator and flight engineer control the craft from the flight deck.

The anti-bounce web helps support the skirt. Holes allow air in, but not out of, the outer chamber.

The outer chamber is kept full of air. This keeps the craft stable in rough weather.

Large fans suck in air to fill the skirt.

Air is blown down through a flexible rubber skirt to form a cushion that lifts the vehicle gently off the ground.

Flexible flaps at the bottom of the skirt help the craft travel over rough surfaces, while trapping the air beneath it.

Engines

The engines of modern vessels range in size, from tiny outboards a child can lift, to diesels the size of a room and gas turbines as powerful as the jets on an airliner.

Some marine engines run on a mixture of petrol and oil, others use diesel fuel. Most are designed to run at a steady speed for long periods of time while the vessel cruises. Stop-start driving (such as a car faces in traffic) is unusual. Engines mostly drive propellers that range from the size of your hand, to about 7m (23ft) across in the case of supertankers. On some fast ships, engines drive water jets instead, because they reach much higher speeds with less wear and tear.

Electric power

This Yamaha electric drive outboard engine can propel a small boat with hardly any noise. It weighs less than 9 kg (20lbs), runs on a 12- volt car battery and produces 1/3 *hp** of thrust. It's perfect for watching wildlife, or finding fish without disturbing them.

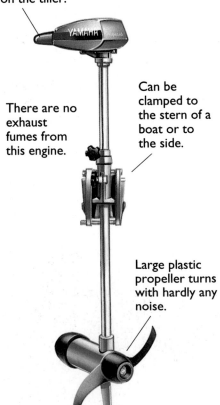

Speed is controlled by twisting the handgrip on the tiller.

There are no exhaust fumes from this engine.

Can be clamped to the stern of a boat or to the side.

Large plastic propeller turns with hardly any noise.

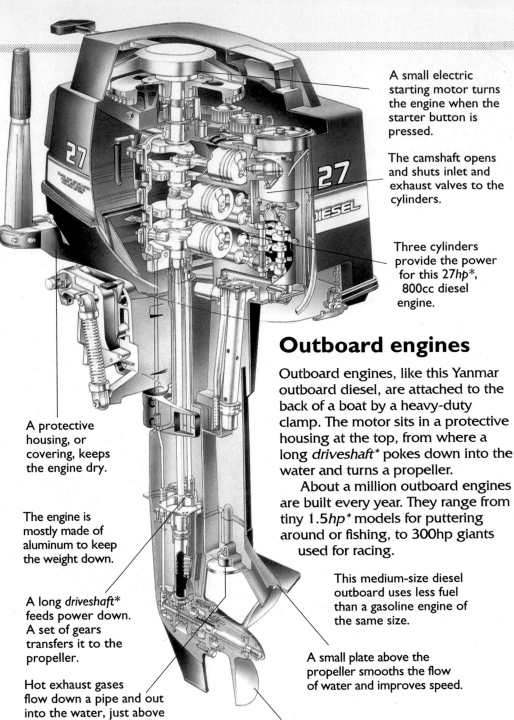

A small electric starting motor turns the engine when the starter button is pressed.

The camshaft opens and shuts inlet and exhaust valves to the cylinders.

Three cylinders provide the power for this 27*hp**, 800cc diesel engine.

A protective housing, or covering, keeps the engine dry.

The engine is mostly made of aluminum to keep the weight down.

A long *driveshaft** feeds power down. A set of gears transfers it to the propeller.

Hot exhaust gases flow down a pipe and out into the water, just above the propeller.

Outboard engines

Outboard engines, like this Yanmar outboard diesel, are attached to the back of a boat by a heavy-duty clamp. The motor sits in a protective housing at the top, from where a long *driveshaft** pokes down into the water and turns a propeller.

About a million outboard engines are built every year. They range from tiny 1.5*hp** models for puttering around or fishing, to 300hp giants used for racing.

This medium-size diesel outboard uses less fuel than a gasoline engine of the same size.

A small plate above the propeller smooths the flow of water and improves speed.

Propeller

How do propellers push?

As they spin, propeller blades force water to rush backward. The flow creates a strong thrust that shoves a boat forward. Big, slow-turning propellers have the strongest thrust of all.

Because propeller blades are curved, like those of a plane engine, (see page 43) water flows faster over the front of the blade than the back. This creates a second strong force, of *suction**, that also pulls the propeller forward as it turns.

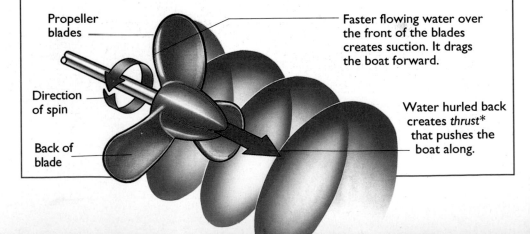

Propeller blades

Direction of spin

Back of blade

Faster flowing water over the front of the blades creates suction. It drags the boat forward.

Water hurled back creates *thrust** that pushes the boat along.

Inboard engines

Inboard diesel engines are the workhorses of the sea. They are used by yachts, fishing boats and all kinds of work boats, from tugs to supertankers. They are tough, strong, thrifty with fuel and can run for hours with next to no servicing.

This small diesel engine is used by sailing yachts to motor in and out of port, or to cruise when the sails are down. It runs quietly and smoothly and is extremely reliable.

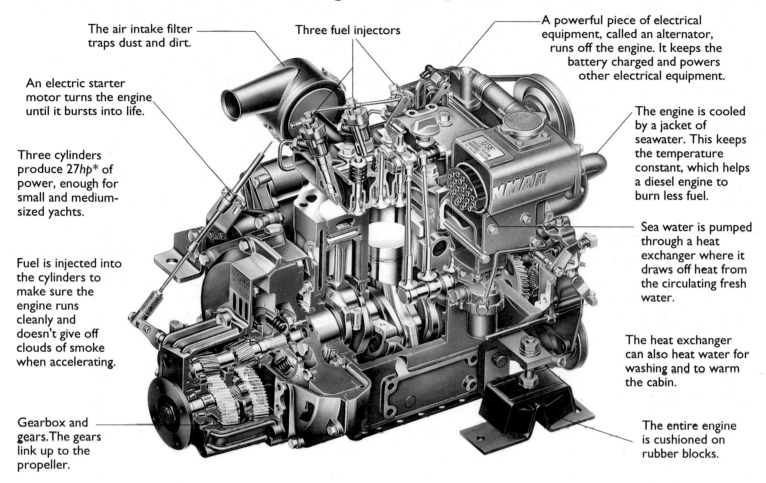

The air intake filter traps dust and dirt.

Three fuel injectors

A powerful piece of electrical equipment, called an alternator, runs off the engine. It keeps the battery charged and powers other electrical equipment.

An electric starter motor turns the engine until it bursts into life.

Three cylinders produce 27hp* of power, enough for small and medium-sized yachts.

Fuel is injected into the cylinders to make sure the engine runs cleanly and doesn't give off clouds of smoke when accelerating.

The engine is cooled by a jacket of seawater. This keeps the temperature constant, which helps a diesel engine to burn less fuel.

Sea water is pumped through a heat exchanger where it draws off heat from the circulating fresh water.

The heat exchanger can also heat water for washing and to warm the cabin.

Gearbox and gears. The gears link up to the propeller.

The entire engine is cushioned on rubber blocks.

Turbine engines

Ships which need to travel fast (ferries, ACVs and warships) all have gas turbine engines. Turbines allow a boat to go faster because of their small size and light weight. (They can be up to 80% lighter and 60% smaller than diesel engines of the same power.) The gas turbines found in ships are versions of the same engines that power jet planes. You can learn about turbine engines in aircraft on pages 42-43.

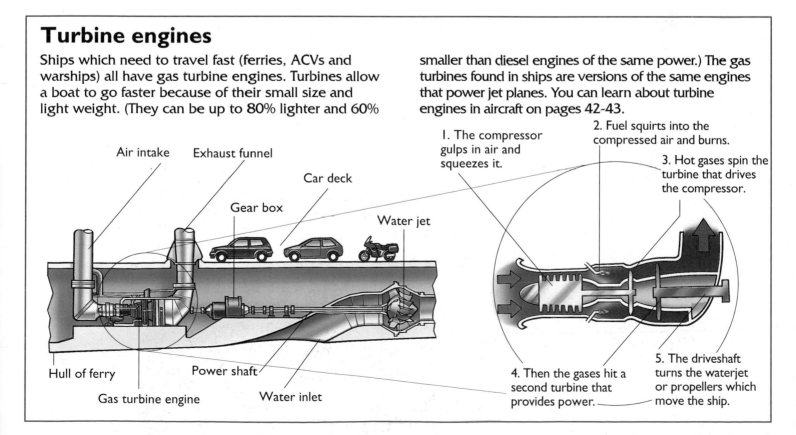

Air intake

Exhaust funnel

Car deck

Gear box

Water jet

Hull of ferry

Power shaft

Gas turbine engine

Water inlet

1. The compressor gulps in air and squeezes it.

2. Fuel squirts into the compressed air and burns.

3. Hot gases spin the turbine that drives the compressor.

4. Then the gases hit a second turbine that provides power.

5. The driveshaft turns the waterjet or propellers which move the ship.

Lifeboats

Lifeboats are some of the toughest working boats in the world. They are built to go to sea in really foul weather, and to work in waters strewn with rocks and sandbanks. Bucking high winds and breaking seas, they steer right alongside stricken ships to pass towlines or lift off crew.

Trent Class lifeboat

Some of the busiest shipping lanes in the world are next to Britain and Ireland. Apart from oil tankers, cargo ships and ferries, thousands of small fishing boats and yachts go to sea every day. Each year, lifeboats are called out over 6000 times (that's some 16 launches a day), saving more than 1,600 lives. The boats, like the Trent class lifeboat shown here, are all run by the RNLI (the Royal National Lifeboat Institution).

The Trent Lifeboat
Length: 14.26m (46ft 9in)
Weight: 26.5 tonnes
                 (26 tons)
Speed: 25 knots
Range: 400km (250 miles)
Crew: 6
Engines: Two 800hp diesels

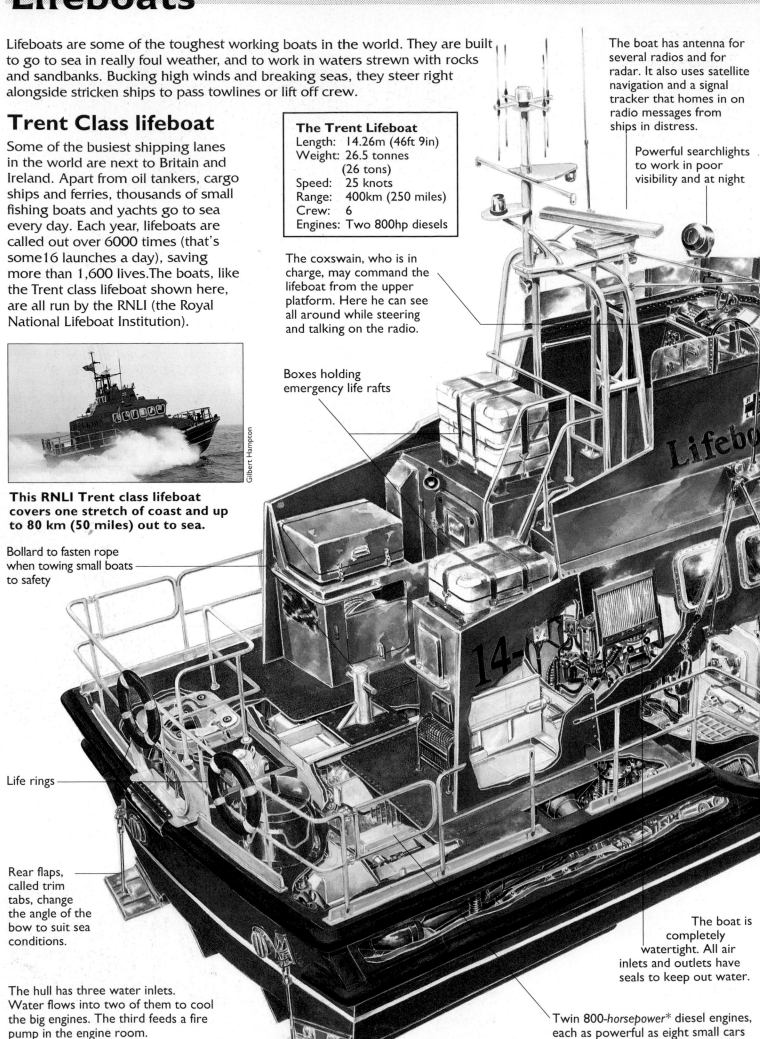

Gilbert Hampton

This RNLI Trent class lifeboat covers one stretch of coast and up to 80 km (50 miles) out to sea.

The boat has antenna for several radios and for radar. It also uses satellite navigation and a signal tracker that homes in on radio messages from ships in distress.

Powerful searchlights to work in poor visibility and at night

The coxswain, who is in charge, may command the lifeboat from the upper platform. Here he can see all around while steering and talking on the radio.

Boxes holding emergency life rafts

Bollard to fasten rope when towing small boats to safety

Life rings

Rear flaps, called trim tabs, change the angle of the bow to suit sea conditions.

The hull has three water inlets. Water flows into two of them to cool the big engines. The third feeds a fire pump in the engine room.

The boat is completely watertight. All air inlets and outlets have seals to keep out water.

Twin 800-*horsepower** diesel engines, each as powerful as eight small cars

The right way up!

Lifeboats are built of tough lightweight materials that are completely watertight. They will bob upright almost at once if a wave ever knocks them flat. As they flip over, their engines automatically slow down. Then, as soon as the boats right themselves, the coxswain simply opens the throttle and continues on his way.

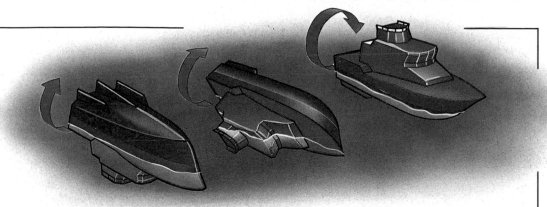

1. All new lifeboats are capsize-tested for safety. A crane tilts the boat into the water until it is lying completely upside down.

2. As the crane lines are dropped, the boat quickly turns itself the right way up. Water pours from the upper decks as it rights itself.

3. The heavy engines are so low down, and there is so much air in the cabin and hull, that the lifeboat flips upright without needing help.

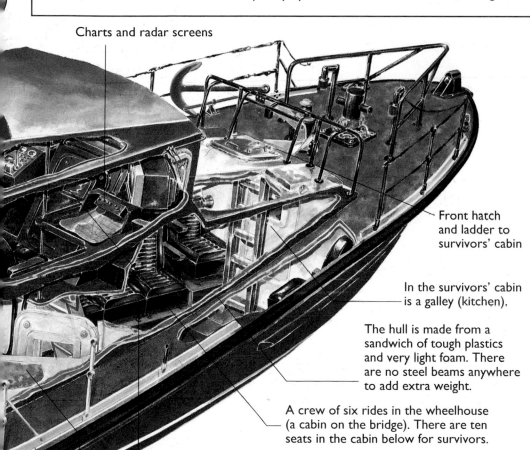

Charts and radar screens

Front hatch and ladder to survivors' cabin

In the survivors' cabin is a galley (kitchen).

The hull is made from a sandwich of tough plastics and very light foam. There are no steel beams anywhere to add extra weight.

A crew of six rides in the wheelhouse (a cabin on the bridge). There are ten seats in the cabin below for survivors.

Crewmen wear helmets and sit harnessed in highback seats that stop them from flying about as waves smash into the boat.

Fuel tanks are filled with foam, just like tanks in some racing cars. It stops fuel from sloshing around as the boat rolls.

The sides of the deck are extra low to make it easier to snatch people from the sea.

Side keels

A lifeboat may work so close to shore that a really big wave can make it touch bottom. To protect the propellers, it has a pair of very deep keels on either side of the main keel. These reach further down than the propeller blades and so will touch bottom first. They also keep the boat upright at low tide if it gets stranded away from base.

Propellers tucked close to the hull, protected by the keels.

Side keel   Main keel   Side keel

A quick launch

Some lifeboats are moored afloat, but others are stationed in boathouses. In order to put to sea, they use a greased slope called a slipway. First their engines are started. Then, once the single holding wire is released, the lifeboat slides down the slipway and gathers speed. It hits the water at almost nine *knots**.

A groove in the slipway guides the keel.

The side keels keep the lifeboat upright.

Racing boats

Racing powerboats are designed to rise out of the water and skim the surface at high speed. There are three basic types: monohulls, catamarans and hydroplanes.

A monohull is another name for a single-hulled boat. (Most non-racing boats belong to this category.) A catamaran has two narrow hulls, one on each side of the driver. The hulls are set wide apart to make the boat stable. A hydroplane is a half-breed. It has two hulls in front, while the back half narrows into a single hull.

Hull shapes

Monohulls have a flaring V-shape that helps the front section of the hull to rise out of the water at high speed.

Only the rear hulls of catamarans (and their propeller and rudder) stay wet at race speeds, making them the fastest class of racer.

The twin front hulls of hydroplanes create *lift**. At full speed they become airborne. Only the back hull stays in the water.

Monohull

Catamaran

Hydroplane

Ocean racer

Surfury was a monohull cruiser designed for offshore races in heavy seas and winds. It was built in 1965 and, over the next five years, carved out a reputation as one of the world's best racers in long distance events.

A third crew member tended the engines. He stood behind the drivers.

Surfury won the British Cowes-Torquay race in 1967 with an average speed of 85km/h (53 mph).

Two big Daytona engines, one behind the other, provided 1050 *horsepower**.

Surfury was 11m (36ft) long. It was built from sheets of laminated cedar wood, pressed into shape.

Two drivers rode half-standing, supported by reclining seats that cushioned them from the battering of high-speed travel over waves.

Part of the cabin roof was replaced with a tarpaulin to save weight.

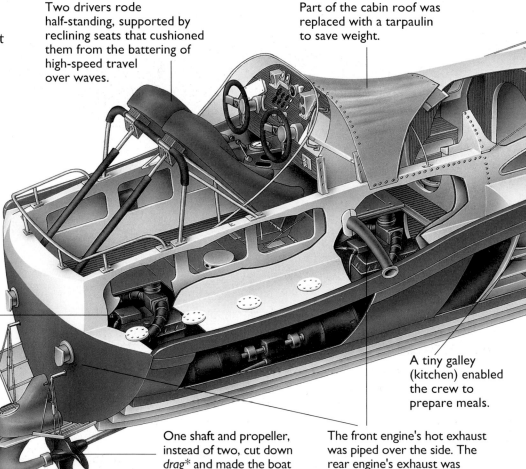

A tiny galley (kitchen) enabled the crew to prepare meals.

One shaft and propeller, instead of two, cut down *drag** and made the boat much faster.

The front engine's hot exhaust was piped over the side. The rear engine's exhaust was vented through the stern.

A formula 1 circuit

Marker *buoys**

About 20 boats compete in races of 55-60 laps.

Finish line

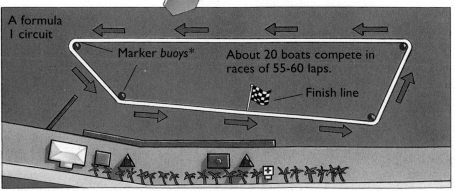

Formula 1 racing

Formula 1 boats are small, streamlined catamarans with a huge outboard engine. Their hulls are built from synthetic materials that are light but immensely strong, to withstand pounding at top speeds. Like Formula 1 cars, these boats compete all over the world. There are usually about 12 events a year, held in sheltered waters where boats can reach top speeds of 260 km/h (165 mph).

Plane speed

Racing boats are built with specially shaped bottoms, so their hulls can plane (or skim) across the surface, rather than carve a path through the water. This increases their speed enormously, because the engines avoid wasting power by having to push aside a heavy weight of water.

Chris Davies / Formula Photo

A Victory boat is a type of big catamaran that has won many offshore races in recent years.

Circuit racing ranges from Formula I boats, to little J250 craft, like this, that children of nine and up can race.

Chris Davies / Formula Photo

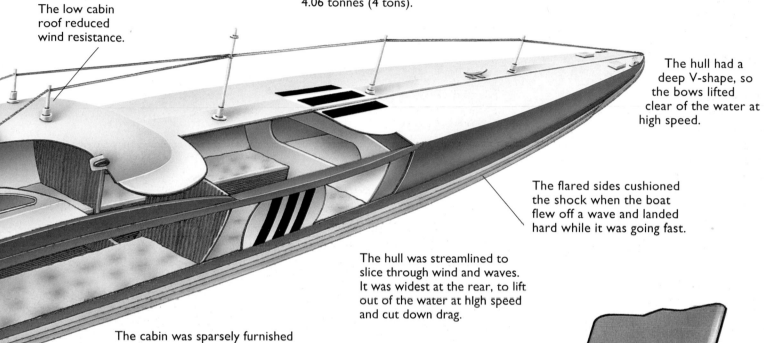

The low cabin roof reduced wind resistance.

The racing weight was 4.06 tonnes (4 tons).

The hull had a deep V-shape, so the bows lifted clear of the water at high speed.

The flared sides cushioned the shock when the boat flew off a wave and landed hard while it was going fast.

The hull was streamlined to slice through wind and waves. It was widest at the rear, to lift out of the water at high speed and cut down drag.

The cabin was sparsely furnished to save weight. The dining table doubled as the door to the toilet.

Hydrofoils

The speed of any vessel in water is limited by a force called *drag**, created by the friction between the boat and the water. This means that ordinary boats cannot travel much faster than 35 km/h (20mph). So, with a given size of boat and engine, the easiest way to boost a boat's speed is by lifting the hull out of the water altogether. One of the best ways of doing this is with hydrofoils.

Hydrofoils are flat struts fixed to the hull below water. They are shaped like the wings of a plane (see page 35). As a boat gathers speed, water flows faster over the curved upper side of a hydrofoil than the flat surface beneath it. Low pressure forms above the foil and, as with a plane wing, creates *lift**. The strut rises up. As the hull lifts out of the water, drag decreases. Now, running with the same power, the boat swiftly picks up speed. Big passenger hydrofoils can accelerate up to more than 90km/h (almost 60 mph).

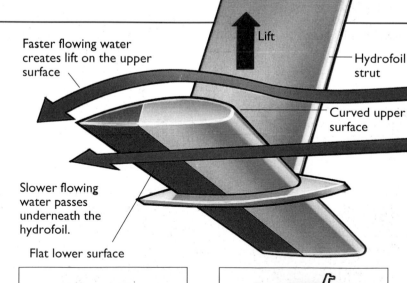

Faster flowing water creates lift on the upper surface

Lift

Hydrofoil strut

Curved upper surface

Slower flowing water passes underneath the hydrofoil.

Flat lower surface

At slow speed, the hull sits in the water like any other boat.

Going fast, the hull rides in the air. Only the foils stay underwater.

Container ships

Modern cargo ships are huge and expensive to build. So they are designed to spend as little time as possible resting in port. To make loading quicker, nearly all freight goes on board in gigantic, prepacked metal boxes, called containers. Other freight is designed to be driven, or towed by trailers, on and off - just like cars on a ferry. This kind of freight is known as roll-on roll-off (or ro-ro). It can include anything from railway carriages to helicopters and earth-moving equipment.

The *Atlantic Companion* (below) is one of five 53,000-tonne (52,000-ton) G3 models owned by the Atlantic Container Line. They are among the largest combination container/ro-ro ships afloat.

ACL

The *Atlantic Companion* carries containers and ro-ro cargo from the USA to Europe. Each crossing takes six to eight days.

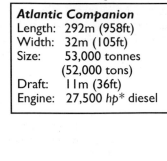

Atlantic Companion
Length: 292m (958ft)
Width: 32m (105ft)
Size: 53,000 tonnes
         (52,000 tons)
Draft: 11m (36ft)
Engine: 27,500 *hp** diesel

Dining room and day room where the crew can take breaks

Indoor swimming pool and sauna

Five levels of cars can park in the upper garage.

Library and TV/video room

The whole ship is controlled from a room called a wheelhouse that runs the full width of the ship. The ship is steered by computer, while at sea.

There are two 50-person lifeboats - one on each side of the ship.

Refrigerated containers

A wide ramp lowers from the back of the ship. Two lanes of traffic at a time can use the ramp - one loading and the other unloading.

Stern *thruster** for docking (see box opposite)

A single main propeller can drive a loaded ship at a cruising speed of 18 *knots**.

Fully loaded, the ship carries 1045 cars, over 1900 containers, 175 refrigerated containers, and hundreds of roll-on roll-off pieces of freight.

A giant six-cylinder diesel engine drives the ship.

Steering

Almost all ships steer with the help of one or two rudders fixed behind their propellers.

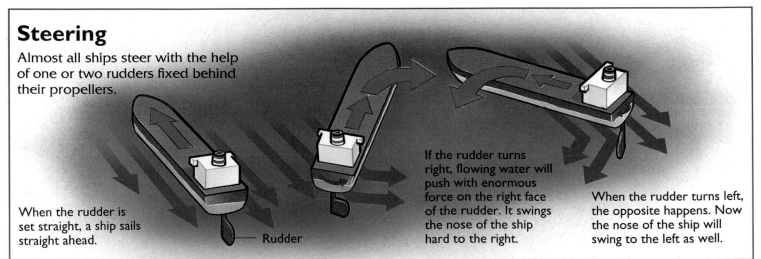

When the rudder is set straight, a ship sails straight ahead.

Rudder

If the rudder turns right, flowing water will push with enormous force on the right face of the rudder. It swings the nose of the ship hard to the right.

When the rudder turns left, the opposite happens. Now the nose of the ship will swing to the left as well.

Container ports

Some of the busiest ports in the world, such as Hong Kong and Singapore, each handle over 10 million containers a year.

After a ship docks, giant cranes, able to lift 50 tonnes (49 tons) at a time, roll into position to unload the containers.

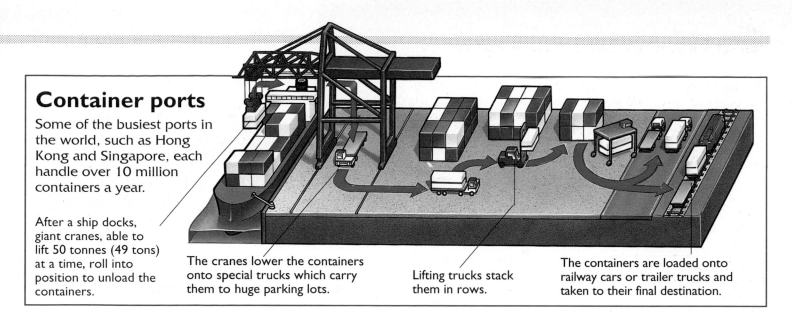

The cranes lower the containers onto special trucks which carry them to huge parking lots.

Lifting trucks stack them in rows.

The containers are loaded onto railway cars or trailer trucks and taken to their final destination.

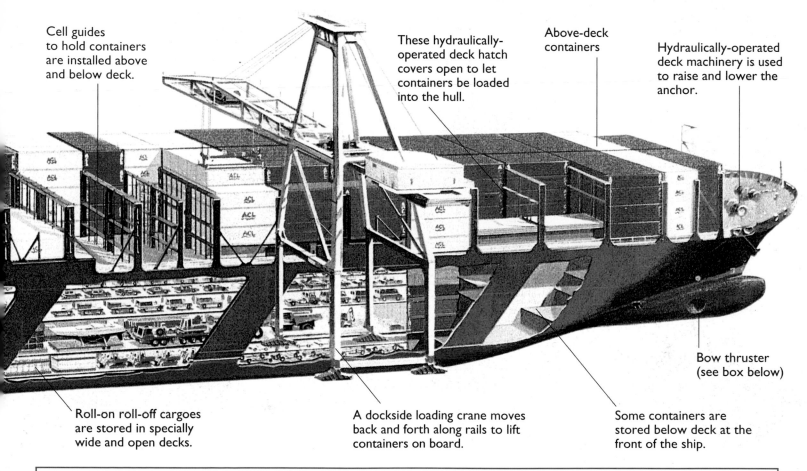

Cell guides to hold containers are installed above and below deck.

These hydraulically-operated deck hatch covers open to let containers be loaded into the hull.

Above-deck containers

Hydraulically-operated deck machinery is used to raise and lower the anchor.

Bow thruster (see box below)

Roll-on roll-off cargoes are stored in specially wide and open decks.

A dockside loading crane moves back and forth along rails to lift containers on board.

Some containers are stored below deck at the front of the ship.

Thrusters

All G3 ships can dock without help from tugboats. They use big propellers, called thrusters, attached to the bow and stern to create a sideways blast of water.

Run together, in the same direction, the thrusters slowly nudge the ship sideways as it docks. Pushing on opposite sides, they turn the ship around within its own length.

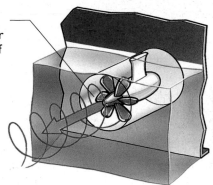

Thrusters work by pushing water from one side of the ship to the other through a large tunnel in the hull.

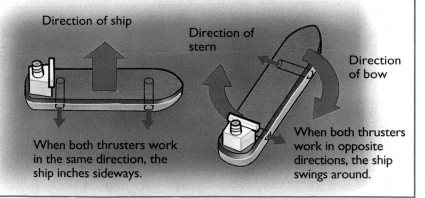

Direction of ship

Direction of stern

Direction of bow

When both thrusters work in the same direction, the ship inches sideways.

When both thrusters work in opposite directions, the ship swings around.

Tugs

Ocean-going ships are so big that they are difficult to steer in enclosed waters. This means they have trouble sailing in and out of port. That's where tugs come in.

Tugs are stubby little boats that stop, start and turn with ease. They handle so well they can work in even the tightest spaces, alongside piers, or in closed-off sections of canals or rivers called locks.

Tucked into a tug's hull is an incredibly powerful engine that drives a huge propeller. This provides the power to tow cargo ships and oil tankers well over a hundred times as heavy as the tug.

A 20 year-old tug	
Length:	32m (105ft)
Draught:	4.7m (15ft)
Engines:	Twin diesels
Top speed:	About 12 knots
Crew:	Up to 12
Pulling power:	around 40 to 50 tonnes (39-49 tons)

Exhaust funnel for diesel engine

All-purpose tugs

A general purpose tug doesn't work only with ships. It may also tow barges and dredgers, fight fires (see right) with its pumps and hoses, or mop up oil spills left by tankers. Tugs are sometimes hired to carry crews and other passengers from ship to shore, or as rescue craft to help ships that get into trouble.

Steel bars to keep tow lines from snagging on the deck

Tow ropes are 15cm (6in) thick and able to take a strain of over 100 tonnes (98 tons).

Capstan winch for reeling in heavy tow ropes

Pumps to feed water or foam to fire guns

Howard Smith Towage & Salvage

This is a deep-sea tug, which is longer and heavier than the ones used in ports. Their high bows are built to shrug off ocean waves, while their huge engines can tow anything from oil rigs to crippled supertankers.

Rudder

Two diesel engines can produce 3,000hp - a huge amount of power for such a small boat.

Propeller power

Many new tugs have two sets of special high-powered propellers called Voith-Schneider propellers. They look a bit like egg-beaters, and sit mid-hull instead of at the stern. Unlike ordinary propellers, they can thrust in any direction. This lets tugs tow at full power in whatever direction the captain wants to go.

Each blade looks like a stubby little wing.

When the blades swing at an angle during part of each turn, the ship starts to move - in this case forward.

When the ship is at rest, the blades turn without an angle and so create no thrust.

A deep keel helps to steer.

Struts around the blades boost the thrust of the propellers.

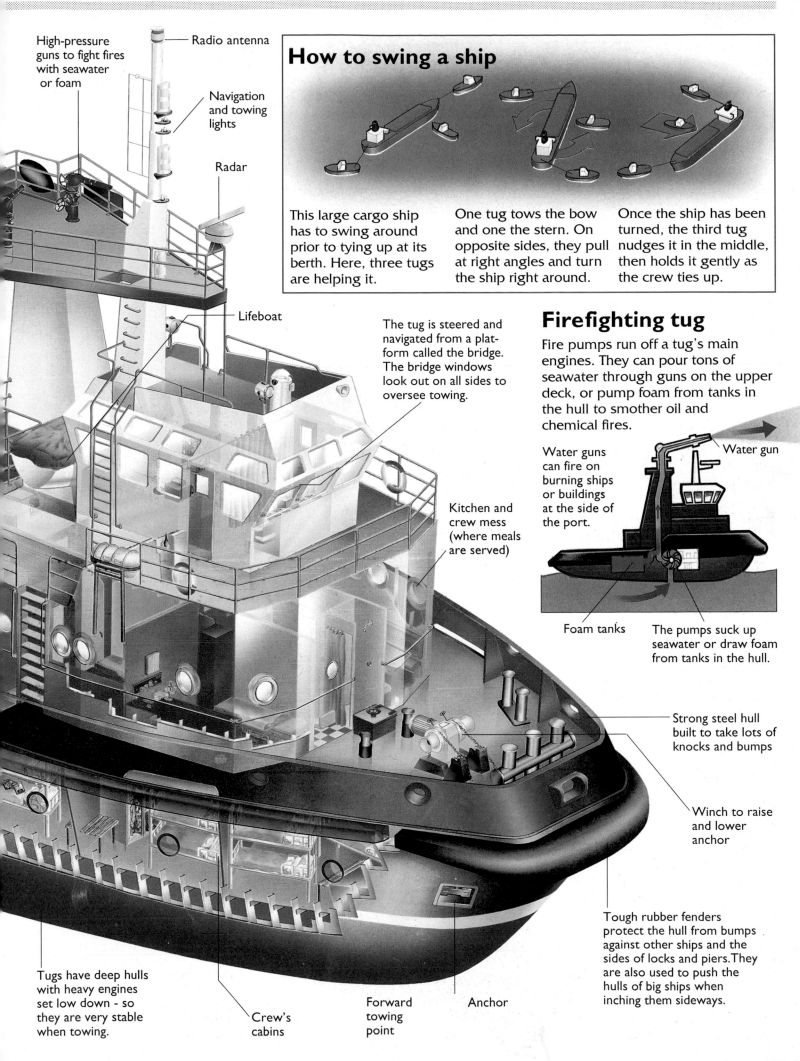

High-pressure guns to fight fires with seawater or foam

Radio antenna

Navigation and towing lights

Radar

How to swing a ship

This large cargo ship has to swing around prior to tying up at its berth. Here, three tugs are helping it.

One tug tows the bow and one the stern. On opposite sides, they pull at right angles and turn the ship right around.

Once the ship has been turned, the third tug nudges it in the middle, then holds it gently as the crew ties up.

Lifeboat

The tug is steered and navigated from a platform called the bridge. The bridge windows look out on all sides to oversee towing.

Firefighting tug

Fire pumps run off a tug's main engines. They can pour tons of seawater through guns on the upper deck, or pump foam from tanks in the hull to smother oil and chemical fires.

Water guns can fire on burning ships or buildings at the side of the port.

Water gun

Kitchen and crew mess (where meals are served)

Foam tanks

The pumps suck up seawater or draw foam from tanks in the hull.

Strong steel hull built to take lots of knocks and bumps

Winch to raise and lower anchor

Tough rubber fenders protect the hull from bumps against other ships and the sides of locks and piers. They are also used to push the hulls of big ships when inching them sideways.

Tugs have deep hulls with heavy engines set low down - so they are very stable when towing.

Crew's cabins

Forward towing point

Anchor

Cruise ships

Few people cross oceans by ship any more. Planes are much faster and more convenient. Although ocean liners have long gone, their place has now been taken by cruise liners. These ships are designed specifically for pleasure trips, usually calling at a number of different ports.

The *Sun Princess*

The *Sun Princess, launched in 1995,* is one of the newest big ships to join the fleet that sails the Caribbean in winter and the Alaska Coast in summer. Cruise ships take over 4.5 million people on trips every year.

At 78,250 tonnes (77,000 tons) and 261m (856ft), the *Sun Princess* is the biggest cruise ship afloat.

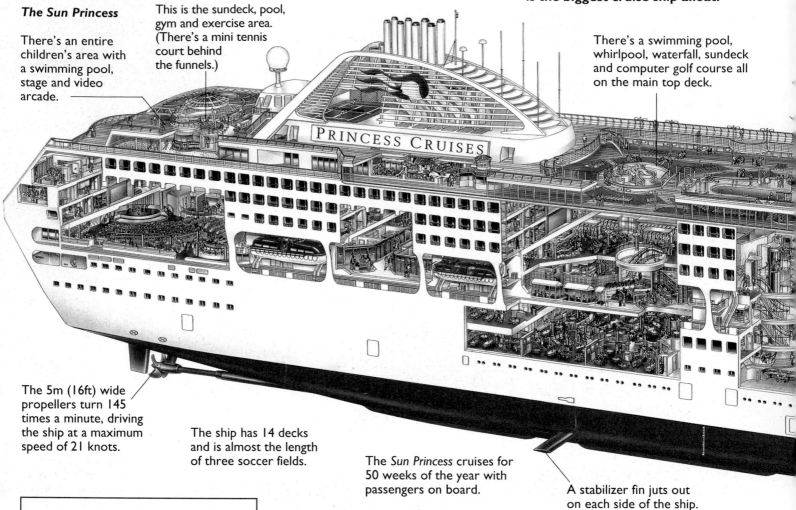

The Sun Princess

There's an entire children's area with a swimming pool, stage and video arcade.

This is the sundeck, pool, gym and exercise area. (There's a mini tennis court behind the funnels.)

There's a swimming pool, whirlpool, waterfall, sundeck and computer golf course all on the main top deck.

The 5m (16ft) wide propellers turn 145 times a minute, driving the ship at a maximum speed of 21 knots.

The ship has 14 decks and is almost the length of three soccer fields.

The *Sun Princess* cruises for 50 weeks of the year with passengers on board.

A stabilizer fin juts out on each side of the ship.

Silent night

The cruising speed of the *Sun Princess* is 21 knots (a good 10 knots slower than older passenger liners like the *QE2*). Its two propellers each have six curved blades, which draw water past the hull with little turbulence. Each propeller is driven by an electric motor, mounted on rubber to cut down noise.

How stabilizers work

Two stubby wings called stabilizers poke from the hull of the ship below the water line. They smooth out the rolling motion of the waves.

These wings waggle back and forth all the time, controlled by computers in the ship that sense exactly what the waves are doing.

As waves wash past, they set up a side-to-side rolling motion.

The stabilizer helps to keep the ship in a more upright position.

The stabilizers fold into a bay in the sides when the sea is calm. As the sea gets rougher, a single stabilizer is brought into use.

It acts like the wing of a plane, lifting one side of the ship in the opposite direction to the rolling motion of the waves.

The two opposing rolling motions cancel each other out. This means the ship continues in a steadier, more upright manner.

A floating hotel

Part resort, part luxury hotel, cruise ships are amazingly comfortable. In the best suites, passengers can enjoy marble bathrooms, whirlpool tubs, TVs and private bars. Over 400 cabins come with outside balconies overlooking the sea.

In the heart of the ship is a four-floor high lobby where people can glide up and down in glass elevators.

Radar antennae, radio equipment and satellite links for phones, faxes, computers and TV.

The ship can take as many as 2,022 passengers at a time, with a crew of 920.

The bridge, the area from which the captain and his officers run the ship

Sea fare

With four restaurants and cafés, and five bars scattered around the ship, passengers can eat and drink just about any time, day or night.
A typical shopping list for a seven-day cruise might include the following groceries:

10,886 kg (24,000 lbs) of meat
2994 kg (6600 lbs) of fish
726 kg (1600 lbs) of fresh shrimp
4082 kg (9000 lbs) of potatoes
15,876 kg (35,000 lbs) of fruit
Enough coffee to brew 8865 ltrs (1,950 gallons)

Computers guide and steer the ship. They can stop her outside a port and hold her steady there without ever needing to drop the anchor.

P&O

SUN PRINCESS

The bulb shaped bow parts the waves to enable the ship to slip through the sea with less effort.

The ship has a large auditorium in the front for shows and concerts.

Bulkheads

The hull of a cruise ship, below the water line, is divided into compartments by watertight walls called bulkheads. These are designed so that if water gets into one compartment it doesn't spread through the ship.
   Above this lies the watertight bulkhead deck. No water can rise above it, even if the lower hull is entirely flooded. So, even if a ship is sinking, bulkheads stop it from capsizing (rolling over) due to water rushing to one side. This gives people more time to escape.

The compartments below the bulkhead deck hold the engines, air-conditioning, supplies, laundries, and cabins for the crew.

Bulkhead deck

Bulkheads

All watertight bulkhead doors can be shut by remote control from the bridge.

The ship will still stay afloat, even if two compartments are flooded.

Submersibles

Submarines are built for military use. Navies use them to launch missiles or to sink surface ships.

Submersibles are something altogether different. They are small diving craft built for scientific research, archeology, or to work in oil and mineral exploration. Some map the seabed, others repair pipes and cables, and a few are used for rescue work. They can all dive far deeper (about four times as deep) than any military submarine.

Length:	7.6m (25ft)
Width:	2.4m (8ft)
Engines:	6 small electric *thrusters**
Cruising speed:	1 *knot**
Top speed:	1.5 knots
Max depth:	4000m (13,000ft)
Range:	8 kms (5 miles)

Alvin can dive to about 4,000m (15,000ft) - about as far as a person can walk in an hour.

Two still cameras are fixed outside to take pictures while three video cameras record everything on film.

Alvin the submersible

One of the best-known submersibles is a little research vessel called *Alvin*. First launched in 1964, it has since made thousands of dives around the world. It was the first vessel to explore the wreck of the *Titanic*, and to discover belching vents of hot water at the bottom of the sea. These occur where cracks in the seabed have caused heat deep inside the Earth to raise the temperature of water seeping in by hundreds of degrees. In these isolated spots, scientists have found colonies of strange tube worms and shrimps not known anywhere else.

The robot arm collects rocks and other samples from the ocean floor.

Three small portholes allow the crew to see out.

*Thrusters**

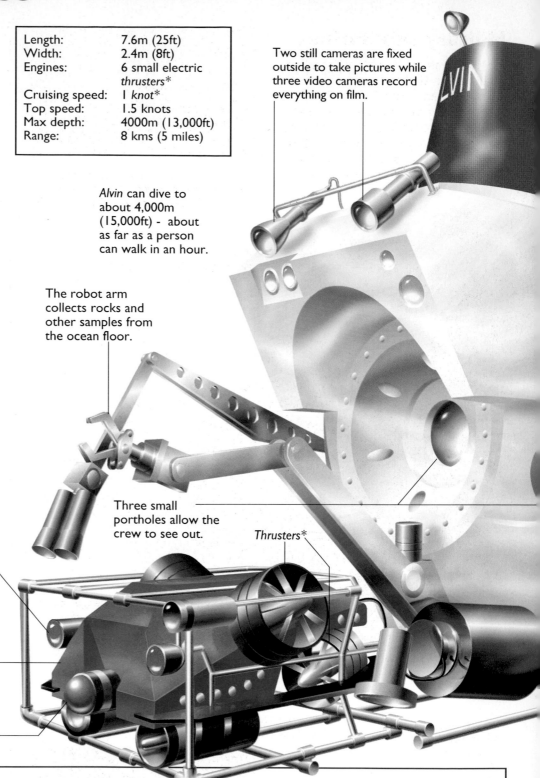

The seafloor where *Alvin* works is pitch black. Its powerful lights can only light up a small patch of seabed.

This is a remote-controlled robot called *Jason Jr*, that was used to explore the wreck of the *Titanic*. It was taken down in a cage, bolted to the front of *Alvin*, and steered by cable into the ship.

Video camera

Using special equipment, divers like this one from *Norbert* can work up to 250m (820ft) deep.

Big squeeze

The amount of air pressure at sea level is called 'one atmosphere'. Underwater, pressure builds up very quickly, as water is far heavier than air. Every 10m (33ft) farther down adds another 'atmosphere' of pressure.

The limit of *Alvin's* range is just under 4,000m (13,120ft). In the deepest parts of the ocean, almost 11,000m (36,000ft) down, pressure may be 1,000 times greater than at the surface. Here a submersible would crumple like an empty can.

Air Pressure and Underwater Pressure

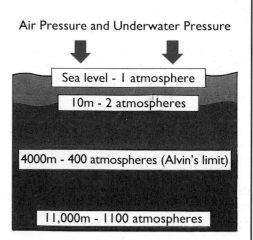

Sea level - 1 atmosphere

10m - 2 atmospheres

4000m - 400 atmospheres (Alvin's limit)

11,000m - 1100 atmospheres

Military submarines

Military submarines are designed to operate in a shallow band of water, no more than about 200-300m (600-900ft) below the surface. They are used to attack surface ships, or hunt enemy submarines and fire missiles. Their hulls are strong, but very few can go deeper than 500m (1640ft).

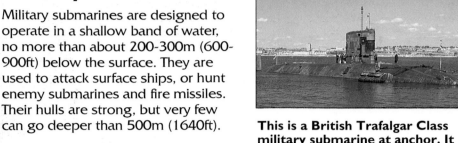

This is a British Trafalgar Class military submarine at anchor. It can reach a top speed of 30 *knots**.

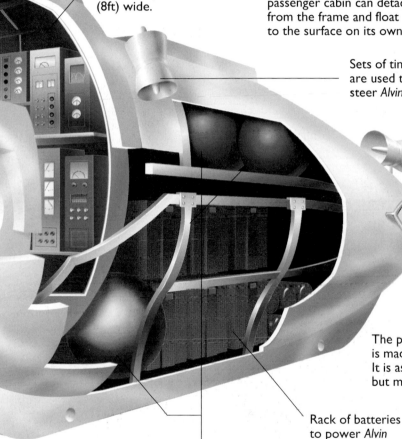

The cramped cabin is a metal ball just over 2m (8ft) wide.

In an emergency, the passenger cabin can detach from the frame and float to the surface on its own.

Sets of tiny thrusters are used to drive and steer *Alvin*.

The passenger cabin is made of titanium. It is as hard as steel, but much stronger.

Rack of batteries to power *Alvin*

Air tanks and ballast tanks

The sub stays in contact with the surface by radio telephone.

Mini-subs

Mini submersibles are widely used, for example, in the oil business, to move divers, or to work at depths that are too dangerous for free-swimming humans. They are equipped with floodlights, cameras, robot arms, and a highly accurate navigation system so they can find their way about in pitch darkness.

As all these subs run on batteries, they can only stay under for a very short time (usually less than a day) before they surface and recharge.

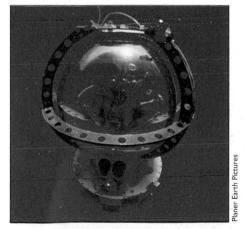

***Nemo* (Naval Experimental Manned Observatory) operates at a depth of 183m (600ft), with a crew of two.**

How do subs dive?

Submersibles can only go up and down. They carry heavy lead weights as they dive that are dumped at the bottom when the vessels need to stop going down.

A submarine is different. As well as being able to travel on the surface and dive, it can also hover at whatever depth it wants to. This is possible because it has air tanks, called ballast tanks, all along the outside of its hull. They are open to the sea at the bottom and have vents at the top.

Floating on the surface, the ballast tanks are full of air and their vents are closed.

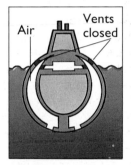

To dive, the vents are opened to let water flood into the tanks. This makes the sub heavier and so it sinks.

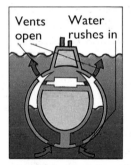

To hover or travel at the desired depth, the vents are closed, so the sub stops sinking. The tanks are full of water.

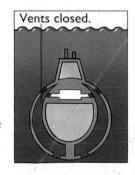

To go up, high-pressure air is blown into the tanks, forcing out the water. The submarine rises to the surface.

Water is blown out.

The future

The look of boats has changed out of all recognition in the past 150 years. During this time, they have grown bigger, faster and much more comfortable. If change continues like this, it is likely that boats of the future will look very different from the way they do today. Since the main problem is the way water slows boats down, many of the newest ideas are concentrating on raising them out of the water, to make them go faster.

Air superliner

A group of Japanese companies are testing the idea of fast catamaran freighters, able to carry 1,000 tonnes (984 tons) at over 50 knots, with a range of 800 km (500 miles) or more. One model, the TSL-A, uses a cushion of air to lift much of its body out of the water in order to reach top speed. So far, only half-size models, like the *Hisho* (below), have been tested at sea, but they have been a great success.

Japan Ship Centre

Hisho is a 70m (230ft) half-size model of the TSL-A. It is driven by two 16,000hp engines, linked to water jets.

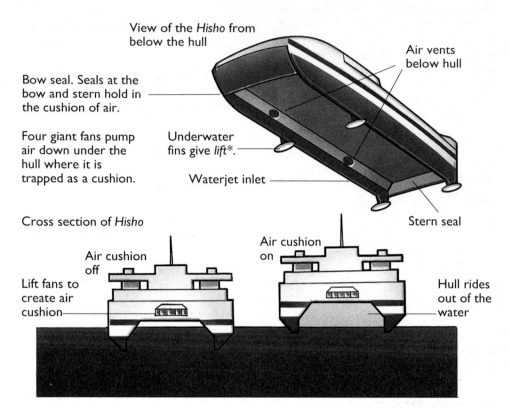

View of the *Hisho* from below the hull

Air vents below hull

Bow seal. Seals at the bow and stern hold in the cushion of air.

Four giant fans pump air down under the hull where it is trapped as a cushion.

Underwater fins give *lift*.

Waterjet inlet

Stern seal

Cross section of *Hisho*

Air cushion off

Lift fans to create air cushion

Air cushion on

Hull rides out of the water

The boat with no propellers

Japanese engineers have built an experimental boat that runs without propellers or *thrusters*. Instead it is powered by two *superconducting* electromagnetic thrusters. The *Yamato 1* was tested in Kobe, Japan, in 1992, proving that a motor with no moving parts really can work.

The *Yamato 1* has two water tunnels in its hull, wrapped with magnets and electrodes. When these are switched on, they create a force that pushes a jet of seawater through both tunnels and out at the stern with enough power to drive the boat along at eight knots.

The *Yamato 1* is 30m (98ft) long, weighs 188 tonnes (185 tons) and has a crew of ten.

Main generators to provide electric current

Wheelhouse for steering

In a special refrigerator, electromagnets are cooled to -270°C with liquid helium.

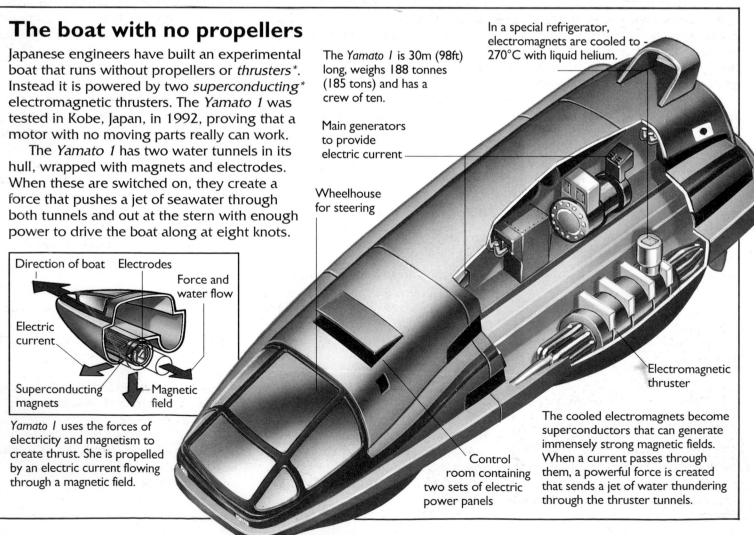

Direction of boat   Electrodes

Force and water flow

Electric current

Superconducting magnets

Magnetic field

Yamato 1 uses the forces of electricity and magnetism to create thrust. She is propelled by an electric current flowing through a magnetic field.

Control room containing two sets of electric power panels

Electromagnetic thruster

The cooled electromagnets become superconductors that can generate immensely strong magnetic fields. When a current passes through them, a powerful force is created that sends a jet of water thundering through the thruster tunnels.

94

Wave cutter

The knife-blade bows of fast catamaran ferries work so well that they may one day be used on cargo ships too. In the model below, the crew's quarters and the bridge are pushed up front, while as much deck space as possible is left free for freight. Up to 70 containers are stored out in the open, without hatches or covers. This saves weight and so makes the ship much faster.

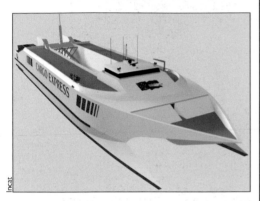

This 40 knot wave-piercing freighter, designed by Incat, Sydney, Australia, is powered by four jet thrusters.

Flying boats

The most dramatic way to make boats faster is to lift them right out of the water altogether. One design that does this is the wing in ground-effect craft, or wingship.

The *Flarecraft L-325* rides smoothly on a cushion of air. Short stubby wings flying just above the surface of the water create a pocket of high air pressure (called ground effect) when they are moving at high speed. This will lift the 9.5m (31ft) craft into the air once it reaches 80km/h (50mph). But it cannot fly higher than 2m (6ft) above the waves, which is why it is registered with the US Coast Guard as a boat.

This *Flarecraft L-325* is a five-seat water taxi, which cruises at 120km/h (75mph).

Glossary

Ballast. Heavy weights, often lead or tanks of water, packed into the deepest parts of the hull or keel to give a boat better balance. Ballast stops a boat from rolling over in heavy winds and waves.

Bow. The narrow front end of a boat, pointed to cut cleanly into the water.

Bridge. The place from which ships are steered. Usually one of the highest places above deck with a good view.

Bulkheads. Walls and watertight doors that run from side to side inside the hull and divide it into watertight compartments.

Buoy. A bright float, anchored near ports, used for navigation or mooring.

Coxswain. The person who steers a boat. Also called a helmsman.

Deck. The floors of a ship.

Dinghy. Any small boat powered by sail, oars or outboard motor.

Drag. The force created by the action of water against the hull and propeller of a ship which slows it down. Ships with long, narrow hulls and pointed ends usually suffer less drag than those with wide hulls and blunt ends.

Driveshaft. The shaft that transmits power from the engine to the propeller in a ship. Also called the propeller shaft.

Funnel. The chimney of a ship which releases smoke and exhaust gases.

Horsepower. A measurement of a boat's engine power, equivalent to 746 watts.

Heat exchanger. An attachment to a ship's engine to pipe cold seawater past the hot water that cools an engine. The seawater draws off heat, without coming into direct contact with the engine.

Hull. The part of a ship which sits in the water.

Hydrofoil. A boat with underwater "wings" designed to generate lift. As speed increases, the hull is raised out of the water, so reducing drag.

Keel. The lowest structure of a ship's hull, running lengthways, upon which the framework of the hull is built.

Knots. The speed of a ship in water is measured in knots, or nautical miles per hour. One knot is 1.85km (1.15 miles).

Lift. The upward force created by wings.

Port. Facing toward the bow of a ship, its left-hand side is known as the port side.

Propeller. A rotating device, with two or more curved blades, that provides thrust for moving a ship forward. A propeller is attached to a shaft (usually at the back of the boat) that is turned by the engine.

Radar. A method of finding the position and speed of a distant ship or other object, by transmitting radio waves which are reflected back to the sender.

Rudder. A large blade at the back of a ship behind the propeller, for steering.

Stabilizers. Fins projecting from the sides of the hull, to help keep a ship steady.

Starboard. Facing toward the bow of a ship, the right side is known as starboard.

Stern. The back end of a boat, usually rounded so water flows smoothly past.

Superconducting. Having no electrical resistance. In metals this occurs when they are cooled to very low temperatures.

Thrust. The force which drives boats forward, provided by the turning action of the propellers which throws a powerful surge of water backward.

Thrusters. Extra propellers in the hull of a ship for moving sideways.

Turbine engines. High-speed engines that work like the jets that power planes.

Upthrust. The force pushing up on a boat when it is floating in water.

Wheelhouse. An enclosed platform from which a ship is steered. Also called the pilothouse or bridge.

Winches. Winding wheels for raising and lowering heavy anchors, or for hauling ropes to raise sails or tie up to a dock.

Index

ABS (anti-locking brakes), 22, 25, 29
acceleration, 25
accelerator, 27, 31
accelerometers, 58, 59
active safety features, 6
active suspension, 20
actuators, 39
Adolphus, Gustavus, 71
aerobatics, 49
aerodynamics, 16, 17, 29, 30, 31, 46, 47, 63
aeroscreen, 19
ailerons, 36, 37, 48, 61
air bag, 6, 7
air brake, 37, 40, 51, 53
Airbus A300-600ST, 41
Airbus A340, 39, 40, 64
Airbus A3XX, 62
air corridors, 59
aircraft carrier, 52
air-cushioned vehicles (ACVs), 79
air filter, 4, 15
airflow, 67
airfoil, 63
air intake, 35, 37, 55, 60
airliners, 40, 41, 46, 47, 54, 62
air pressure, 14, 31, 35, 39, 63
airspeed indicator (ASI), 38, 39
air traffic control, 59
alloy, 42, 63
alternator, 11, 26, 31, 81
altimeter, 38, 39
altitude, 39, 54, 61
Alvin, 92
anchors, 77, 87
anti-G suit, 55
anti-roll bar, 21, 29
Antonov AN76, 43
arrester hook, 51
artificial horizon, 38, 58
Atlantic Companion, 86
automatic gearbox, 13, 28
autopilot, 59
avionics, 35, 45, 53
axle, 3, 20, 29

BAe/Aerospatiale Concorde, 43, 46, 47
BAe Hawk 200, 34, 35, 45
BAe Sea Harrier, 52, 53
balance weight, 10
ballast, 73, 95
ballast tanks, 93
ball bearings, 17
banked turn, 37, 38
barges, 88
battens, 77
battle, 69
Bell X-15, 62
Bentley 4 1/2 Litre, 18, 19
Benz Velo, 3
bias ply tyres, 31
biplanes, 46, 49, 63
black box, 54
boathouses, 83
Boeing 747, 39, 47, 50, 62, 64
Boeing 757, 42
Boeing AWACS, 56
boilers, 67, 72, 73, 74
boom, 77
bow, 66, 67, 68, 75, 77, 79, 85, 87, 91, 95

brake horsepower (bhp), 11, 18, 19, 25, 28, 31
brake lights, 15, 26
brake pads, 22
brake parachutes, 51, 61
brakes, 51
bridge, 89, 91, 95
British Navy, 72
bucket seats, 8
bulkheads, 72, 91, 95
bunkers, 72
buoys, 78, 95
bypass duct, 42, 43

Cabins, 40, 66, 70, 74, 83, 85
cage, 7
caliper, 22
cam, 31
cambelt, see *timing belt*
camouflage, 61
camshaft, 11, 80
cannons, 70, 71
canoes, 66
canopy, 54, 55, 56, 60
captain, 70, 79, 91
cargo, 74
cargo hold, 41, 62
cargo planes, 35
cargo ships, 82, 86, 89, 95
catalytic converter, 25, 29
catamarans, 84, 85, 94
catamaran ferries, 95
catapult, 51
Cessna 150, 48
chassis, 4, 31
chocks, 52
clutch, 12, 27, 31
coal, 66, 67, 72
cockpit, 14, 35, 36, 37, 38, 39, 48, 49, 52, 57, 58, 62
co-driver, 8, 9
cogs, 12, 13
coil, 26, 27
combustion chamber, 43, 63
combustion cycle, 10
compass, 58
composites, 45, 61
compression chamber, 42
compressor, 53, 63
compressor blades, 42, 43
Computer Aided Design (CAD), 4, 45
computers, 86, 90, 91
Concorde, 46, 47
connecting rod, 10
contact points, 27
container ports, 87
containers, 95
container ships, 86-87
control cables, 36, 37
control column, 37, 38
control surfaces, 36, 37, 38, 46, 61, 63
coxswain, 82, 83, 95
crank, 31
crankshaft, 10, 11, 27
crash test dummy, 6
cruiseships, 90, 91
crumple path, 7
crumple zone, 7
Cuban Eight, 49
Curtiss Hawk, 44
cylinder, 10, 11, 20, 22, 25, 26, 38, 42

Damper, 20, 28, 29
Dassault Rafale, 54
dead reckoning, 58
deck, 67, 68, 69, 70, 71, 74, 75, 76, 87, 90, 95
deck winch, 72
De Havilland Leopard Moth, 38
Delaunay-Belleville F6, 2, 3
delta wings, 35
depth finder, 76
DHC-2 Beaver, 50
diesel engines, 76, 80, 82, 86
differential, 12, 13, 31
dinghies, 77, 95
dipped headlights, 27
dipstick, 4
disc brake, 5, 15, 22
distributor, 26, 27, 31
downforce, 14, 25
drag, 36, 37, 46, 51, 55, 85, 95
drag coefficient, 16
dredgers, 88
driveshaft, 12, 13, 80, 95
drogue basket, 47
drogue chute, 55
drum brake, 5, 22, 25
duralumin, 44, 63

ECM pod, 57
EFA EuroFighter, 54
Egyptians, Ancient, 66
ejection seat, 45, 52, 54, 55
electric engines, 11, 31
elevators, 36, 37, 48, 50, 51, 61
emergency brake, 31
engine room, 68
engines, 34, 40, 42, 43, 44, 50, 51, 67, 72, 78, 80-81, 84
exhaust gases, 61
exhaust nozzles, 52, 53, 57
exhaust pipe, 5, 8, 15, 29
exhaust valve, 10

Facetting, 60, 61
Falcon 900, 50
fan, 4, 24
fan blades, 40
ferries, 78-79, 81, 82
fighting ship, 71
fire extinguisher, 9
firefighting tug, 89
fishing boats, 81
flaps, 79, 82
Flarecraft L-325, 95
floating, 66, 68, 73
flying boats, 95
fog lamp, 26
Ford Escort RS Cosworth, 8, 9
Ford Trimotor, 40
foremast, 68, 77
Formula I boats, 84
four forces of flight, 36, 63
four wheel drive (4WD), 12, 24, 28
freight, 67, 74, 86, 95
friction, 16, 17, 31, 85
fuel, 67, 80, 83
fuel injection system, 10
fuel management systems, 47
fuel pipe, 10
fuel tank, 34, 45, 47, 52, 56, 57, 61, 62, 83
funnel, 67, 72, 73, 88, 95
furnace, 72, 73

Galley, 46, 63, 70
gas turbine engine, 42, 43, 46, 62
gearbox, 12, 13
gears, 12, 13, 27, 31
gear stick, 13, 27
General Dynamics F16, 39, 49
gliders, 38, 48
gravity, 36, 55, 63
Greeks, Ancient, 68, 69
gudgeon pin, 11
gyroscope, 38, 58, 59

Handling, 20
hard point, 53, 57, 61
Hawker Hunter, 46
headlight, 3, 4, 9, 19, 26, 27
head-up displays (HUDs), 30
heat exchanger, 95
helmsman, 76, 95
high tension lead, 27, 31
Hisho, 94
H.M.S. Gannet, 72, 73
Honda Dream, 31
horizon, 58
horsepower, 82, 95
HOTAS, 63
hull, 67, 68, 69, 71, 72, 73, 74, 76, 77, 82, 83, 84, 85, 87, 94, 95
hydraulic cylinder, 20, 22
hydraulics, 20, 31, 38, 39, 45, 49
hydraulic system, 22
hydrofoils, 85, 95
hydroplaning, 23

Idler gear, 13
ignition, 25, 26, 27, 31
inboard engines, 81
inlet manifold, 10
inlet valve, 10
input gear, 13
input shaft, 12, 13
INS, 63
intake fan, 42, 43, 52
internal combustion (I.C.) engine, 3, 10, 11
IZA electric car, 11

J250 craft, 85
jet engine, see *gas turbine engine*

Keel, 71, 77, 83, 95
Kevlar, 45
knots, 68, 73, 83, 95

Laminated glass, 5
layshaft, 13
leading edge, 35
Le Mans race, 18, 24
lifeboats, 82-83, 89
life jackets, 54
life rafts, 54, 55
lift, 35, 36, 37, 46, 50, 51, 67, 84, 85, 94, 95
light aircraft, 36, 38
lightweight boats, 70
Lockheed C17, 56